Science 100
Teacher's Guide Part 1

CONTENTS

Author: **Phyllis A. MacDonald, M.Ed.**

Revision Editor: Alan Christopherson, M.S.

804 N. 2nd Ave. E., Rock Rapids, IA 51246-1759

CURRICULUM

OVERVIEW

SCIENCE

Curriculum Overview
Grades 1–12

	Grade 1	Grade 2	Grade 3
LIFEPAC 1	YOU LEARN WITH YOUR EYES • Name and group some colors • Name and group some shapes • Name and group some sizes • Help from what you see	THE LIVING AND NONLIVING • What God created • Rock and seed experiment • God-made objects • Man-made objects	YOU GROW AND CHANGE • Air we breathe • Food for the body • Exercise and rest • You are different
LIFEPAC 2	YOU LEARN WITH YOUR EARS • Sounds of nature and people • How sound moves • Sound with your voice • You make music	PLANTS • How are plants alike • Habitats of plants • Growth of plants • What plants need	PLANTS • Plant parts • Plant growth • Seeds and bulbs • Stems and roots
LIFEPAC 3	MORE ABOUT YOUR SENSES • Sense of smell • Sense of taste • Sense of touch • Learning with my senses	ANIMALS • How are animals alike • How are animals different • What animals need • Noah and the ark	ANIMAL AND ENVIRONMENT CHANGES • What changes an environment • How animals are different • How animals grow • How animals change
LIFEPAC 4	ANIMALS • What animals eat • Animals for food • Animals for work • Pets to care for	YOU • How are people alike • How are you different • Your family • Your health	YOU ARE WHAT YOU EAT • Food helps your body • Junk foods • Food groups • Good health habits
LIFEPAC 5	PLANTS • Big and small plants • Special plants • Plants for food • House plants	PET AND PLANT CARE • Learning about pets • Caring for pets • Learning about plants • Caring for plants	PROPERTIES OF MATTER • Robert Boyle • States of matter • Physical changes • Chemical changes
LIFEPAC 6	GROWING UP HEALTHY • How plants and animals grow • How your body grows • Eating and sleeping • Exercising	YOUR FIVE SENSES • Your eye • You can smell and hear • Your taste • You can feel	SOUNDS AND YOU • Making sounds • Different sounds • How sounds move • How sounds are heard
LIFEPAC 7	GOD'S BEAUTIFUL WORLD • Types of land • Water places • The weather • Seasons	PHYSICAL PROPERTIES • Colors • Shapes • Sizes • How things feel	TIMES AND SEASONS • The earth rotates • The earth revolves • Time changes • Seasons change
LIFEPAC 8	ALL ABOUT ENERGY • God gives energy • We use energy • Ways to make energy • Ways to save energy	OUR NEIGHBORHOOD • Things not living • Things living • Harm to our world • Caring for our world	ROCKS AND THEIR CHANGES • Forming rocks • Changing rocks • Rocks for buildings • Rock collecting
LIFEPAC 9	MACHINES AROUND YOU • Simple levers • Simple wheels • Inclined planes • Using machines	CHANGES IN OUR WORLD • Seasons • Change in plants • God's love never changes • God's Word never changes	HEAT ENERGY • Sources of heat • Heat energy • Moving heat • Benefits and problems of heat
LIFEPAC 10	WONDERFUL WORLD OF SCIENCE • Using your senses • Using your mind • You love yourself • You love the world	LOOKING AT OUR WORLD • Living things • Nonliving things • Caring for our world • Caring for ourselves	PHYSICAL CHANGES • Change in man • Change in plants • Matter and time • Sound and energy

	Grade 4	Grade 5	Grade 6
LIFEPAC 1	PLANTS • Plants and living things • Using plants • Parts of plants • The function of plants	CELLS • Cell composition • Plant and animal cells • Life of cells • Growth of cells	PLANT SYSTEMS • Parts of a plant • Systems of photosynthesis • Transport systems • Regulatory systems
LIFEPAC 2	ANIMALS • Animal structures • Animal behavior • Animal instincts • Man protects animals	PLANTS: LIFE CYCLES • Seed producing plants • Spore producing plants • One-celled plants • Classifying plants	ANIMAL SYSTEMS • Digestive system • Excretory system • Skeletal system • Diseases
LIFEPAC 3	MAN'S ENVIRONMENT • Resources • Balance in nature • Communities • Conservation and preservation	ANIMALS: LIFE CYCLES • Invertebrates • Vertebrates • Classifying animals • Relating function and structure	PLANT AND ANIMAL BEHAVIOR • Animal behavior • Plant behavior • Plant-animal interaction • Balance in nature
LIFEPAC 4	MACHINES • Work and energy • Simple machines • Simple machines together • Complex machines	BALANCE IN NATURE • Needs of life • Dependence on others • Prairie life • Stewardship of nature	MOLECULAR GENETICS • Reproduction • Inheritance • DNA and mutations • Mendel's work
LIFEPAC 5	ELECTRICITY AND MAGNETISM • Electric current • Electric circuits • Magnetic materials • Electricity and magnets	TRANSFORMATION OF ENERGY • Work and energy • Heat energy • Chemical energy • Energy sources	CHEMICAL STRUCTURE • Nature of matter • Periodic Table • Diagrams of atoms • Acids and bases
LIFEPAC 6	PROPERTIES OF MATTER • Properties of water • Properties of matter • Molecules and atoms • Elements	RECORDS IN ROCK: THE FLOOD • The Biblical account • Before the flood • The flood • After the flood	LIGHT AND SOUND • Sound waves • Light waves • The visible spectrum • Colors
LIFEPAC 7	WEATHER • Causes of weather • Forces of weather • Observing weather • Weather instruments	RECORDS IN ROCK: FOSSILS • Fossil types • Fossil location • Identifying fossils • Reading fossils	MOTION AND ITS MEASUREMENT • Definition of force • Rate of doing work • Laws of motion • Change in motion
LIFEPAC 8	THE SOLAR SYSTEM • Our solar system • The big universe • Sun and planets • Stars and space	RECORDS IN ROCK: GEOLOGY • Features of the earth • Rock of the earth • Forces of the earth • Changes in the earth	SPACESHIP EARTH • Shape of the earth • Rotation and revolution • Eclipses • The solar system
LIFEPAC 9	THE PLANET EARTH • The atmosphere • The hydrosphere • The lithosphere • Rotation and revolution	CYCLES IN NATURE • Properties of matter • Changes in matter • Natural cycles • God's order	ASTRONOMY AND THE STARS • History of astronomy • Investigating stars • Major stars • Constellations
LIFEPAC 10	GOD'S CREATION • Earth and solar system • Matter and weather • Using nature • Conservation	LOOK AHEAD • Plant and animal life • Balance in nature • Biblical records • Records of rock	THE EARTH AND THE UNIVERSE • Plant systems • Animal systems • Physics and chemistry • The earth and stars

Science LIFEPAC Overview

	Grade 7	Grade 8	Grade 9
LIFEPAC 1	WHAT IS SCIENCE • Tools of a scientist • Methods of a scientist • Work of a scientist • Careers in science	SCIENCE AND SOCIETY • Definition of science • History of science • Science today • Science tomorrow	OUR ATOMIC WORLD • Structure of matter • Radioactivity • Atomic nuclei • Nuclear energy
LIFEPAC 2	PERCEIVING THINGS • History of the metric system • Metric units • Advantages of the metric system • Graphing data	STRUCTURE OF MATTER I • Properties of matter • Chemical properties of matter • Atoms and molecules • Elements, compounds, & mixtures	VOLUME, MASS, AND DENSITY • Measure of matter • Volume • Mass • Density
LIFEPAC 3	EARTH IN SPACE I • Ancient stargazing • Geocentric Theory • Copernicus • Tools of astronomy	STRUCTURE OF MATTER II • Changes in matter • Acids • Bases • Salts	PHYSICAL GEOLOGY • Earth structures • Weathering and erosion • Sedimentation • Earth movements
LIFEPAC 4	EARTH IN SPACE II • Solar energy • Planets of the sun • The moon • Eclipses	HEALTH AND NUTRITION • Foods and digestion • Diet • Nutritional diseases • Hygiene	HISTORICAL GEOLOGY • Sedimentary rock • Fossils • Crustal changes • Measuring time
LIFEPAC 5	THE ATMOSPHERE • Layers of the atmosphere • Solar effects • Natural cycles • Protecting the atmosphere	ENERGY I • Kinetic and potential energy • Other forms of energy • Energy conversions • Entropy	BODY HEALTH I • Microorganisms • Bacterial infections • Viral infections • Other infections
LIFEPAC 6	WEATHER • Elements of weather • Air masses and clouds • Fronts and storms • Weather forecasting	ENERGY II • Magnetism • Current and static electricity • Using electricity • Energy sources	BODY HEALTH II • Body defense mechanisms • Treating disease • Preventing disease • Community health
LIFEPAC 7	CLIMATE • Climate and weather • Worldwide climate • Regional climate • Local climate	MACHINES I • Measuring distance • Force • Laws of Newton • Work	ASTRONOMY • Extent of the universe • Constellations • Telescopes • Space explorations
LIFEPAC 8	HUMAN ANATOMY I • Cell structure and function • Skeletal and muscle systems • Skin • Nervous system	MACHINES II • Friction • Levers • Wheels and axles • Inclined planes	OCEANOGRAPHY • History of oceanography • Research techniques • Geology of the ocean • Properties of the ocean
LIFEPAC 9	HUMAN ANATOMY II • Respiratory system • Circulatory system • Digestive system • Endocrine system	BALANCE IN NATURE • Photosynthesis • Food • Natural cycles • Balance in nature	SCIENCE AND TOMORROW • The land • Waste and ecology • Industry and energy • New frontiers
LIFEPAC 10	CAREERS IN SCIENCE • Scientists at work • Astronomy • Meteorology • Medicine	SCIENCE AND TECHNOLOGY • Basic science • Physical science • Life science • Vocations in science	SCIENTIFIC APPLICATIONS • Measurement • Practical health • Geology and astronomy • Solving problems

	Grade 10	Grade 11	Grade 12
LIFEPAC 1	TAXONOMY • History of taxonomy • Binomial nomenclature • Classification • Taxonomy	INTRODUCTION TO CHEMISTRY • Metric units and instrumentation • Observation and hypothesizing • Scientific notation • Careers in chemistry	KINEMATICS • Scalars and vectors • Length measurement • Acceleration • Fields and models
LIFEPAC 2	BASIS OF LIFE • Elements and molecules • Properties of compounds • Chemical reactions • Organic compounds	BASIC CHEMICAL UNITS • Alchemy • Elements • Compounds • Mixtures	DYNAMICS • Newton's Laws of Motion • Gravity • Circular motion • Kepler's Laws of Motion
LIFEPAC 3	MICROBIOLOGY • The microscope • Protozoan • Algae • Microorganisms	GASES AND MOLES • Kinetic theory • Gas laws • Combined gas law • Moles	WORK AND ENERGY • Mechanical energy • Conservation of energy • Power and efficiency • Heat energy
LIFEPAC 4	CELLS • Cell theories • Examination of the cell • Cell design • Cells in organisms	ATOMIC MODELS • Historical models • Modern atomic structure • Periodic Law • Nuclear reactions	WAVES • Energy transfers • Reflection and refraction of waves • Diffraction and interference • Sound waves
LIFEPAC 5	PLANTS: GREEN FACTORIES • The plant cell • Anatomy of the plant • Growth and function of plants • Plants and people	CHEMICAL FORMULAS • Ionic charges • Electronegativity • Chemical bonds • Molecular shape	LIGHT • Speed of light • Mirrors • Lenses • Models of light
LIFEPAC 6	HUMAN ANATOMY AND PHYSIOLOGY • Digestive and excretory system • Respiratory and circulatory system • Skeletal and muscular system • Body control systems	CHEMICAL REACTIONS • Detecting reactions • Energy changes • Reaction rates • Equilibriums	STATIC ELECTRICITY • Nature of charges • Transfer of charges • Electric fields • Electric potential
LIFEPAC 7	INHERITANCE • Gregor Mendel's experiments • Chromosomes and heredity • Molecular genetics • Human genetics	EQUILIBRIUM SYSTEMS • Solutions • Solubility equilibriums • Acid-base equilibriums • Redox equilibriums	CURRENT ELECTRICITY • Electromotive force • Electron flow • Resistance • Circuits
LIFEPAC 8	CELL DIVISION & REPRODUCTION • Mitosis and meiosis • Asexual reproduction • Sexual reproduction • Plant reproduction	HYDROCARBONS • Organic compounds • Carbon atoms • Carbon bonds • Saturated and unsaturated	MAGNETISM • Fields • Forces • Electromagnetism • Electron beams
LIFEPAC 9	ECOLOGY & ENERGY • Ecosystems • Communities and habitats • Pollution • Energy	CARBON CHEMISTRY • Saturated and unsaturated • Reaction types • Oxygen groups • Nitrogen groups	ATOMIC AND NUCLEAR PHYSICS • Electromagnetic radiation • Quantum theory • Nuclear theory • Nuclear reaction
LIFEPAC 10	APPLICATIONS OF BIOLOGY • Principles of experimentation • Principles of reproduction • Principles of life • Principles of ecology	ATOMS TO HYDROCARBONS • Atoms and molecules • Chemical bonding • Chemical systems • Organic chemistry	KINEMATICS TO NUCLEAR PHYSICS • Mechanics • Wave motion • Electricity • Modern physics

LIFEPAC

MANAGEMENT

STRUCTURE OF THE LIFEPAC CURRICULUM

The LIFEPAC curriculum is conveniently structured to provide one teacher handbook containing teacher support material with answer keys and ten student worktexts for each subject at grade levels two through twelve. The worktext format of the LIFEPACs allows the student to read the textual information and complete workbook activities all in the same booklet. The easy to follow LIFEPAC numbering system lists the grade as the first number(s) and the last two digits as the number of the series. For example, the Language Arts LIFEPAC at the 6th grade level, 5th book in the series would be LAN0605.

Each LIFEPAC is divided into 3 to 5 sections and begins with an introduction or overview of the booklet as well as a series of specific learning objectives to give a purpose to the study of the LIFEPAC. The introduction and objectives are followed by a vocabulary section which may be found at the beginning of each section at the lower levels, at the beginning of the LIFEPAC in the middle grades, or in the glossary at the high school level. Vocabulary words are used to develop word recognition and should not be confused with the spelling words introduced later in the LIFEPAC. The student should learn all vocabulary words before working the LIFEPAC sections to improve comprehension, retention, and reading skills.

Each activity or written assignment has a number for easy identification, such as 1.1. The first number corresponds to the LIFEPAC section and the number to the right of the decimal is the number of the activity.

Teacher checkpoints, which are essential to maintain quality learning, are found at various locations throughout the LIFEPAC. The teacher should check 1) neatness of work and penmanship, 2) quality of understanding (tested with a short oral quiz), 3) thoroughness of answers (complete sentences and paragraphs, correct spelling, etc.), 4) completion of activities (no blank spaces), and 5) accuracy of answers as compared to the answer key (all answers correct).

The self test questions are also number coded for easy reference. For example, 2.015 means that this is the 15th question in the self test of Section II. The first number corresponds to the LIFEPAC section, the zero indicates that it is a self test question, and the number to the right of the zero the question number.

The LIFEPAC test is packaged at the centerfold of each LIFEPAC. It should be removed and put aside before giving the booklet to the student for study.

Answer and test keys have the same numbering system as the LIFEPACs and appear at the back of this handbook. The student may be given access to the answer keys (not the test keys) under teacher supervision so that he can score his own work.

A thorough study of the Curriculum Overview by the teacher before instruction begins is essential to the success of the student. The teacher should become familiar with expected skill mastery and understand how these grade level skills fit into the overall skill development of the curriculum. The teacher should also preview the objectives that appear at the beginning of each LIFEPAC for additional preparation and planning.

TEST SCORING and GRADING

Answer keys and test keys give examples of correct answers. They convey the idea, but the student may use many ways to express a correct answer. The teacher should check for the essence of the answer, not for the exact wording. Many questions are high level and require thinking and creativity on the part of the student. Each answer should be scored based on whether or not the main idea written by the student matches the model example. "Any Order" or "Either Order" in a key indicates that no particular order is necessary to be correct.

Most self tests and LIFEPAC tests at the lower elementary levels are scored at 1 point per answer; however, the upper levels may have a point system awarding 2 to 5 points for various answers or questions. Further, the total test points will vary; they may not always equal 100 points. They may be 78, 85, 100, 105, etc.

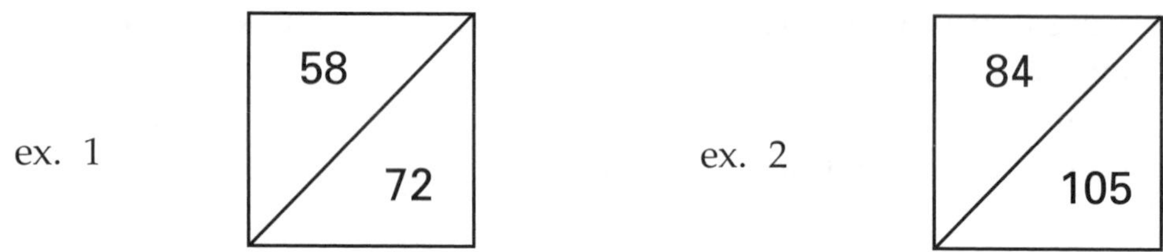

A score box similar to ex.1 above is located at the end of each self test and on the front of the LIFEPAC test. The bottom score, 72, represents the total number of points possible on the test. The upper score, 58, represents the number of points your student will need to receive an 80% or passing grade. If you wish to establish the exact percentage that your student has achieved, find the total points of his correct answers and divide it by the bottom number (in this case 72.) For example, if your student has a point total of 65, divide 65 by 72 for a grade of 90%. Referring to ex. 2, on a test with a total of 105 possible points, the student would have to receive a minimum of 84 correct points for an 80% or passing grade. If your student has received 93 points, simply divide the 93 by 105 for a percentage grade of 89%. Students who receive a score below 80% should review the LIFEPAC and retest using the appropriate Alternate Test found in the Teacher's Guide.

The following is a guideline to assign letter grades for completed LIFEPACs based on a maximum total score of 100 points.

LIFEPAC Test = 60% of the Total Score (or percent grade)
Self Test = 25% of the Total Score (average percent of self tests)
Reports = 10% or 10* points per LIFEPAC
Oral Work = 5% or 5* points per LIFEPAC
*Determined by the teacher's subjective evaluation of the student's daily work.

Example:

LIFEPAC Test Score	=	92%	92 x .60	=	55 points
Self Test Average	=	90%	90 x .25	=	23 points
Reports				=	8 points
Oral Work				=	4 points
TOTAL POINTS				=	90 points

Grade Scale based on point system:

100	–	94	=	A
93	–	86	=	B
85	–	77	=	C
76	–	70	=	D
Below		70	=	F

TEACHER HINTS and STUDYING TECHNIQUES

LIFEPAC Activities are written to check the level of understanding of the preceding text. The student may look back to the text as necessary to complete these activities; however, a student should never attempt to do the activities without reading (studying) the text first. Self tests and LIFEPAC tests are never open book tests.

Language arts activities (skill integration) often appear within other subject curriculum. The purpose is to give the student an opportunity to test his skill mastery outside of the context in which it was presented.

Writing complete answers (paragraphs) to some questions is an integral part of the LIFEPAC Curriculum in all subjects. This builds communication and organization skills, increases understanding and retention of ideas, and helps enforce good penmanship. Complete sentences should be encouraged for this type of activity. Obviously, single words or phrases do not meet the intent of the activity, since multiple lines are given for the response.

Review is essential to student success. Time invested in review where review is suggested will be time saved in correcting errors later. Self tests, unlike the section activities, are closed book. This procedure helps to identify weaknesses before they become too great to overcome. Certain objectives from self tests are cumulative and test previous sections; therefore, good preparation for a self test must include all material studied up to that testing point.

The following procedure checklist has been found to be successful in developing good study habits in the LIFEPAC curriculum.

1. Read the introduction and Table of Contents.
2. Read the objectives.
3. Recite and study the entire vocabulary (glossary) list.
4. Study each section as follows:
    a. Read the introduction and study the section objectives.
    b. Read all the text for the entire section, but answer none of the activities.
    c. Return to the beginning of the section and memorize each vocabulary word and definition.
    d. Reread the section, complete the activities, check the answers with the answer key, correct all errors, and have the teacher check.
    e. Read the self test but do not answer the questions.
    f. Go to the beginning of the first section and reread the text and answers to the activities up to the self test you have not yet done.
    g. Answer the questions to the self test without looking back.
    h. Have the self test checked by the teacher.
    i. Correct the self test and have the teacher check the corrections.
    j. Repeat steps a–i for each section.

5. Use the SQ3R* method to prepare for the LIFEPAC test.
6. Take the LIFEPAC test as a closed book test.
7. LIFEPAC tests are administered and scored under direct teacher supervision. Students who receive scores below 80% should review the LIFEPAC using the SQ3R* study method and take the Alternate Test located in the Teacher Handbook. The final test grade may be the grade on the Alternate Test or an average of the grades from the original LIFEPAC test and the Alternate Test.

   *SQ3R: **S**can the whole LIFEPAC.
   Question yourself on the objectives.
   Read the whole LIFEPAC again.
   Recite through an oral examination.
   Review weak areas.

GOAL SETTING and SCHEDULES

Each school must develop its own schedule, because no single set of procedures will fit every situation. The following is an example of a daily schedule that includes the five LIFEPAC subjects as well as time slotted for special activities.

Possible Daily Schedule

8:15	–	8:25	Pledges, prayer, songs, devotions, etc.
8:25	–	9:10	Bible
9:10	–	9:55	Language Arts
9:55	–	10:15	Recess (juice break)
10:15	–	11:00	Mathematics
11:00	–	11:45	Social Studies
11:45	–	12:30	Lunch, recess, quiet time
12:30	–	1:15	Science
1:15	–		Drill, remedial work, enrichment*

*Enrichment: Computer time, physical education, field trips, fun reading, games and puzzles, family business, hobbies, resource persons, guests, crafts, creative work, electives, music appreciation, projects.

Basically, two factors need to be considered when assigning work to a student in the LIFEPAC curriculum.

The first is time. An average of 45 minutes should be devoted to each subject, each day. Remember, this is only an average. Because of extenuating circumstances a student may spend only 15 minutes on a subject one day and the next day spend 90 minutes on the same subject.

The second factor is the number of pages to be worked in each subject. A single LIFEPAC is designed to take 3 to 4 weeks to complete. Allowing about 3-4 days for LIFEPAC introduction, review, and tests, the student has approximately 15 days to complete the LIFEPAC pages. Simply take the number of pages in the LIFEPAC, divide it by 15 and you will have the number of pages that must be completed on a daily basis to keep the student on schedule. For example, a LIFEPAC containing 45 pages will require 3 completed pages per day. Again, this is only an average. While working a 45 page LIFEPAC, the student may complete only 1 page the first day if the text has a lot of activities or reports, but go on to complete 5 pages the next day.

Long range planning requires some organization. Because the traditional school year originates in the early fall of one year and continues to late spring of the following year, a calendar should be devised that covers this period of time. Approximate beginning and completion dates can be noted on the calendar as well as special occasions such as holidays, vacations, and birthdays. Since each LIFEPAC takes 3-4 weeks or eighteen days to complete, it should take about 180 school days to finish a set of ten LIFEPACs. Starting at the beginning school date, mark off eighteen school days on the calendar and that will become the targeted completion date for the first LIFEPAC. Continue marking the calendar until you have established dates for the remaining nine LIFEPACs, making adjustments for previously noted holidays and vacations. If all five subjects are being used, the ten established target dates should be the same for the LIFEPACs in each subject.

FORMS

The sample weekly lesson plan and student grading sheet forms are included in this section as teacher support materials and may be duplicated at the convenience of the teacher.

The student grading sheet is provided for those who desire to follow the suggested guidelines for assignment of letter grades found on page 15. The student's self test scores should be posted as percentage grades. When the LIFEPAC is completed the teacher should average the self test grades, multiply the average by .25, and post the points in the box marked self test points. The LIFEPAC percentage grade should be multiplied by .60 and posted. Next, the teacher should award and post points for written reports and oral work. A report may be any type of written work assigned to the student whether it is a LIFEPAC or additional learning activity. Oral work includes the student's ability to respond orally to questions which may or may not be related to LIFEPAC activities or any type of oral report assigned by the teacher. The points may then be totaled and a final grade entered along with the date that the LIFEPAC was completed.

The Student Record Book which was specifically designed for use with the Alpha Omega curriculum provides space to record weekly progress for one student over a nine week period as well as a place to post self test and LIFEPAC scores. The Student Record Books are available through the current Alpha Omega catalog; however, unlike the enclosed forms these books are not for duplication and should be purchased in sets of four to cover a full academic year.

WEEKLY LESSON PLANNER			
			Week of:
Subject	Subject	Subject	Subject
Monday			
Subject	Subject	Subject	Subject
Tuesday			
Subject	Subject	Subject	Subject
Wednesday			
Subject	Subject	Subject	Subject
Thursday			
Subject	Subject	Subject	Subject
Friday			

WEEKLY LESSON PLANNER				
			Week of:	
	Subject	Subject	Subject	Subject
Monday				
	Subject	Subject	Subject	Subject
Tuesday				
	Subject	Subject	Subject	Subject
Wednesday				
	Subject	Subject	Subject	Subject
Thursday				
	Subject	Subject	Subject	Subject
Friday				

Student Name ______________________ Year ____________

Bible

LP #	Self Test Scores by Sections 1	2	3	4	5	Self Test Points	LIFEPAC Test	Oral Points	Report Points	Final Grade	Date
01											
02											
03											
04											
05											
06											
07											
08											
09											
10											

History & Geography

LP #	Self Test Scores by Sections 1	2	3	4	5	Self Test Points	LIFEPAC Test	Oral Points	Report Points	Final Grade	Date
01											
02											
03											
04											
05											
06											
07											
08											
09											
10											

Language Arts

LP #	Self Test Scores by Sections 1	2	3	4	5	Self Test Points	LIFEPAC Test	Oral Points	Report Points	Final Grade	Date
01											
02											
03											
04											
05											
06											
07											
08											
09											
10											

Student Name ______________________ Year ____________

Mathematics

LP #	Self Test Scores by Sections 1	2	3	4	5	Self Test Points	LIFEPAC Test	Oral Points	Report Points	Final Grade	Date
01											
02											
03											
04											
05											
06											
07											
08											
09											
10											

Science

LP #	Self Test Scores by Sections 1	2	3	4	5	Self Test Points	LIFEPAC Test	Oral Points	Report Points	Final Grade	Date
01											
02											
03											
04											
05											
06											
07											
08											
09											
10											

Spelling/Electives

LP #	Self Test Scores by Sections 1	2	3	4	5	Self Test Points	LIFEPAC Test	Oral Points	Report Points	Final Grade	Date
01											
02											
03											
04											
05											
06											
07											
08											
09											
10											

TEACHER

NOTES

INSTRUCTIONS FOR FIRST GRADE SCIENCE

The first grade handbooks of the LIFEPAC curriculum are designed to provide a step-by step procedure that will help the teacher prepare for and present each lesson effectively. In the early LIFEPACs the teacher should read the directions and any other sentences to the children. However, as the school year progresses, the student should be encouraged to begin reading and following his own instructional material in preparation for the independent study approach that begins at the second grade level.

This section of the *Teacher's Guide* includes the following teacher aids: 1) Cumulative Word List 2) Teacher Instruction Pages.

The Cumulative Word List is made up of words introduced at least once in one of the ten subject LIFEPACs. An asterisk (*) following a word indicates a direction-word that the children will need to know by sight to complete the work independently. Sight words are words that either are needed before their phonetic presentation or do not follow the standard phonetic rules. These words need to be learned through memorization and children should be drilled on them frequently. The drill may be done by use of a chart posted in a prominent place, by word card drills, word recognition or meaning games. Some words on the Cumulative Word List are not expected to be part of the student's reading vocabulary but part of his speaking vocabulary for better understanding of subject content.

The Teacher Instruction Pages list the Concept to be taught as well as Student Objectives and Goals for the Teacher. The Teaching Page contains directions for teaching that page. Worksheet pages used in some lessons follow this section and may be duplicated for individual student use. The Activities section at the end of each lesson is optional and may be used to reinforce or expand the concepts taught.

Materials needed are usually items such as pencils and crayons which are readily available. Additional items that may be required are LIFEPAC tablets (purchased through the catalog or may be any lined paper), alphabet cards, color and number charts, and flash cards for vocabulary words.

Page 1: YOU LEARN WITH YOUR EYES

CONCEPT: the value of the sense of sight to learning

OBJECTIVE: the introduction of all LIFEPAC objectives

BIBLE REFERENCE: Genesis chapters 1 and 2

PROCESS: observing, using the sense of sight

READING INTEGRATION: vocabulary development, recognizing a sentence, left-to-right, oral directions, plurals, writing name, listening

VOCABULARY: color/colors, shape/shapes, size/sizes, eye/eyes, see, look

MATERIALS NEEDED: pencils, vocabulary-word cards, objects normally found in a classroom, LIFEPAC Tablet, Bible

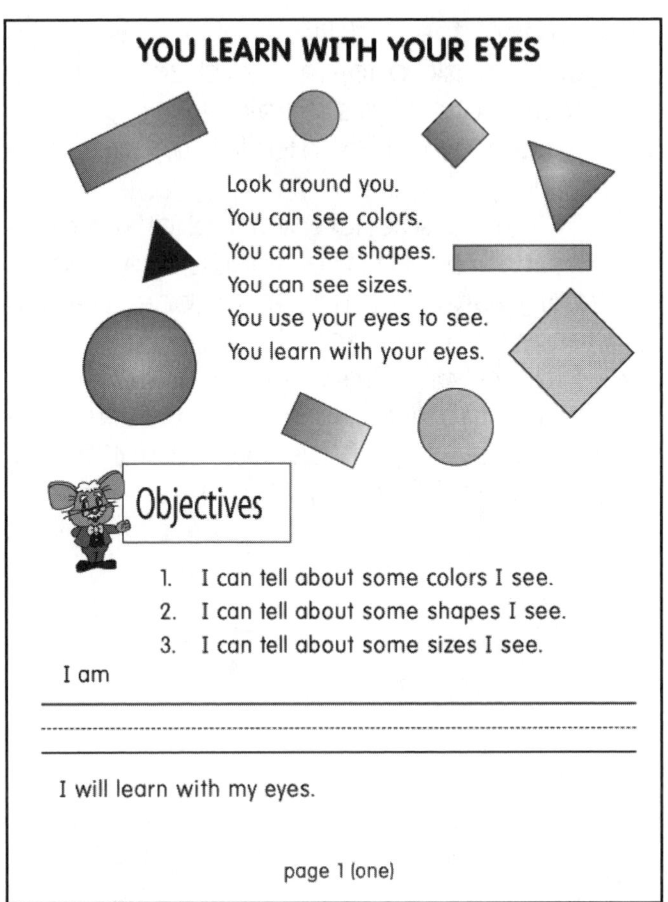

YOU LEARN WITH YOUR EYES
Look around you.
You can see colors.
You can see shapes.
You can see sizes.
You use your eyes to see.
You learn with your eyes.
Objectives
1. I can tell about some colors I see.
2. I can tell about some shapes I see.
3. I can tell about some sizes I see.
I am
I will learn with my eyes.
page 1 (one)

TEACHING PAGE 1:

To prepare for this page and the LIFEPAC, have the children cover their eyes. Hold up two or three objects. Ask the children to uncover their eyes and identify the objects. Ask a few children to come forward in turn and to close their eyes. Hand them familiar objects such as pencils or crayons. The objects will probably be identified. Ask about the color of the object (cannot tell color with eyes closed).

Stress the importance of sight in recognizing color. Use the words *sense, sight,* and *observe* orally, but do not expect the children either to read or to write them at this level.

The teacher may want to extend the discussion to include other properties, such as shape and size, that might be identified by sight.

Read the introduction to the class. Repeat one sentence at a time. Have the children point to the first word and follow the reading, left to right. Identify the vocabulary words. Have the children point to them or circle them with a pencil. Discuss each sentence in turn.

Have the children identify orally the colors and shapes they see in the room. Ask the children to name some big, small, long, short, wide, and narrow things they see.

Read each objective to the class. Discuss the expanded objectives found in the introduction to this Handbook. Be sure the children understand that these objectives are things they will be able to do when they finish the LIFEPAC. Have the children write their own names. Give help as needed.

ACTIVITIES:

1. Review the vocabulary words. Use the word cards.
Example: Ask a child to find the word card that says *shape* and hold the card up for the class to see. Ask if anyone can tell a way to change the word to mean more than

one. When the addition of *s* has been suggested, ask another child to find the word card that says shapes.

2. Use the LIFEPAC Tablet to write the vocabulary words.

3. Make a science word chart or class dictionary. Record the vocabulary words under the proper letter. This procedure will gradually develop alphabetizing skills.

4. Talk about Creation. Ask the children who gave them the gift of sight. Ask them who created all of the wonderful things they see. Read Genesis, Chapters 1 and 2.

Part 1: YOU SEE COLOR

Page 2

CONCEPT: recognition of color and related color words

OBJECTIVES:

I can tell about some colors I see.
I can name some colors I see.
I can read some color words.

PROCESS: observing, using the sense of sight

READING INTEGRATION: rhyming, vocabulary development, left to right, main idea

VOCABULARY: black, blue, brown, green, orange, pink, purple, red, white, yellow

MATERIALS NEEDED: Color display (individual chart or bulletin board with colors named); color cards (tag board or colored construction paper pieces of the ten colors to be taught); color-word cards (black on white, no color indicator except the word); food coloring (red, yellow, and blue), water, muffin tins or babyfood jars for discovery center; LIFEPAC Tablet; Worksheet l; pencils

TEACHING PAGE 2:

Introduce colors with color words. Use the chart or display to identify the color with the word. Take as much time as needed to get the children used to seeing the word with the color.

Play a matching game with colors and color words. Cover the words on the display. Divide the class into teams. Have the children, in turn, draw a color word from the set of word cards and match it with the color. Score by correct match of word to color.

Have the children look at the page. Discuss the illustration. Help the children determine what colors they want to make the flowers.

I. YOU SEE COLOR
Color the Flowers.
Red and yellow,
Green and blue,
Orange and pink
And purple, too.
Black and white,
And even brown,
Are everywhere.
Just look around.
I use my eyes
And I can see
The colors God
Has made for me.
page 2 (two)

Read the poem aloud to the class. Reread with the children following left to right. Have children identify the color words. Have children identify rhyming words.

Select ten children. Give each a colored card or paper using the ten colors listed in the poem. Reread the poem instructing each of the ten children to listen carefully and to hold up his colored card when the name of his color is read. Ask all ten children to hold up their color cards when the word colors is read in the last stanza. Repeat until all children have had a turn. Children can join in the reading of the poem.

ACTIVITIES:

1. Set up a discovery center in a corner or open area of the room.

Provide food coloring (red, yellow, and blue), water, and muffin tins or baby-food jars. Allow individuals or pairs of children to discover how colors mix together to make new colors. Let them mix colored water in the tins or jars. Mix yellow and blue to make green, yellow and red to make orange, and so on.

Let those children who are able write sentences in their Tablets and tell what they have learned about mixing colors.

Other children should dictate sentences to an aide or to the teacher and then copy the sentences into their Tablets.

2. Worksheet 1 reinforces the first activity. Have individual color charts on a large color display so that children can readily find the word they need .

3. Have all the children practice writing the color words in their Tablets. Provide models for children to copy.

4. For children having difficulty, review the color pages and activities used in Language Arts 101-104 LIFEPAC, Handbook, and Tablet.

5. Read the children books dealing with color.

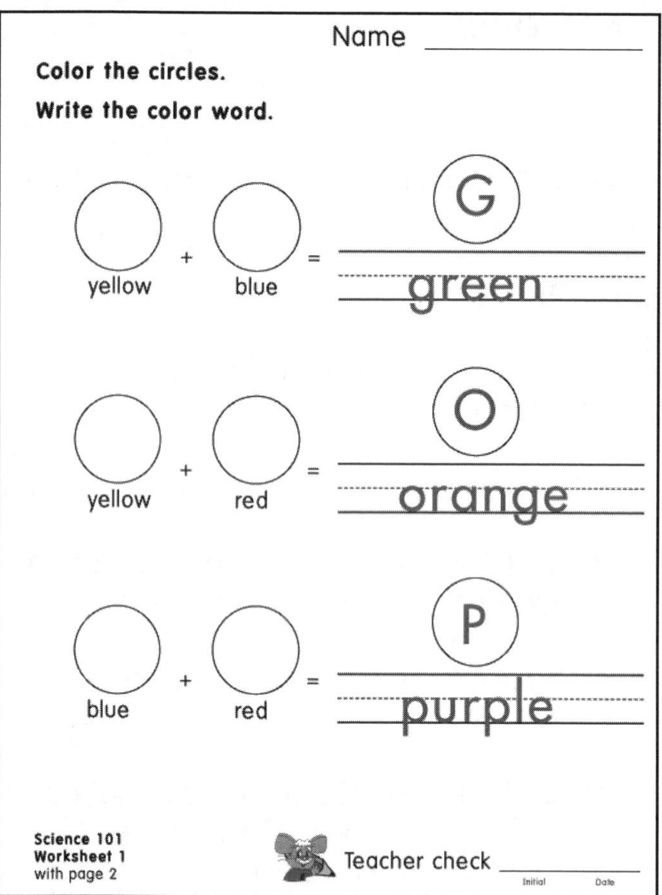
Name

Color the circles.

Write the color word.

yellow + blue = G green

yellow + red = O orange

blue + red = P purple

Science 101
Worksheet 1
with page 2

Teacher check
Initial Date

Page 3: You Name Some Colors

CONCEPT: recognition of color and related color word

OBJECTIVES:

I can tell about some colors I see.
I can name some colors.
I can read some color words.

PROCESS: observing, using the sense of sight

READING INTEGRATION: following oral and written directions, left to right, recognizing color words

VOCABULARY: circle, read, (color)

MATERIALS NEEDED: pencils, crayons, color-word cards, Worksheet 2

TEACHING PAGE 3:

Give additional group practice in matching color word to corresponding color. Use color-word cards to match objects in the classroom.

Read the direction at the top of the page to the class. Emphasize the direction word *circle*. Reread the direction with the children following along from left to right.

Do the first exercise with the group. Have the children identify the color of the apple. Have a volunteer read the two color words next to the picture of the apple. Ask why the word red should be circled. When the correct response has been given, have the children draw a circle around the word red. Be sure they understand the procedure.

The page may be completed independently with help given as needed.

ACTIVITIES

1. Record color words in the science word dictionary.
2. Complete Worksheet 2. Go over the directions carefully. Emphasize the direction words *color* and *read.*
3. Continue use of discovery center until all children have had an opportunity to do the activity (Activity 1, page 2)

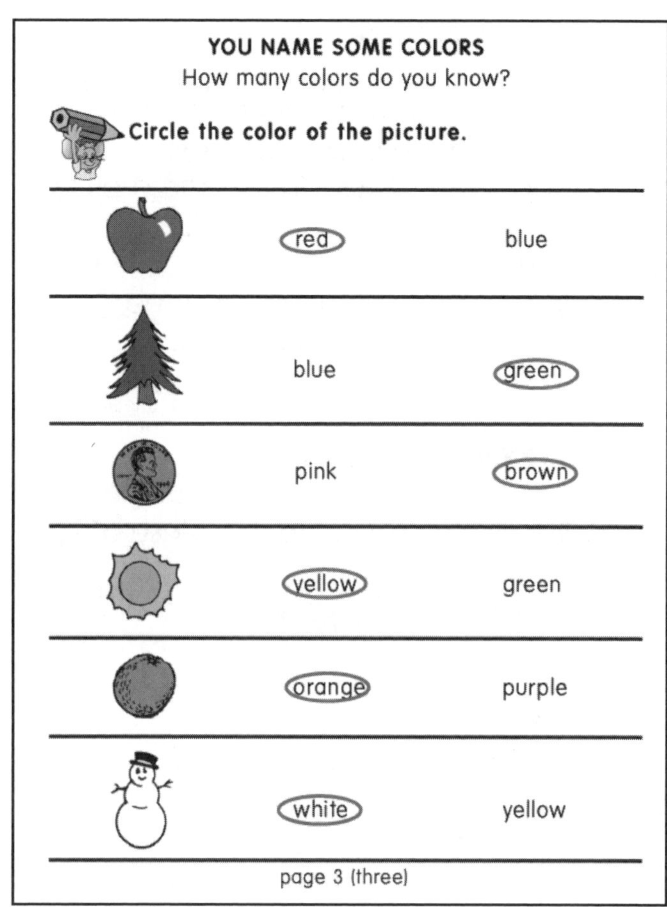

YOU NAME SOME COLORS

How many colors do you know?

Circle the color of the picture.

(apple)	red (circled)	blue
(tree)	blue	green (circled)
(penny)	pink	brown (circled)
(sun)	yellow (circled)	green
(orange)	orange (circled)	purple
(snowman)	white (circled)	yellow

page 3 (three)

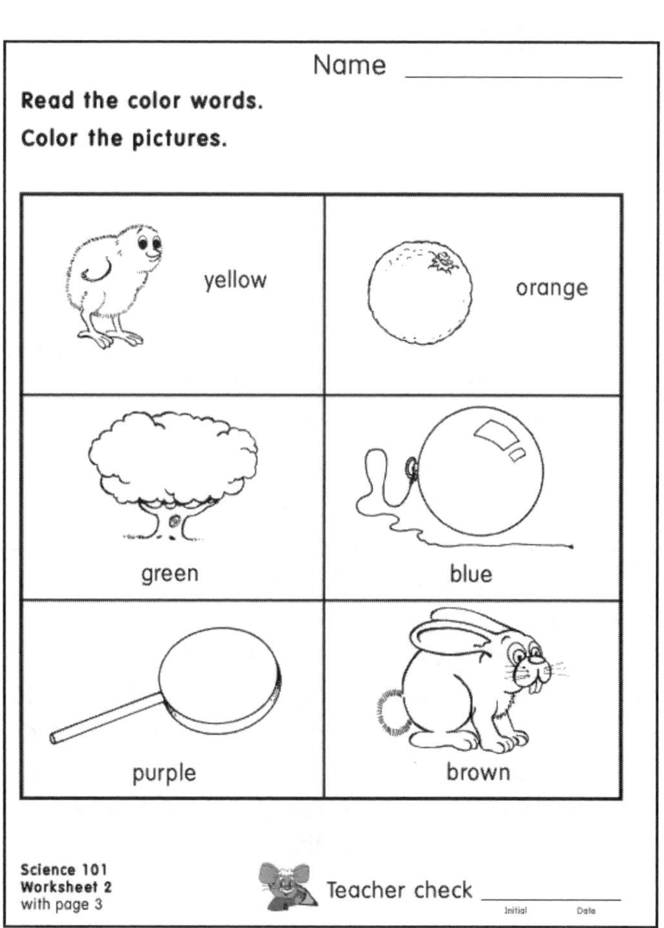

Name ______________

Read the color words.
Color the pictures.

yellow	orange
green	blue
purple	brown

Science 101
Worksheet 2
with page 3

Teacher check ______________
Initial Date

Page 4: Activity Page

CONCEPTS: God used the colors of the rainbow to signify a promise. The colors of the rainbow are always in the same order.

OBJECTIVES:
I can tell about some colors I see.
I can name some colors I see.
I can read some color words.

BIBLE REFERENCE: Genesis 9:8 through 17

PROCESS: observing, using the sense of sight

READING INTEGRATION: listening, main idea, sentence recognition, left-to-right, vocabulary development, sequence

VOCABULARY: rainbow, write, (read)

MATERIALS NEEDED: crayons, pencils, LIFEPAC Tablet, Bible, drawing paper, paints

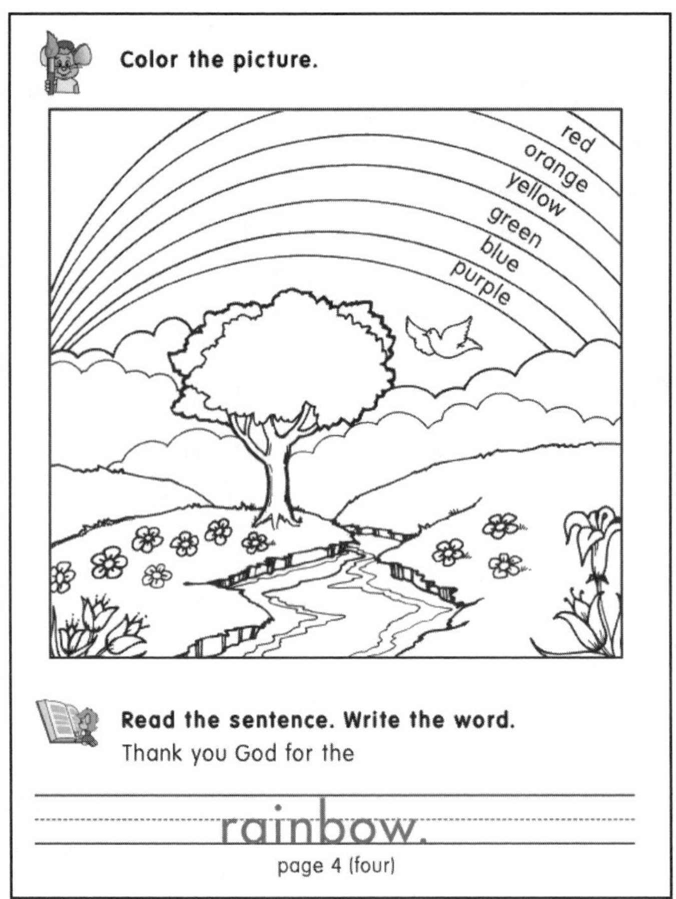
Color the picture.
red
orange
yellow
green
blue
purple
Read the sentence. Write the word.
Thank you God for the
rainbow.
page 4 (four)

TEACHING PAGE 4:

Read or tell the story of Noah and of God's promise not to flood the earth again. Use Genesis 9:8 through 17, the rainbow covenant.

Discuss when the children might see a rainbow.

Ask the children what the weather would be like on a day they could see a rainbow. Ask if they could ever see a rainbow at night. Why not? Ask why they should feel thankful when they see a rainbow.

Read the directions to the children and then with them. Emphasize left to right, the direction word *color,* and the new word *rainbow.*

Call attention to the color words in each stripe of the rainbow. Be sure that the children understand that they are to color each part according to its color word. When they have finished the rainbow, let them color the rest of the picture.

Read the directions for the sentence to the children and with them. Emphasize the direction words *read* and *write.* Read the sentence to the group. Ask the children what word completes the sentence (rainbow). Write the word *rainbow* on the board. Have the children read together the whole sentence, then carefully copy the word *rainbow* on the line to complete the sentence.

ACTIVITIES:

1. Have the children copy the sentence into their LIFEPAC Tablets.
2. Distribute paper and paints. Ask the children to paint their own rainbow picture. Make sure that the correct colors are used in the correct order for the rainbow.
3. Some students may write sentences or a short story to go with their pictures.

Page 5: Activity Page

CONCEPT: matching color to color word

OBJECTIVES:
I can tell about some colors I see.
I can name some colors.
I can read some color words.

PROCESS: observing

READING INTEGRATION: listening, main idea, recalling details

VOCABULARY: match, flag

MATERIALS NEEDED: pencils, crayons, picture of the first American flag, Worksheet 3

TEACHING PAGE 5:

Read or tell this little story about our flag to the class. Display a picture of the first flag.

Long ago, when our country was just beginning, we had no flag. Our leader, George Washington, thought a country should have its own flag. He asked Betsy Ross to make the new flag. Together, they decided how it should look.

The new flag had three colors: red, white, and blue. Red stood for the blood men shed in the fight for our country's freedom. The white showed that the fight for freedom was right and pure. Blue was for the loyalty of all who worked to build a good country.

The new flag had thirteen stars in a circle, to stand for the thirteen states. It had thirteen stripes, too. The stars were on a blue background and the stripes were red and white.

The flag we have today still has thirteen stripes, but it has fifty stars, one for each state in the United States of America.

We can be proud of our country and of our red, white, and blue flag.

Discuss the story. Ask a few specific questions about the story. For example,

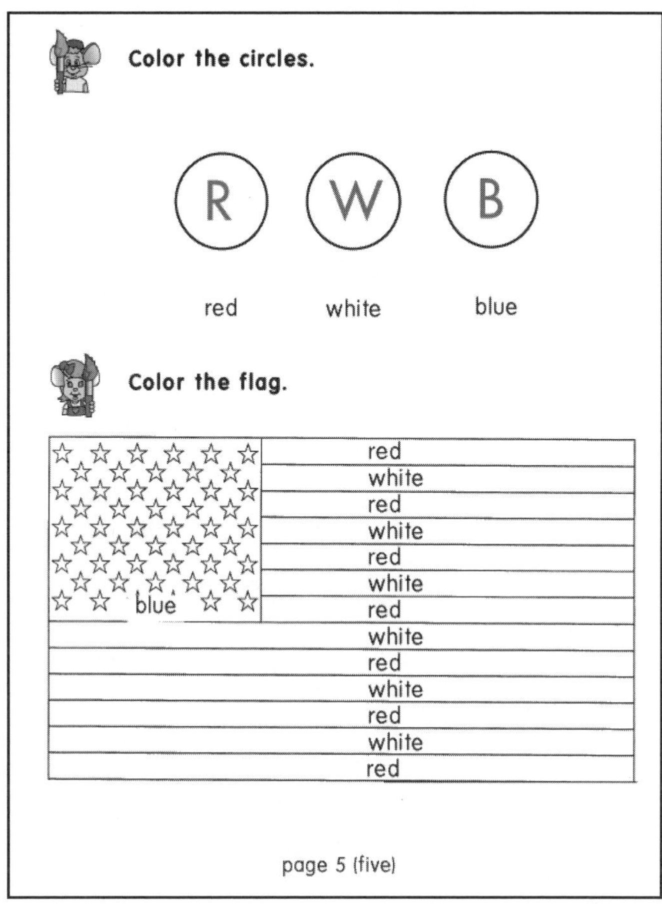

"What did Betsy Ross do?"

"Name the three colors in the flag."

"How many stripes does our flag have?"

Have the children look at the picture of a flag in the LIFEPAC. Note where the colors are to be on the flag pictured. Ask if this pictured flag is the first flag. Read the directions. Repeat and have the children read them with you. Children should complete the page independently.

ACTIVITIES:

1. Complete Worksheet 3. Read the directions. This worksheet should be an independent activity. The flag picture on LIFEPAC page 5 can be used as a reference.
2. Use flash-card or sentence drills for children who are still having difficulty with the three color words.

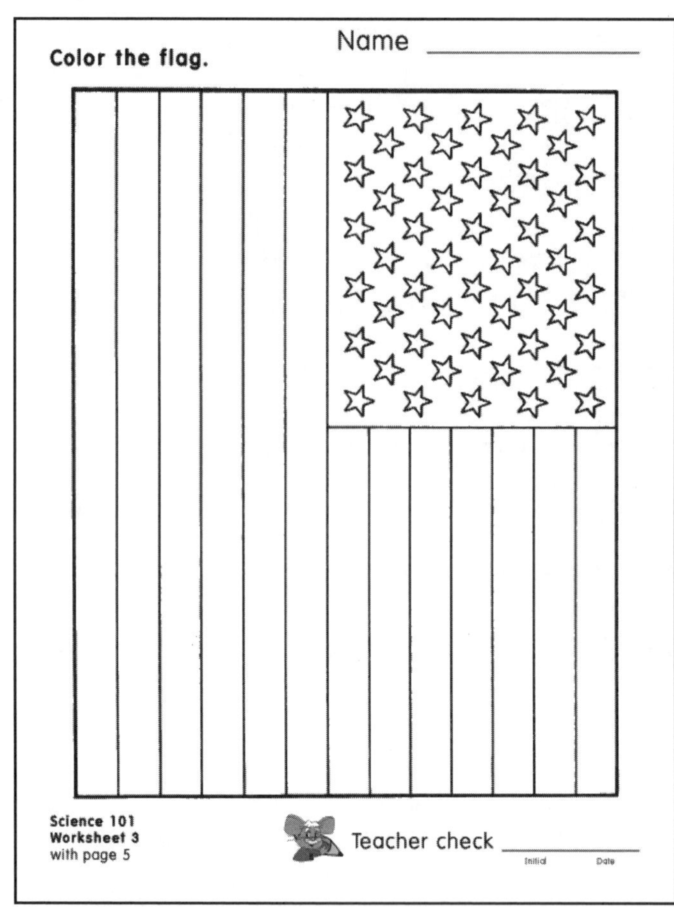
Color the flag.
Name
Science 101
Worksheet 3
with page 5
Teacher check
Initial
Date

Page 6: You Group by Color

CONCEPT: color groups

OBJECTIVES:
I can tell about some colors I see.
I can match objects by color

PROCESSES: observing; classifying, by color

READING INTEGRATION: oral and written directions, left to right

VOCABULARY: group, draw

MATERIALS NEEDED: items of assorted colors (blocks, balls, a box or bag of used crayons, etc.), pencils, LIFEPAC Tablet

YOU GROUP BY COLOR
Some things are all green.
Some things are all brown.
Some things have many colors.
Circle the green pictures.
Draw 3 things that are orange.
page 6 (six)

TEACHING PAGE 6:

On a desk or a table display the items of assorted colors. Tell the children that the items need to be put in groups. Ask for suggestions of how that grouping could be done. When desired response has been received, have volunteers sort the items according to color; all reds together, all blues together, and so on.

Reinforce the idea by having the children group themselves according to color of eyes, color of hair, color of shoes, and so on.

Read the directions to the children. Emphasize the direction word *color* and the direction word *draw.*

The page should be completed independently.

ACTIVITIES:

1. Set up a discovery center. Place the items of assorted color in the center area. Provide boxes or trays for each color group. Task will be to sort the items and have a teacher or helper check on success.
2. Have the child write or copy the sentence *I can group by color* in his Tablet.
3. *At Home Project:* Assign or have children pick a color. Have each child collect and bring in as many small items of that color as he can find. Make a color group display of items collected.

Page 7: Activity Page

CONCEPT: color groups

OBJECTIVES:

I can tell about some colors I see.
I can match objects by color.

PROCESS: classifying, by color

READING INTEGRATION: following directions

VOCABULARY: picture, pick

MATERIALS NEEDED: crayons, pencils, Worksheet 4

TEACHING PAGE 7:

If the children need more practice in grouping by color, repeat some of the activities from page 6.

Read the directions. Emphasize the direction word *color.* The page should be completed with teacher assistance.

ACTIVITIES:

1. Do Worksheet 4. Read the directions to and with the group. Emphasize the direction word *pick.* Have each child pick one crayon. They are to draw four pictures of things that are realistically that color. No purple pickles, please. Have the children label each picture. Have an aide help those who need help spelling words for their pictures.
2. Read one of the many color story books available. Read the story of Joseph's coat of many colors in Genesis chapter 37.

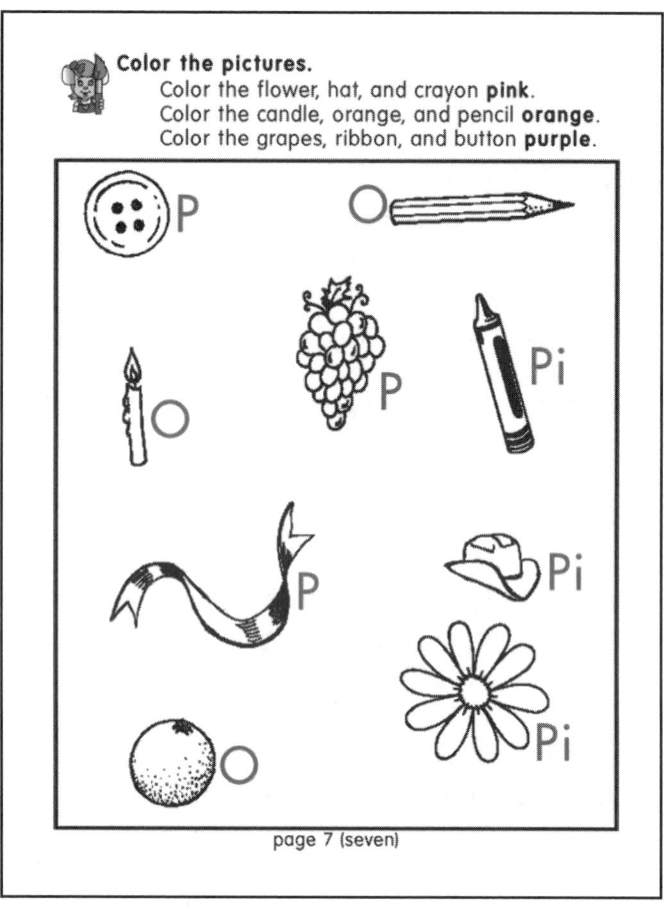

Color the pictures.
Color the flower, hat, and crayon **pink**.
Color the candle, orange, and pencil **orange**.
Color the grapes, ribbon, and button **purple**.

page 7 (seven)

Name ______________

Pick a color.
Draw 4 things that are that color.

Science 101
Worksheet 4
with page 7

Teacher check ______________
Initial Date

Page 8: Colors Can Help You

CONCEPT: purposes of color

OBJECTIVES:
I can tell about some colors I see.
I can tell some ways color helps.

PROCESS: observing

READING INTEGRATION: main idea, listening, oral and written directions, left to right

VOCABULARY: eat, help, banana, (look)

MATERIALS NEEDED: pencils, LIFEPAC Tablet, pictures of animals with protective coloration (examples: spotted coat of a fawn, fur that turns white in winter, as a snowshoe rabbit, etc.)

TEACHING PAGE 8:

Point out that color not only helps us to identify things around us, but also helps us in other ways. Go directly to the page for an example.

Ask the children to look at the picture. Ask them what they see (a traffic light). Read the text and let the children answer the questions. Ask them what the yellow light tells them. Direct children to color traffic light.

Read the directions with the children. Emphasize the direction word *look*. Ask what part of the body is used to look (eyes).

Have the children read the colors of the three bananas. Ask how they might taste or feel. Have the children color the bananas and circle the one they would eat. Accept whatever answer the child circles as long as he can give a reason. Go over the next direction. Children may write the word.

Read the second direction for the children. Check to see that they write the color word below the circled banana.

Discuss the question at the bottom of the page.

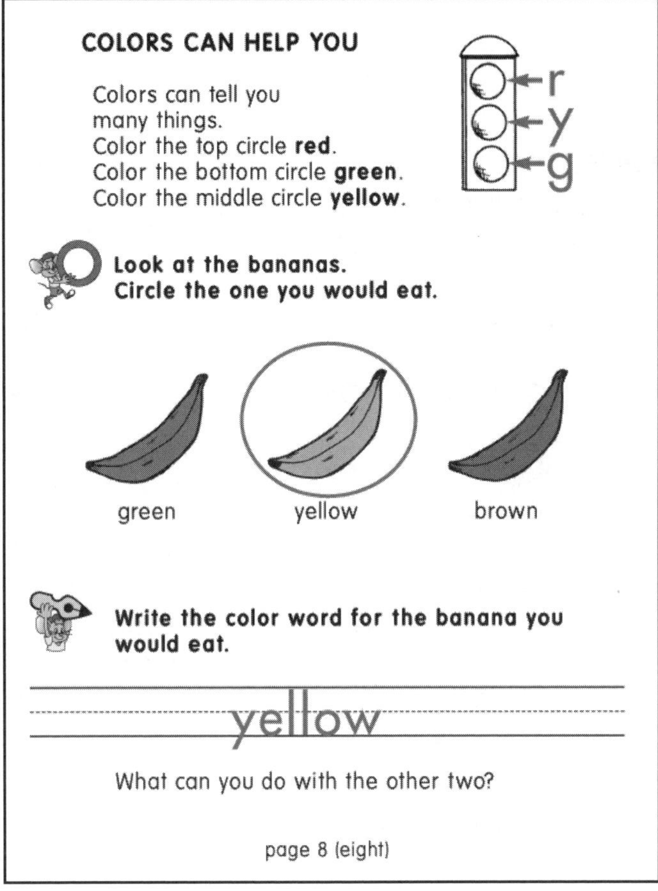

Help the children write an answer in their Tablets.

ACTIVITIES:

1. Use the pictures of animals with protective coloration to show another way in which color can be helpful.
2. Discuss some other ways that color is helpful, such as red burner on a stove is **HOT** and brown grass needs water.

Page 9: Color Groups

CONCEPT: color groups

OBJECTIVES:

I can tell about some colors I see.
I can match objects by color.

PROCESSES: classifying, by color; observing

READING INTEGRATION: listening, classifying, speaking in a group

TEACHING PAGE 9:

Have the children use their eyes to find color groups in the classroom. Choose three colors that are prominent in the room.

Children may contribute orally to a list of objects that fit into each group. Record lists on the chalkboard.

Read the directions to the children. Allow time to look, discuss, and color. List the groups on the board or make a chart for display.

Students who are able may copy the lists into the Tablet.

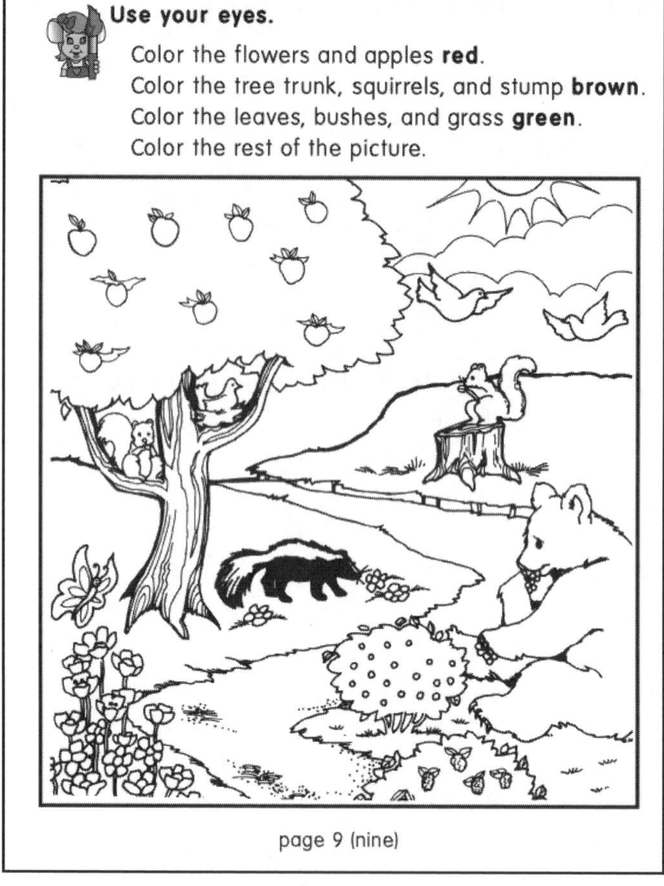

Use your eyes.
Color the flowers and apples red.
Color the tree trunk, squirrels, and stump brown.
Color the leaves, bushes, and grass green.
Color the rest of the picture.
page 9 (nine)

ACTIVITY:

Extend the concept of classifying by asking the children if things in the picture could be grouped in any other way. Possible responses: living/nonliving, plant/animal, things that fly/things that do not fly, things that grow/things that do not grow, and so on.

Allow plenty of time for discussion.

Pages 10 and 11: Self Test 1

CONCEPT: evaluate student progress

OBJECTIVE: I can tell about some colors I see.

READING INTEGRATION: recognition of color words

MATERIALS NEEDED: pencils, color charts, crayons, Worksheets 5 and 6

TEACHING PAGE 10:

Before giving this self test, review the color words with group practice or with a color game.

Practice color classification skills as on teacher's pages 6, 7, or 8.

Read all directions with the children. Be sure they are understood.

Do not stress the aspect of *Test*. Tell the children that these pages will show them what they have learned and what they need to study harder.

Put color charts away before doing page 10 of the test. The general proficiency of your group should dictate whether you choose to direct the self test or to allow the children to proceed independently once the directions are given.

If a child does poorly on page 10, review the color lessons and activities from Science 101 as well as the color activities in Language Arts.

TEACHING PAGE 11:

Read the directions. Let the children complete the activities independently.

Check and provide help for those children who have not done well.

ACTIVITIES:

1. Have the more advanced students tell or write a sentence about each of the two oranges.
2. Worksheets 5 and 6 should be given as extra practice for those children who need it and for review for the others.

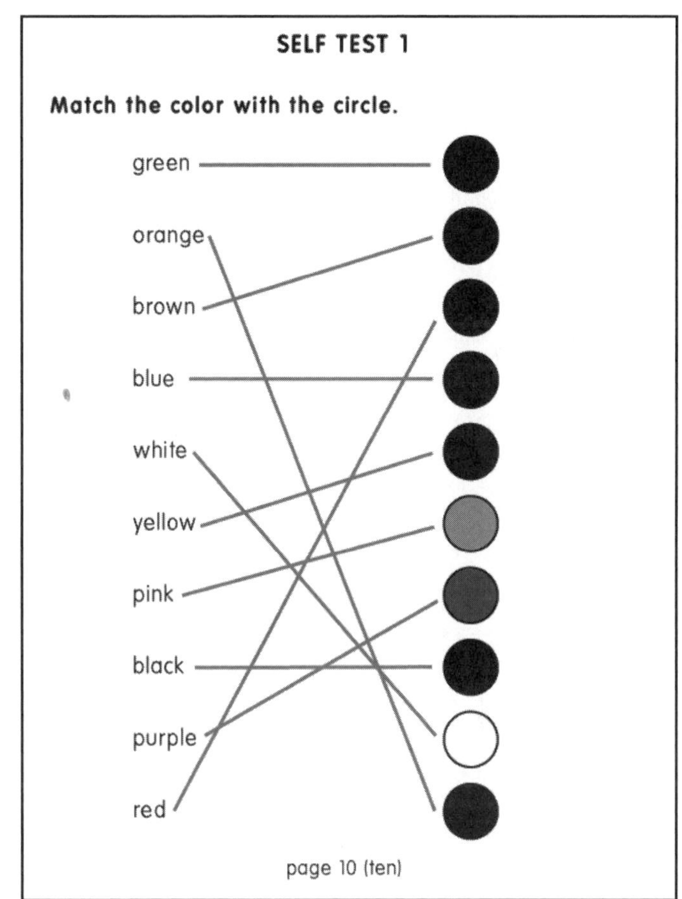

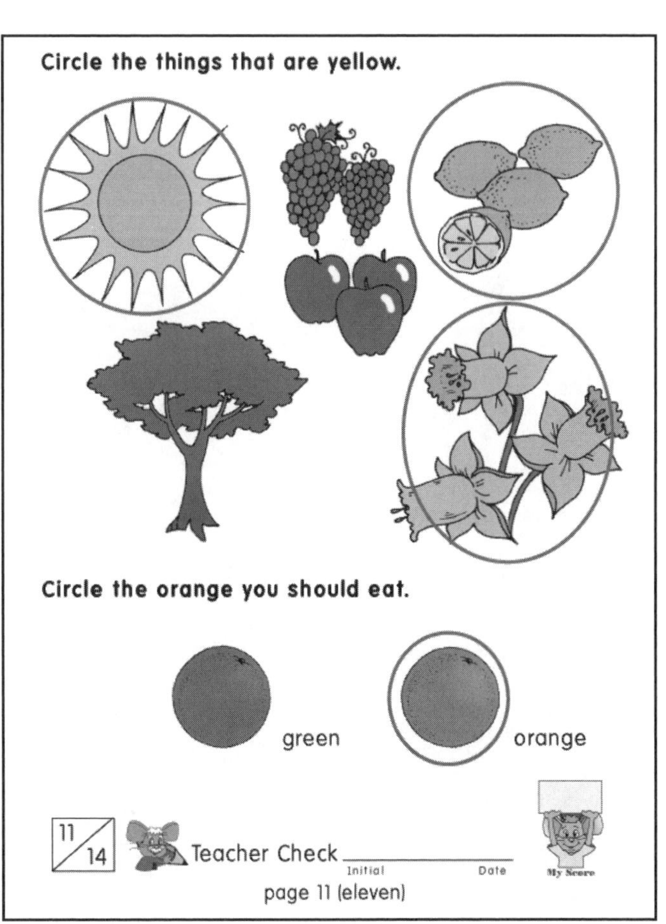

Circle the things that are yellow.
Circle the orange you should eat.
Match the color with the circle.
green
orange
11
14
Teacher Check
Initial
Date
My Score
page 11 (eleven)

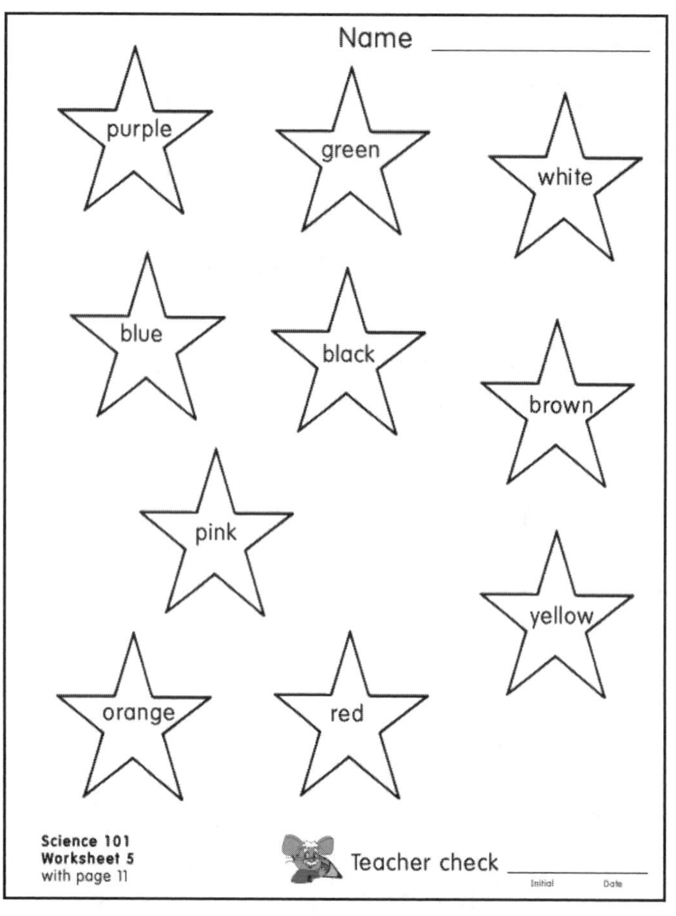
Name
purple
green
white
blue
black
brown
pink
yellow
orange
red
Science 101
Worksheet 5
with page 11
Teacher check
Initial
Date

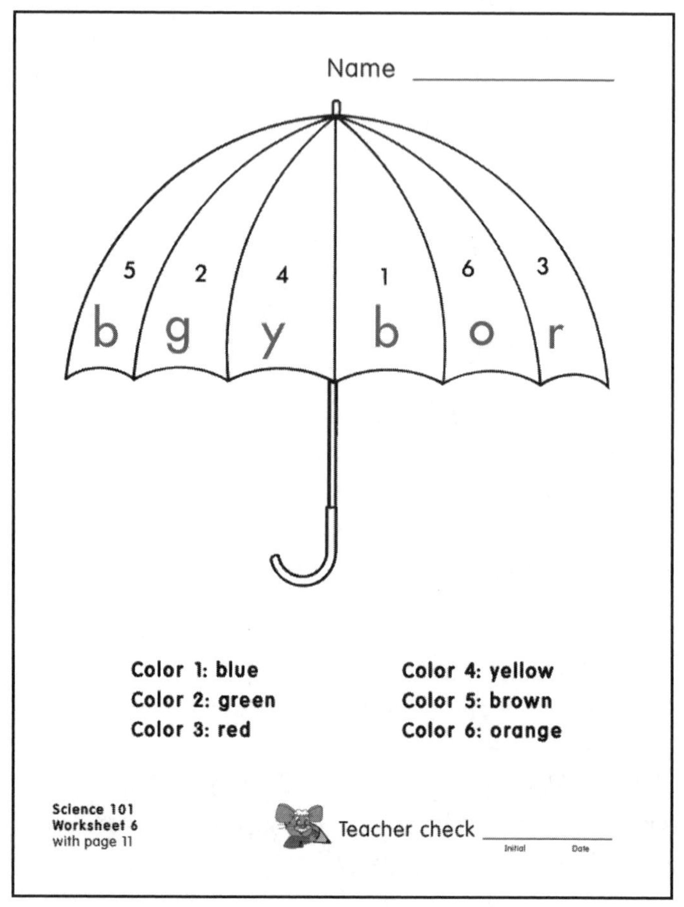
Name
5
2
4
1
6
3
b
g
y
b
o
r
Color 1: blue
Color 2: green
Color 3: red
Color 4: yellow
Color 5: brown
Color 6: orange
Science 101
Worksheet 6
with page 11
Teacher check
Initial
Date

PART 11. YOU SEE SHAPE
Page 12

CONCEPT: identification of basic shapes

OBJECTIVES:
I can tell about some shapes I see.
I can name some shapes.

PROCESS: observing, using the sense of sight

READING INTEGRATION: listening, rhyming, left to right, vocabulary development

VOCABULARY: square, triangle, shape(s), circle, rectangle

MATERIALS NEEDED: basic shape cards made for Language Arts 100 or tag board shapes, shape-word cards, LIFEPAC Tablet

TEACHING PAGE 12:

To prepare the children for this page, collect the shape cards made for Language Arts 100 or make tag board shapes of circles, triangles (with different angles), rectangles, and squares. Make them different colors and sizes for future use. Make several sets of shape-word cards. Use white cards with black ink.

Play matching games with shapes and shape words as you did with the colors and color words.

Tell the children that shapes can be seen in familiar objects and that shapes can help in identification and classification of matter.

Read the shape poem with children following along. Have the children identify the shape words in the poem.

Pass out the cards with shapes on them. As the poem is reread, have the children holding the shapes hold them up as the corresponding shape word is read .

Repeat several times allowing different children to hold the shapes.
Children should read along in chorus as the poem becomes familiar.

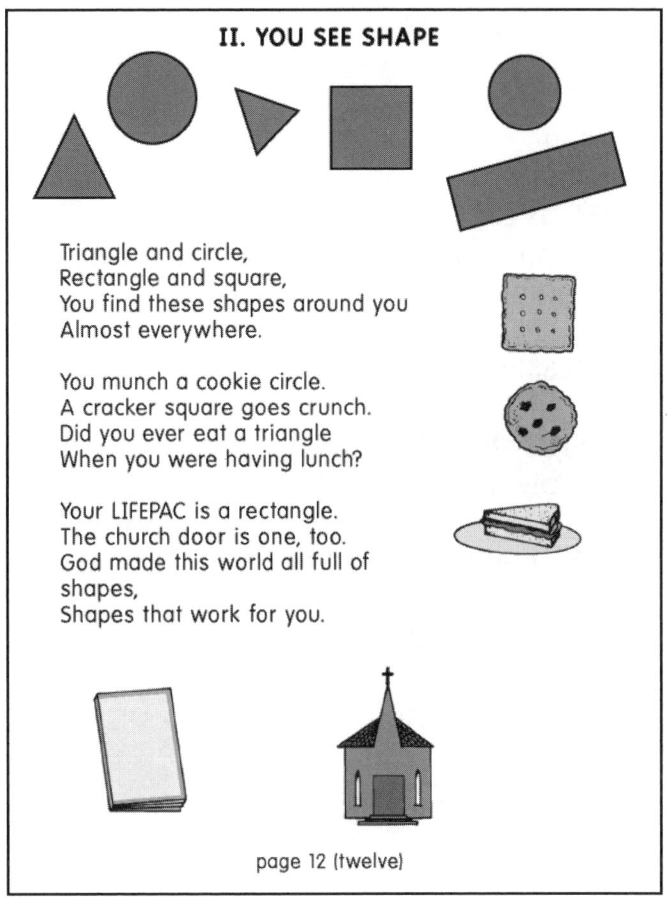
II. YOU SEE SHAPE

Triangle and circle,
Rectangle and square,
You find these shapes around you
Almost everywhere.

You munch a cookie circle.
A cracker square goes crunch.
Did you ever eat a triangle
When you were having lunch?

Your LIFEPAC is a rectangle.
The church door is one, too.
God made this world all full of shapes,
Shapes that work for you.

page 12 (twelve)

ACTIVITIES:

1. Add the vocabulary words to the science dictionary or chart.
2. Have the children practice writing the words in their Tablets.
3. Read books dealing with shapes.

Page 13: You Name Some Shapes

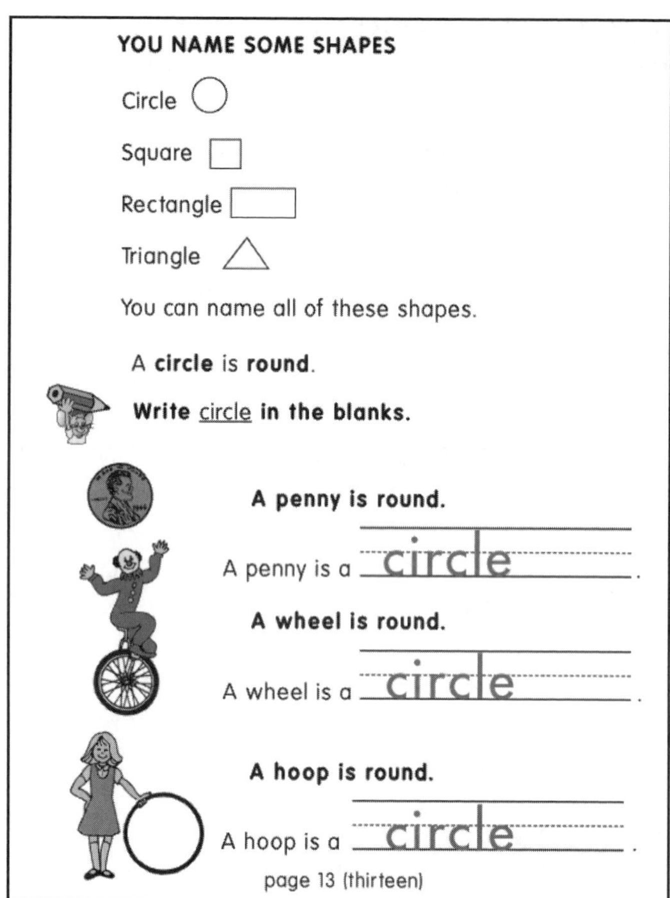

CONCEPT: shape seen in familiar objects (circles)

OBJECTIVES:
I can tell about some shapes I see.
I can name some shapes.

PROCESS: observing, using the sense of sight

READING INTEGRATION: following written and oral directions, sentence recognition

VOCABULARY: round, (circle)

MATERIALS NEEDED: vocabulary word cards (include direction-word card, write), pencils, three-dimensional shapes made of heavy cardboard or purchased commercially, drawing paper

TEACHING PAGE 13:

Have the children look around the room for things that are round. List them on the chalkboard or on a "circle chart."

Provide practice in vocabulary recoginiton with the word cards.

Review the direction word *write* and the shape word *circle*. Note the *circle* is also a direction word.

Read the directions with the children. Identify the pictures. If your students are able, teach the words *penny, wheel,* and *hoop*. This vocabulary is for enrichment and is not to be used as part of the reading vocabulary.

Read the sentences with the children. Have them fill in the lines. The first one is dotted and is to be traced.

ACTIVITIES:

1. Set up a discovery center providing various sized shapes made of sturdy material. Such sets are available commerically or can be constructed of wood or heavy cardboard and painted in the primary colors (red, blue, and yellow). These shapes can be used for patternmaking, classifiying, tracing and so on. The children can use these patterns throughout the LIFEPAC.
2. Give the children drawing paper and have them make a drawing using only circles.
3. More advanced students may work with and expand the sentences to tell about the picture.

Page 14: Squares and Rectangles

CONCEPT: identification of squares and rectangles alone and in familiar objects

OBJECTIVES:
I can tell about some shapes I see.
I can name some shapes I see.
I can read some shapes words.

PROCESSES: observing, using the senses of sight; comparing, likes and differences

READING INTEGRATION: vocabulary development, sentence recognition, left to right, written and oral directions, main idea

VOCABULARY: side, long, short, (rectangle, square)

MATERIALS NEEDED: squares and rectangles of different sizes and proportions, shape-word cards, LIFEPAC Tablet, Worksheet 7

TEACHING PAGE 14:

Have ready the models of squares and rectangles. Have children discuss ways they are alike and different. Remind them that they are using their eyes to learn about these shapes. Have them find shapes of squares and rectangles in the classroom (desk top, book, etc.). Have the children match the shape to the shape word.

Practice the vocabulary with the word cards. Have the children use the words in sentences. Read the descriptive sentences with the children. Emphasize the vocabulary words. Note the left to right reading. Use the shape models to point out the important ideas of the sentences.

Read the directions. Let the children complete the page independently. Give help as needed.

ACTIVITIES:

1. Do Worksheet 7. Give help with the directions as needed.
2. Continue use of discovery center.
3. Use Tablet to practice vocabulary words.
4. Add vocabulary to science dictionary.

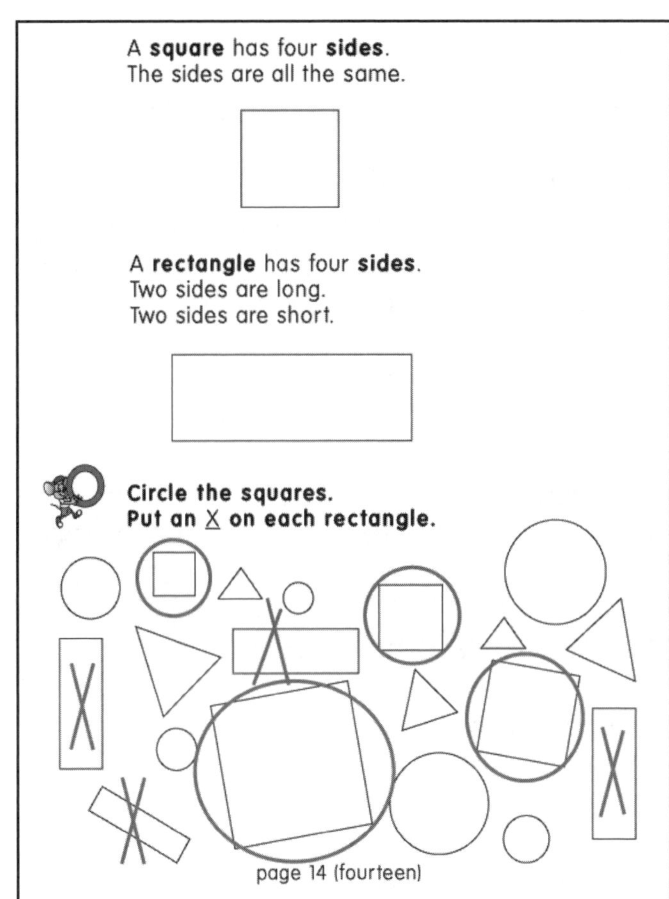

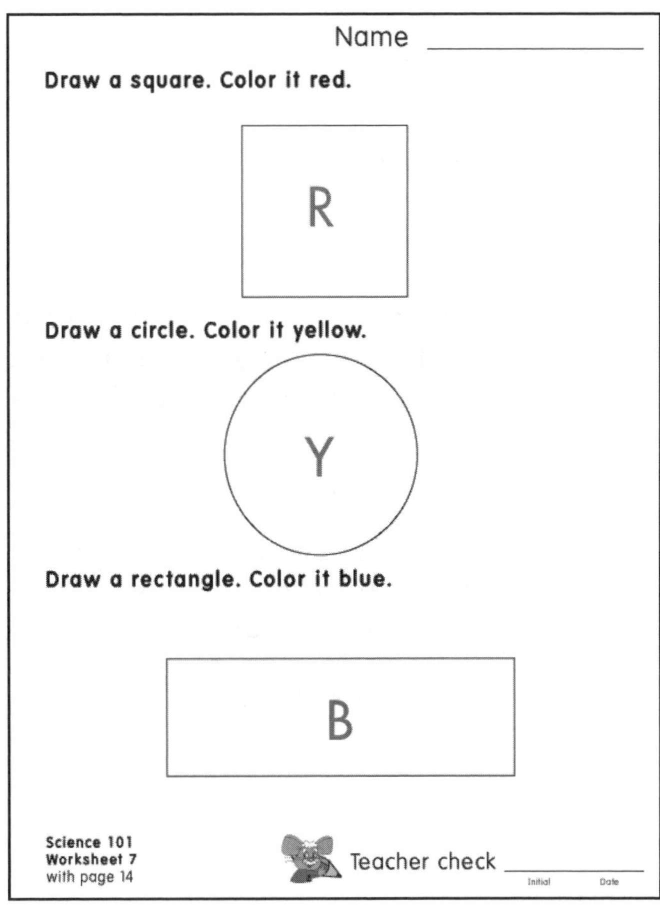

A **square** has four **sides**.

A **rectangle** has four **sides**.
Two sides are long.
Two sides are short.
Circle the squares.
Put an X on each rectangle.

Name
Draw a square. Color it red.
R
Draw a circle. Color it yellow.
Y
Draw a rectangle. Color it blue.
B
Science 101
Worksheet 7
with page 14
Teacher check
Initial
Date

Page 15: Triangles

CONCEPT: Triangles have three sides.

OBJECTIVES:

I can tell about some shapes I see.
I can name some shapes I see.
I can read some shape words.

PROCESSES: observing, using the sense of sight; comparing, likes and differences

READING INTEGRATION: vocabulary development, sentence recognition, main idea

VOCABULARY: same, different

MATERIALS NEEDED: models of triangles, assorted sizes and proportions, vocabulary-word cards

TEACHING PAGE 15:

Compare triangle models with the class. Have the children volunteer their observations of how all triangles are alike and how they are different. Note triangles in the classroom.

Read the descriptive sentences with the children. Ask for a volunteer to use the models to show the main idea of each sentence.

Read the direction to the children. Have them read it with you as you repeat it. Have the page completed independently. Give help as needed.

ACTIVITIES:

1. Continue use of discovery center. Have the children group shapes, build things, and work with shapes.
2. Do Worksheet 8. Review of shapes and color. Read directions. Give help as needed.

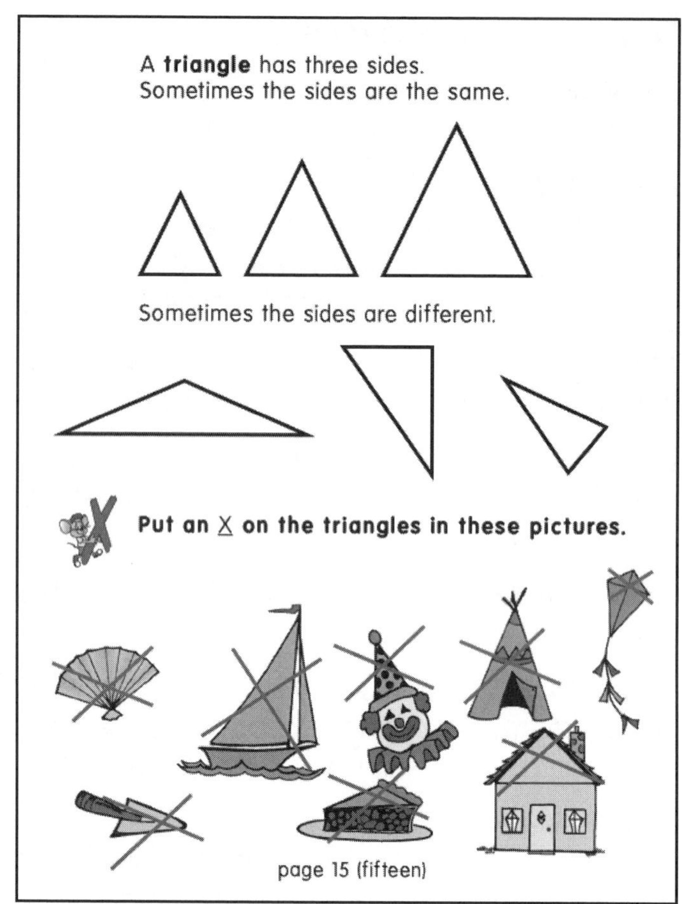

A **triangle** has three sides.
Sometimes the sides are the same.
Sometimes the sides are different.
Put an X on the triangles in these pictures.
page 15 (fifteen)

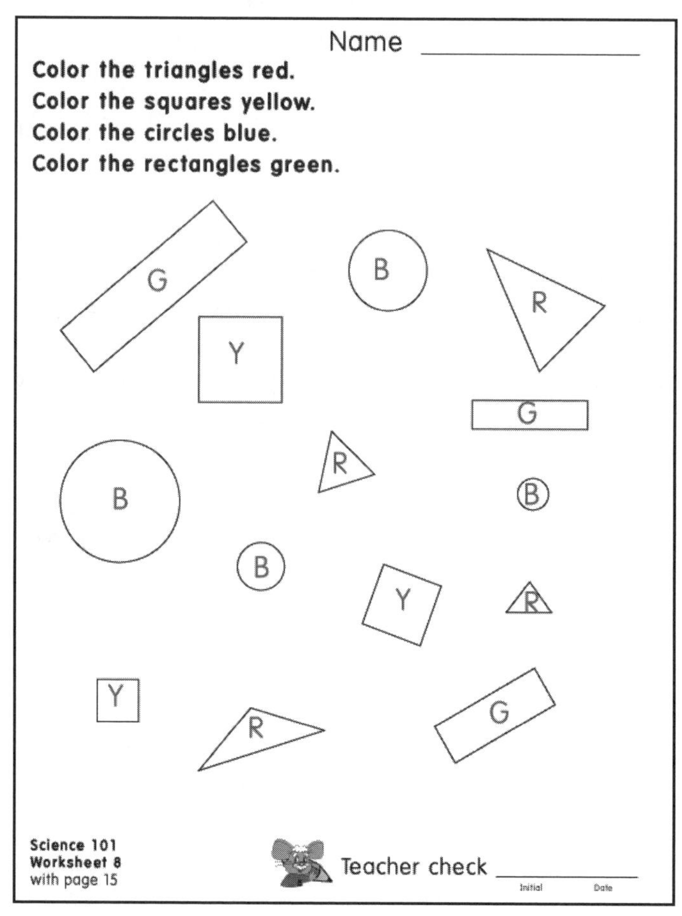

Page 16: You Group by Shape

CONCEPT: Objects can be grouped by common properties.

OBJECTIVES:
I can tell about some shapes I see.
I can match objects by shape.

PROCESSES: observing, using the sense of sight; classifying, by shape

READING INTEGRATION: written and oral directions

VOCABULARY: (circle, rectangle, square, triangle)

MATERIALS NEEDED: pencils, flannel board or chart, flannel shapes or paper shapes with rolled tape to hold shapes to surface, familiar objects of assorted shapes, four shoeboxes, set of small shapes to be sorted

TEACHING PAGE 16:

Use the flannel board or chart to have the children practice putting the shapes into groups. Be sure the chart is visible to all. Label the chart with the shape word and the letter as used on the page.

Using the objects of assorted shapes, have the children take turns putting them into groups by shape.

Read the title and text. Discuss differing shapes in objects in the room, in nature, and so on.

Read the directions together. Be sure the children understand that they are to write only the letter that stands for the shape.

ACTIVITY:

Set up the four shoe boxes in the discovery center. Label each box with the name of a different shape.

Put the set of small shapes in a box near the shoe boxes. Give the children the following directions and then write the directions on tag board and put near the boxes.

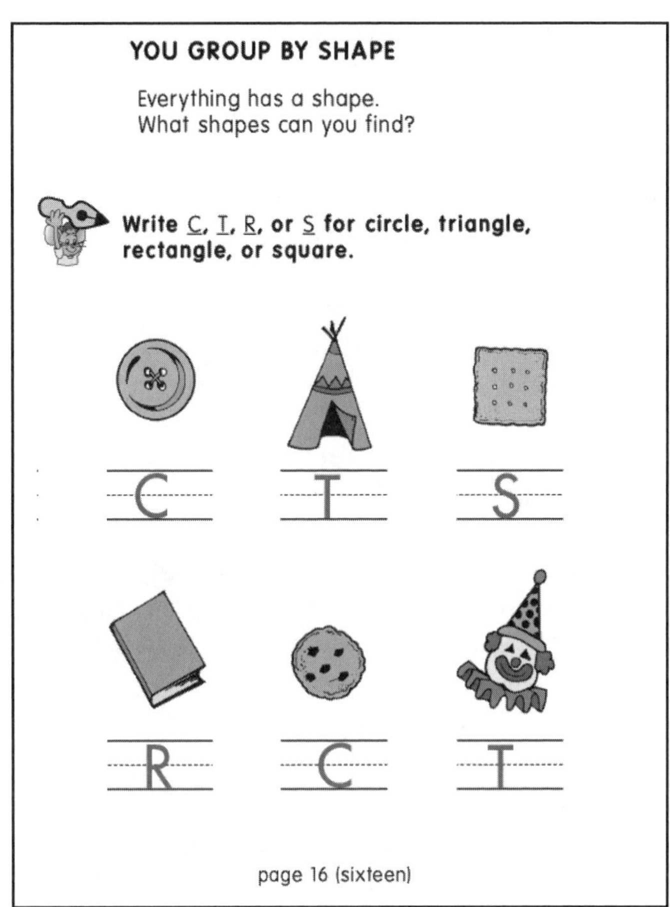

YOU GROUP BY SHAPE
Everything has a shape.
What shapes can you find?
Write C, T, R, or S for circle, triangle, rectangle, or square.
C
T
S
R
C
T
page 16 (sixteen)

Put the shape in the right box.
Have a helper check your work.

Page 17: Shape Groups

CONCEPT: Shapes are all around.

OBJECTIVES:
I can tell about some shapes I see.
I can match objects by shape.

PROCESSES: observing, by using the sense of sight; classifying, by shape

READING INTEGRATION: sentence form—the question(?)

MATERIALS NEEDED: chart or chalkboard, an assortment of three-dimensional objects that will demonstrate flat shapes (circle, square, etc.) when projected, overhead projector, LIFEPAC Tablet

TEACHING PAGE 17:

Use the overhead projector to show how shadows of common objects are flat shapes. Use objects that will project the shapes learned thus far (an unsharpened pencil will project as a long rectangle and an ice cream cone will project as a triangle and a circle depending on how it is laid on the projector).

After the demonstration have the children use their eyes to discover shape groups in the classroom. Lists should be recorded on a chart or the chalkboard.

Read the sentence to and with the children. Call attention to the question.

Note the question mark. The page should be done as a group with the shapes found recorded on a class chart. If the group is capable, have them copy the lists in their Tablets.

ACTIVITIES:

1. To extend the concept of grouping (classifying), have the children find other kinds of groups in the picture. Examples: color groups, living and non living things.
2. Have the children draw color groups.

Use your eyes.
Can you find groups of shapes?
page 17 (seventeen)

3. Have the more advanced students make up a story for the picture and dictate it to an aide. Have the children illustrate the story.

Page 18: Shapes Can Help You

CONCEPT: Shapes can serve useful purposes.

OBJECTIVES:
I can tell about some shapes I see.
I can tell some ways shapes help.

PROCESSES: observing, by using the sense of sight; predicting

READING INTEGRATION: sentence form—question (?), following directions

VOCABULARY: (help)

MATERIALS NEEDED: blocks, drawing paper, crayons, pencils

TEACHING PAGE 18:

Discuss ways in which shapes are used to help us. Builders use shapes to make buildings strong. Demonstrate with the blocks.

Read the title and the text. Make note of the sentence form and the question marks. The children should be given time to examine the picture carefully. Ask for a volunteer to tell what will happen to the vase of flowers. Do not discuss what shape will work better than the circle. Let each child complete the picture at the bottom of the page independently. Be sure they know to fill in the name of the shape they choose to answer the question.

Check to see if they have drawn the correct shape. If they have not, show them the consequences of putting the wrong shape under the table.

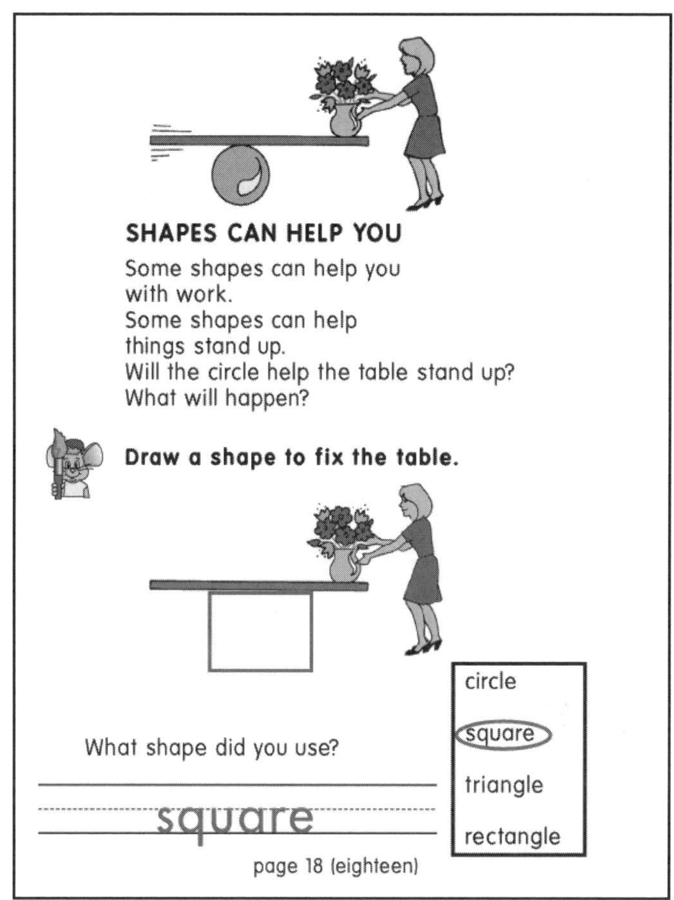

SHAPES CAN HELP YOU
Some shapes can help you
with work.
Some shapes can help
things stand up.
Will the circle help the table stand up?
What will happen?
Draw a shape to fix the table.
What shape did you use?
square
circle
square
triangle
rectangle
page 18 (eighteen)

ACTIVITIES:

1. Do Worksheet 9. Read directions and key. Let the children complete the page independently.
2. Continue use of discovery center until all the children have competed the sorting activity.
3. Give each child a sheet of drawing paper. Have the children fold the paper into four boxes Have them draw a circle in the first box, a triangle in the second, a square in the third, and a rectangle in the fourth.

Ask them to make something real from each shape.

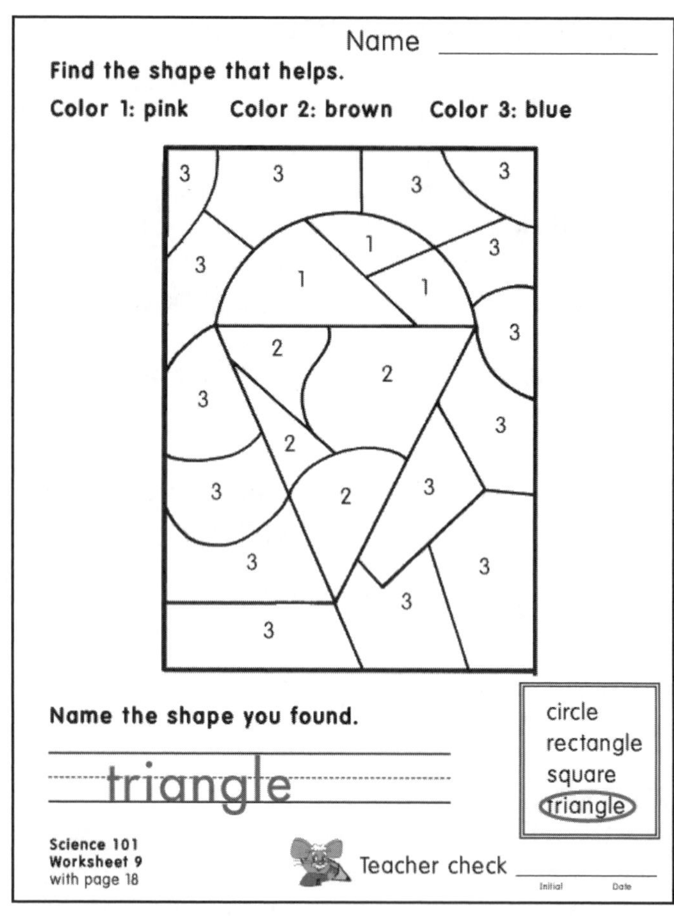
Name
Find the shape that helps.
Color 1: pink Color 2: brown Color 3: blue
3
3
3
3
3
1
1
1
3
3
3
2
2
3
2
3
2
3
3
3
3
3
3
Name the shape you found.
triangle
circle
rectangle
square
triangle
Science 101
Worksheet 9
with page 18
Teacher check
Initial Date

Page 19: Activity Page

VOCABULARY: work

MATERIALS NEEDED: pencils, crayons, LIFEPAC Tablet

TEACHING PAGE 19:

Review the idea that shapes can be useful. Encourage discussion of other ways shapes can be useful.

Read the direction sentence. Be sure the children understand that the shape in each picture is to be doing a useful job. The triangle, for example, is useful in holding the ice cream.

ACTIVITY:

If your class is capable, have the children write a sentence about each shape in their Tablets. If they are not able to do this task, copy this sentence.

Shapes can do work.

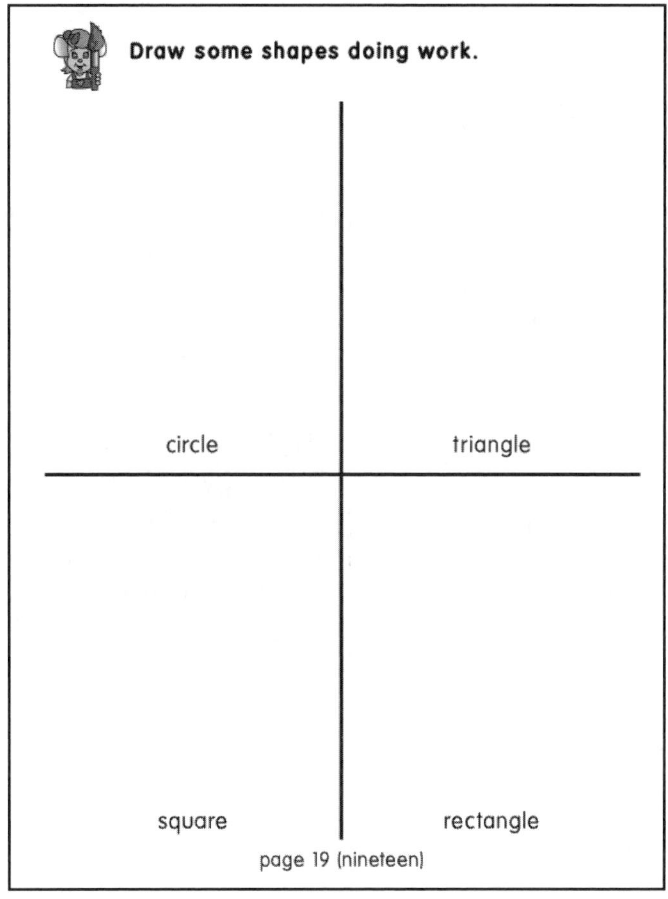

Draw some shapes doing work.
circle
triangle
square
rectangle
page 19 (nineteen)

Page 20: Self Test 2

MATERIALS NEEDED: pencils

TEACHING PAGE 20:

Before beginning the test, review shapes and shape words, color and color words, and direction words. Read all directions with the children.

The proficiency of your class should dictate whether you will do the self test as a group or allow the children to proceed independently once the directions are given. If you choose to do it together, read each direction, answer any questions, and then allow enough time for every child to complete the activity.

If your group is working independently, be sure that you are available for individual questions.

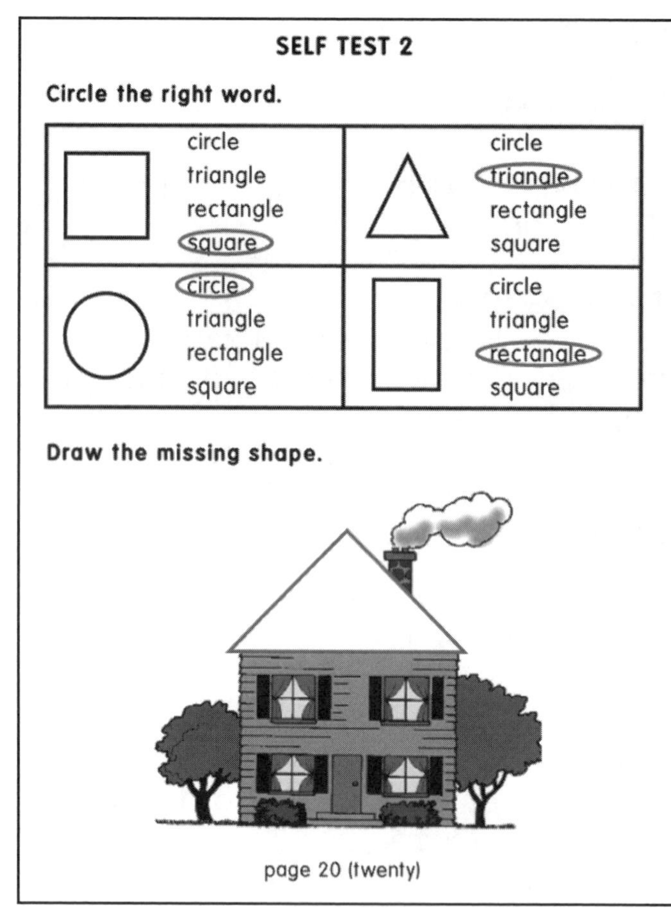

SELF TEST 2

Circle the right word.

	circle triangle rectangle square		circle triangle rectangle square
	circle triangle rectangle square		circle triangle rectangle square

Draw the missing shape.

page 20 (twenty)

Pages 21 and 22: Self Test 2

TEACHING PAGES 21 AND 22:

Read directions.

Check.

Help any students who still have difficulty distinguishing shapes or colors by reviewing pages, activities, and handbook materials for colors and shapes.

ACTIVITY:

Use Worksheet 10 for students who need it for review.

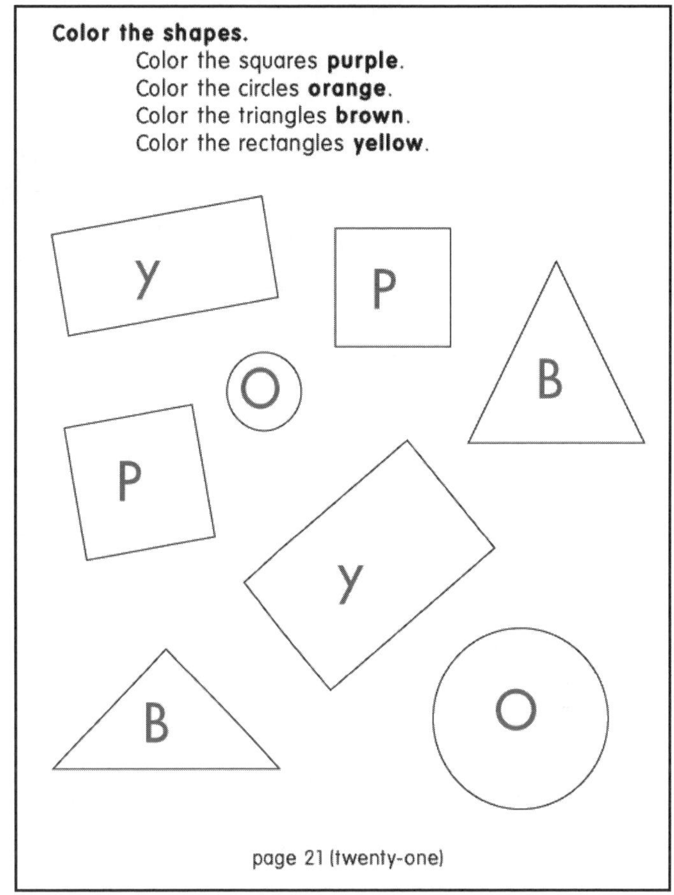

Color the squares **purple**.
Color the circles **orange**.

Write the name of the shapes.
squares circles rectangles
circles
11/14
Teacher Check
Initial
Date
My Score
page 22 (twenty-two)

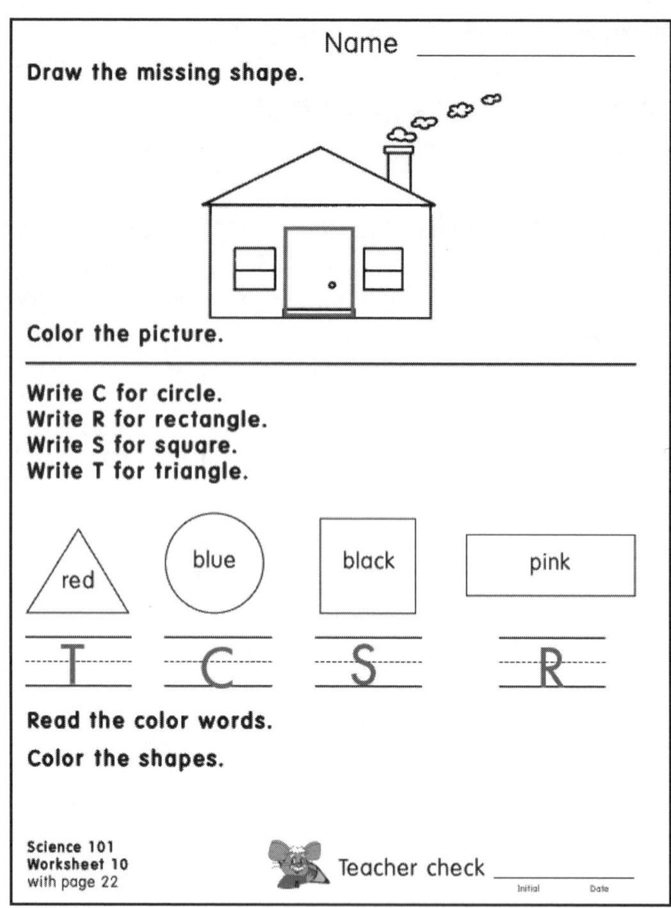
Name ____________

Draw the missing shape.

Color the picture.

Write C for circle.
Write R for rectangle.
Write S for square.
Write T for triangle.

Read the color words.

Color the shapes.

Science 101
Worksheet 10
with page 22

Teacher check ____________
Initial Date

PART III: YOU SEE SIZE

Page 23

CONCEPT: relativity of size

OBJECTIVE: I can tell about some sizes I see.

PROCESSES: observing, using the sense of sight; comparing

READING INTEGRATION: listening, rhyming, main idea

VOCABULARY: big, small, narrow, wide, (long, size, short)

MATERIALS NEEDED: vocabulary-word cards, things to be found in the classroom, buttons, pictures of like objects of differing size

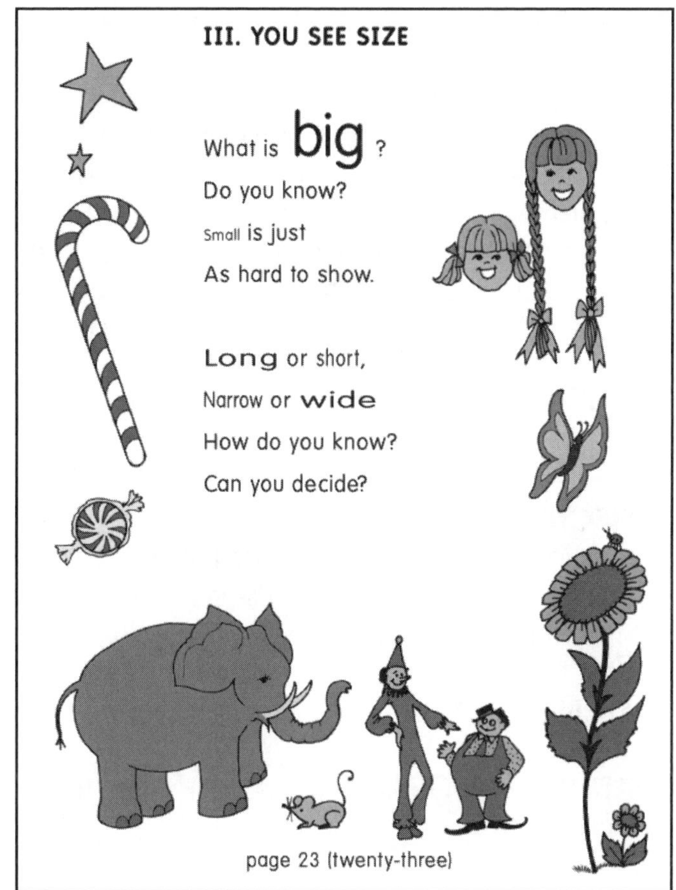
III. YOU SEE SIZE
What is big ?
Do you know?
Small is just
As hard to show.
Long or short,
Narrow or wide
How do you know?
Can you decide?
page 23 (twenty-three)

TEACHING PAGE 23:

Demonstrate how size is relative, that is, how size relates to the objects being compared. *Example:* A *big* button is small when compared to a baby elephant. A baby elephant is small when compared to its mother. A desk is *wide* when compared to a ruler but *narrow* when compared to the width of the room.

Use the word cards to familiarize the children with the vocabulary words.

Read the size poem. Have the children follow along. Have the children identify the size words in the poem.

Pass out the size-word cards. As the poem is reread, have the words held up as the corresponding word is read. Repeat, giving the word cards to other children.

The children should read along in chorus as the poem becomes familiar.

ACTIVITIES:

1. Extend the discussion of size by having the children think of other size words.
2. Record the vocabulary and the extended list in the science dictionary.

Pages 24, 25, and 26: You Name Some Sizes

NOTE TO TEACHER:

Pages 24, 25, and 26 are similar in form and concept. They may be taught together or separately depending on your group. The directions for all three pages are given here. Worksheets 11, 12, and 13 are available to reinforce the concepts of the three pages.

CONCEPTS: big and small (24), long and short (25), wide and narrow (26)

OBJECTIVES:

I can tell about some sizes I see.
I can name some sizes I see.
I can read some size words.

PROCESSES: observing, comparing

READING INTEGRATION: written directions, vocabulary development

MATERIALS NEEDED: pencils; crayons; vocabulary-word cards (size words); LIFEPAC Tablet; Worksheets 11, 12, and 13

TEACHING PAGES 24, 25, and 26:

Review relativity of size. Use objects in the room. Compare sizes of *like* objects. Compare sizes of *unlike* objects.

The students may compare sizes of each other, for example, their height, size of feet, length of hair, and so on.

Emphasize the size words. Use the word cards for extra practice if needed.

Read the introductory sentences. Have the children volunteer to read them. Be sure directions are understood. Pages may be completed independently.

ACTIVITIES:

1. Do Worksheets 11, 12, and 13.
2. Practice the appropriate size words in the Tablets.

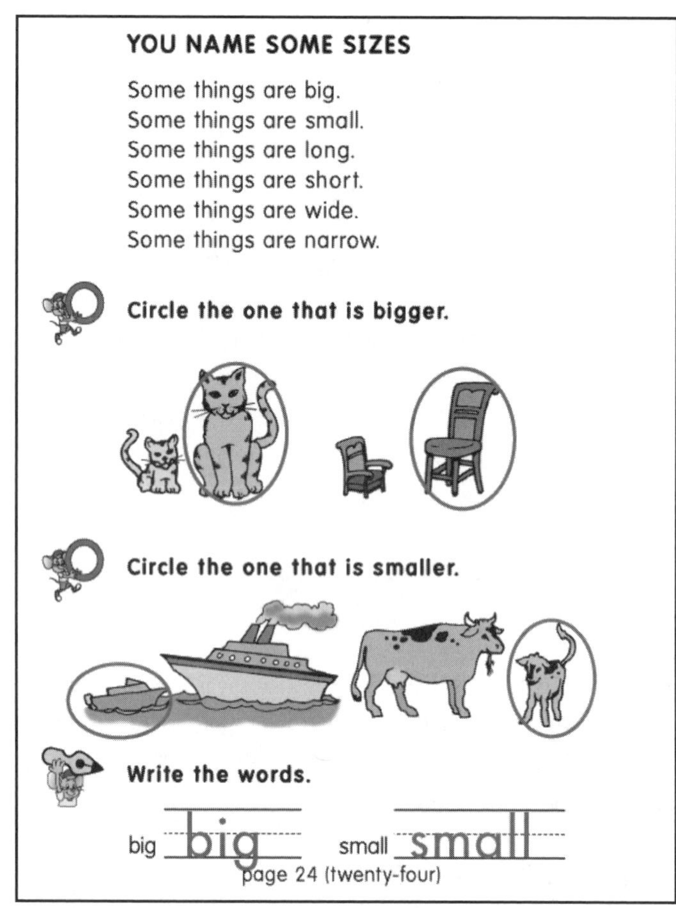

YOU NAME SOME SIZES
Some things are big.
Some things are small.
Some things are long.
Some things are short.
Some things are wide.
Some things are narrow.
Circle the one that is bigger.
Circle the one that is smaller.
Write the words.
big big
small small
page 24 (twenty-four)

Put an X on the one that is longer.
Put an X on the one that is shorter.
Write the words.
long long
short short
page 25 (twenty-five)

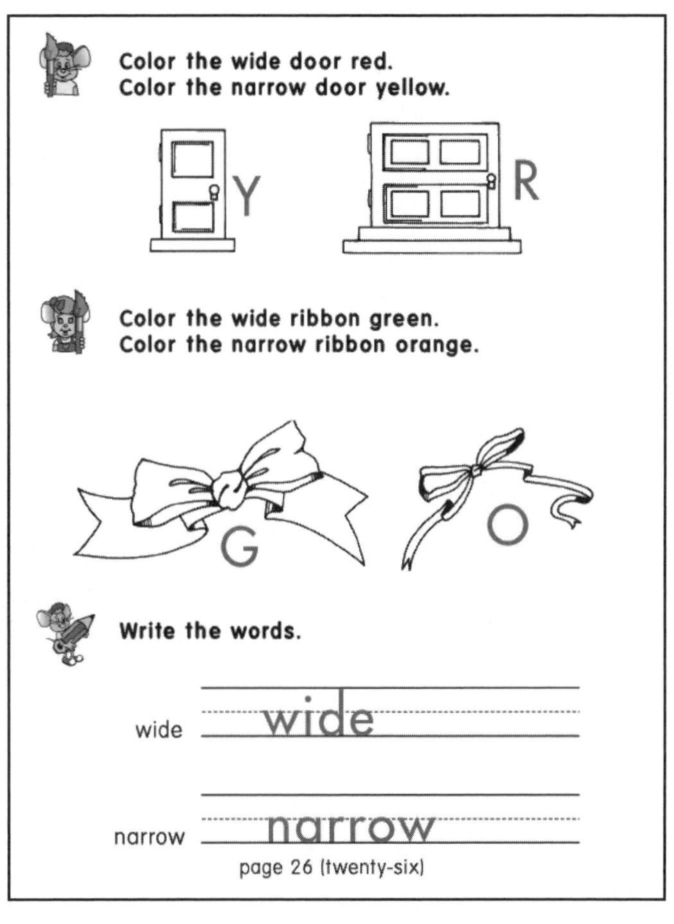
Color the wide door red.
Color the narrow door yellow.
Y
R
Color the wide ribbon green.
Color the narrow ribbon orange.
G
O
Write the words.
wide
wide
narrow
narrow
page 26 (twenty-six)

Name
Draw a big flower. Draw a small flower.
Draw a big balloon. Draw a small balloon.
Color your pictures.
Science 101
Worksheet 11
with page 24
Teacher check
Initial
Date

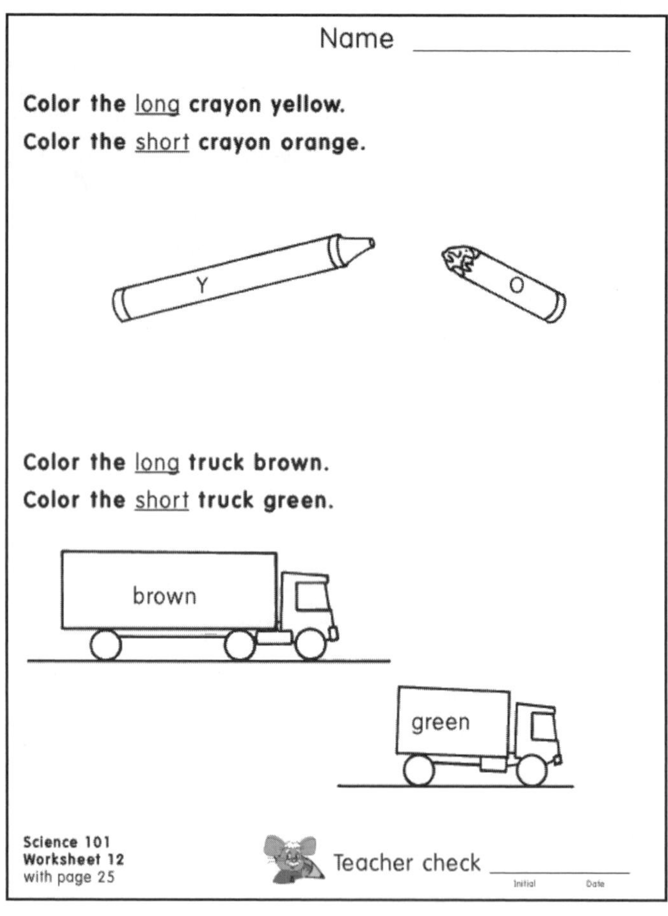
Name
Color the long crayon yellow.
Color the short crayon orange.
Y
O
Color the long truck brown.
Color the short truck green.
brown
green
Science 101
Worksheet 12
with page 25
Teacher check
Initial
Date

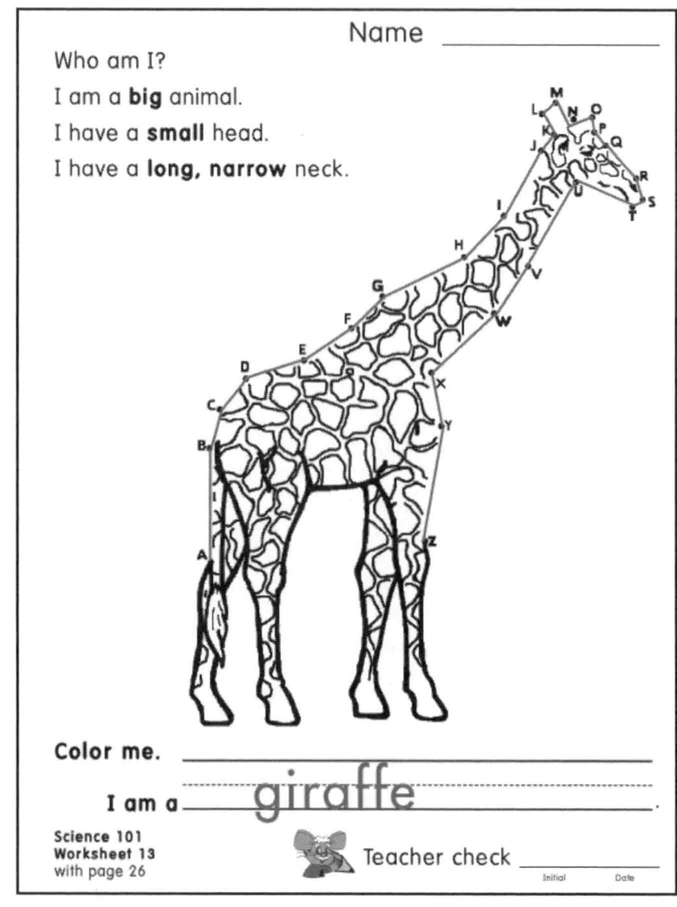
Name
Who am I?
I am a big animal.
I have a small head.
I have a long, narrow neck.
Color me.
I am a giraffe.
Science 101
Worksheet 13
with page 26
Teacher check
Initial
Date

Page 27: You Can Group by Size

CONCEPTS: grouping by size, sequencing by size (supplementary)

OBJECTIVES:

I can tell about some sizes I see.
I can match objects by size.

PROCESSES: observing, classifying

READING INTEGRATION: following written directions

VOCABULARY: belong, different, same, (group)

MATERIALS NEEDED: pencils, 4 rulers (3 long, 1 short or 3 short, 1 long), 4 balloons (3 alike, 1 different) or other similar materials, scissors, paste or glue, Worksheet 14

TEACHING PAGE 27:

Demonstrate grouping by using rulers, balloons, or some similar objects or by drawing such objects on the chalkboard. Put three long rulers and one short ruler on a table. Ask the children to put those together that are alike (three long rulers). Repeat the activity with the balloons or with the other objects chosen. You might also use the children.

Example: three girls with long hair and one with short. Have the children select the one that does not belong. Use word cards to teach the vocabulary.

Ask for a volunteer to read the sentences. Read them to the group if necessary. The page may be completed independently.

ACTIVITIES:

1. Use alternate type of grouping: sequencing according to size. Demonstrate using the children. Have a small group of them stand in order, shortest to tallest.
2. Do Worksheet 14. Be sure the directions are understood. Emphasize the words *paste, order,* and *first.*

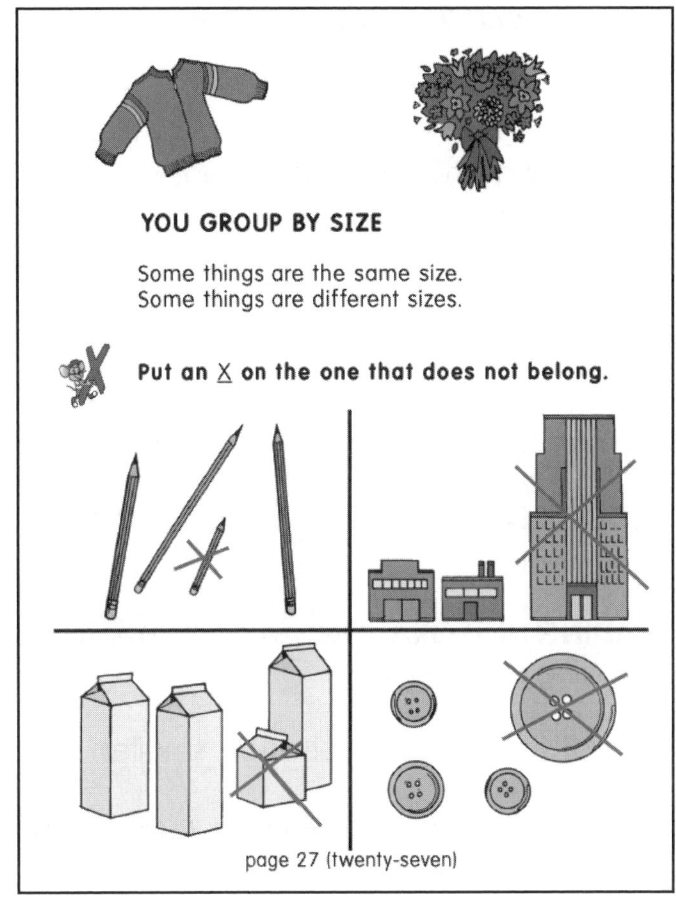

YOU GROUP BY SIZE
Some things are the same size.
Some things are different sizes.
Put an X on the one that does not belong.
page 27 (twenty-seven)

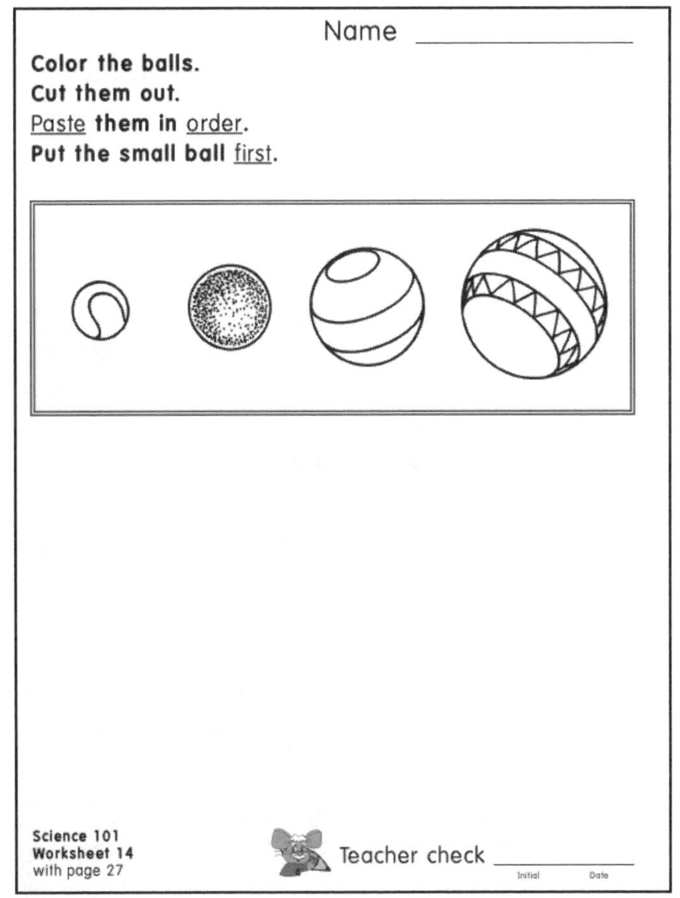

Name
Color the balls.
Cut them out.
Paste them in order.
Put the small ball first.
Science 101
Worksheet 14
with page 27
Teacher check
Initial
Date

Pages 28 and 29: Changing Size

NOTE TO THE TEACHER: Pages 28 and 29 are similar in form and concept. They may be taught together. The directions for both pages are given here.

CONCEPT: Size can change.

OBJECTIVES:

I can tell about some sizes I see.
I can tell some ways size can change.

PROCESSES: observing, comparing, classifying

READING INTEGRATION: written directions, speaking in a group

VOCABULARY: bigger, change, smaller

MATERIALS NEEDED: pencils, pictures of things that grow, pictures of things that get smaller, LIFEPAC Tablet, vocabulary cards

TEACHING PAGES 28 AND 29:

Discuss how some things get bigger. Use living things as examples, both plants and animals. Some things get smaller. Pencils get shorter as they are used. A snowman melts in the sun.

Give the children practice in recognizing the new words. Ask for suggestions of things they know that get bigger or smaller. Record the lists under the proper heading on the chalkboard. Have the children record the lists in their LIFEPAC Tablets.

Read the introductory sentences to and with the children. Pages may be completed independently.

ACTIVITY:

In the discovery center have the children make two collages: one of things that get bigger and one of things that get smaller. Provide magazines from which the children may cut pictures. Scissors and glue or paste will be necessary as well as banner

SIZE CAN CHANGE
Some things get bigger.
Some things get smaller.
Match small to big.
Write the words.
bigger
bigger
smaller
smaller
page 28 (twenty-eight)

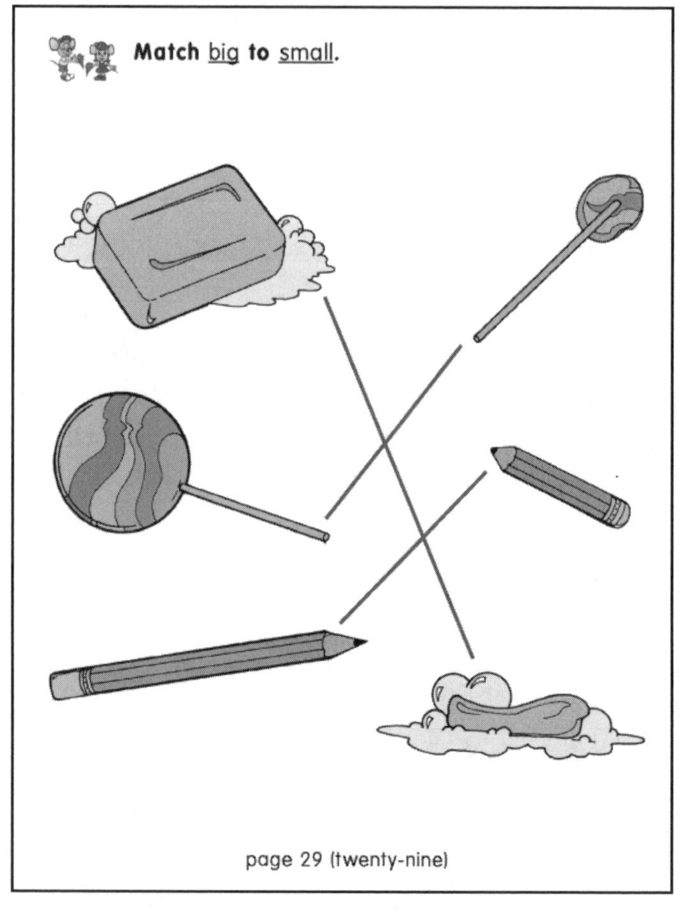
Match big to small.
page 29 (twenty-nine)

paper for the background. Teacher should label the collages with the vocabulary words *bigger* and *smaller.*

Page 30: Size Can Help You

CONCEPT: Size can be helpful.

OBJECTIVES:
I can tell about some sizes I see.
I can tell some ways size helps.

PROCESS: observing

READING INTEGRATION: written directions, listening

VOCABULARY: fit(s)

MATERIALS NEEDED: pencils, crayons, clothing or shoes of varying sizes, child sized desk and chair, teacher-sized desk and chair, other useful objects of varying sizes.

TEACHING PAGE 30:
Introduce the idea of the usefulness of size. *Examples:* Choose a baby shoe or a very large one (an article of clothing will do as well). Ask a child to try it on. Ask if it fits (reinforce the word with a word card). Note the importance of fit in shoes and clothing.

Put a teacher's chair at a student desk or a student's chair at the teacher's desk. Ask if the chair goes with or fits the desk. Why not? Have the children discuss other ways size can be helpful.

Read the introductory sentences and the direction to and with the class. Have the page completed independently.

ACTIVITY:
1. Have objects in the discovery center that fit together (boxes and lids, pieces of puzzles, jars and lids, etc.). Have children select the pieces that fit together.
2. Do Worksheet 15 to review concepts in the LIFEPAC. Read the directions with the children. Be sure they are understood. When the worksheet is completed, check it carefully. The results may determine the extent of review necessary before giving the final self test and the LIFEPAC Test.

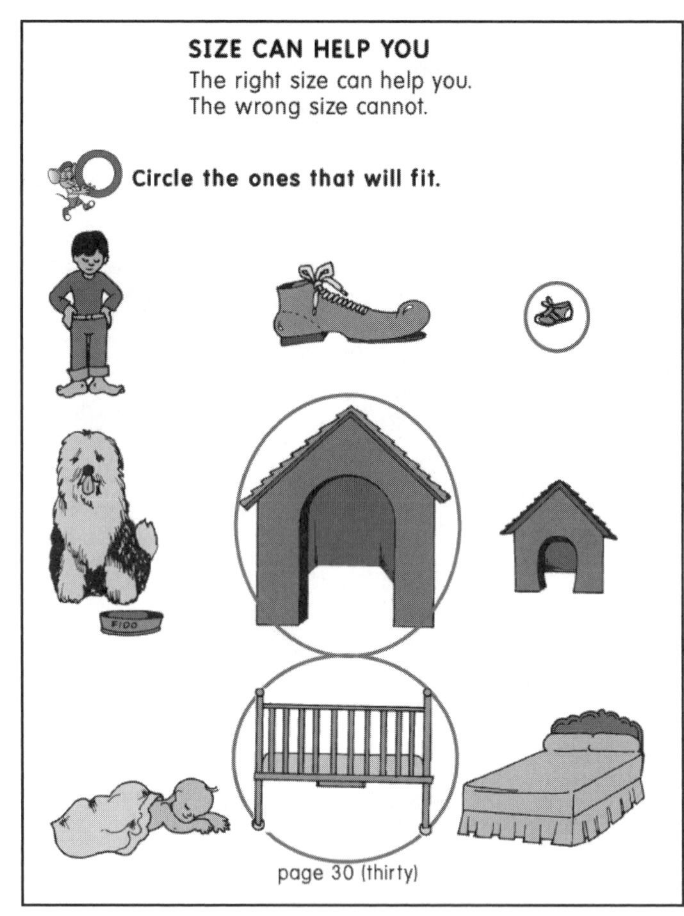

SIZE CAN HELP YOU
The right size can help you.
The wrong size cannot.
Circle the ones that will fit.
FIDO
page 30 (thirty)

Name
Hi, My name is Patches. I need a house.
Draw my house just the right size.
Use a square and a triangle. The door can be a circle or a rectangle.
Color my house red.
Color the roof black.
Science 101
Worksheet 15
with page 30
Teacher check
Initial
Date

Page 31: Size Groups

CONCEPT: grouping by size

OBJECTIVE:
I can tell about some sizes I see.
I can match objects by size.

PROCESSES: observation, classifying

READING INTEGRATION: speaking in a group

MATERIALS NEEDED: objects to be found in the classroom, LIFEPAC Tablet

TEACHING PAGE 31:

Review the idea of relativity of size taught on page 23. Give the children an opportunity to identify groups of sizes in the classroom. They might identify all big things (the chalkboard, teacher's desk, bookcases etc.) and all small things (objects like crayons, pencils, etc.).

Read the introductory sentence to and with the class. Have the children volunteer titles of size groups to be found in the picture. List the groups as they are identified. The lists may be recorded in the Tablets.

ACTIVITY:

Continue collages until all have had a chance to contribute.

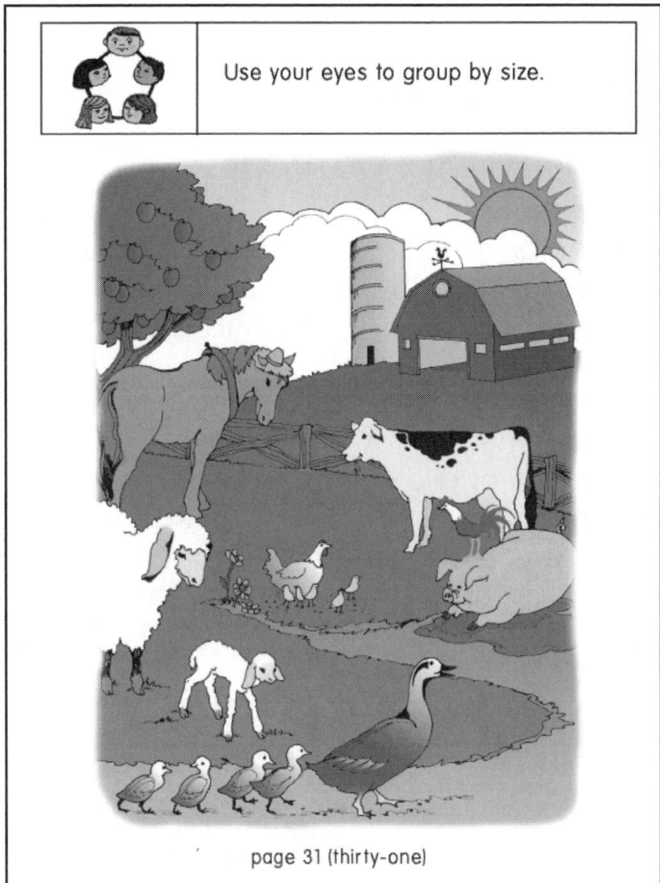

Use your eyes to group by size.
page 31 (thirty-one)

Pages 32 and 33: Self Test 3

MATERIALS NEEDED: pencils

TEACHING PAGES 32 AND 33:

Review colors, shapes, and sizes. Pay particular attention to the vocabulary words. Review the direction words. Read through all of the directions with the children.

The proficiency of your class should dictate whether you will do the self test with the group or allow the children to proceed independently once the directions are given. If you choose to do it together, read each direction, answer any questions, and then allow enough time for every child to complete the activity.

If your group is working independently, be sure that you are available for individual questions.

Check.

Help children who do poorly by reviewing those pages and activities that reinforce the concepts missed. Ask the child questions to determine precisely what was not understood. Check the activities carefully to determine problems. In the first activity, for example, if the child correctly answers the boxes with objects, but misses the three boxes with shapes, his problem is most likely working with shapes rather than size or color.

Analyze other activities accordingly and review as needed.

When the child has reviewed sufficiently, give him this test again. He must complete this test correctly (80%) before taking the LIFEPAC Test.

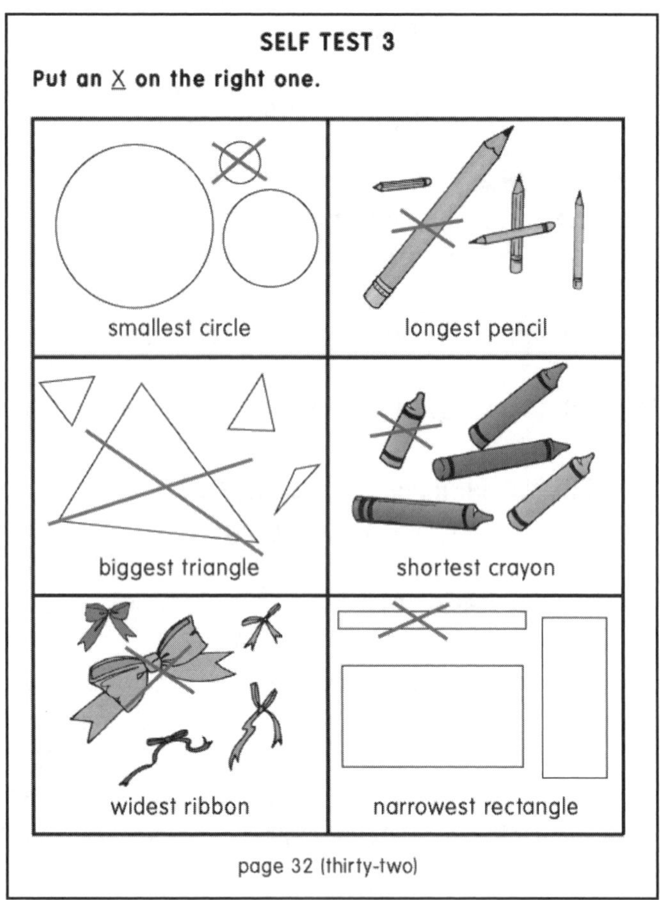

Circle the ones that will get bigger.
Put an X on each one that will get smaller.
Circle the square that does not belong.
Match the one that will fit.
11/14
Teacher Check
Initial
Date
My Score
page 33 (thirty-three)

LIFEPAC TEST AND ALTERNATE LIFEPAC TEST

Administer to the class as a group. Ask to have directions read or read them to the class. In either case, be sure that the children clearly understand what they are to do. Put examples on the board if necessary. Give sufficient time for each activity to be completed before going on to the next one.

When the entire test is complete, collect and score. For those children who do not achieve the acceptable score for passing, return the LIFEPAC for review. Give additional copies of the worksheets and a list of vocabulary words to study. A parent or classroom helper should help in the review. When the child is ready, administer the Alternate LIFEPAC Test. Use the same procedure as for the LIFEPAC Test.

The Alternate LIFEPAC Test is given with answers in this section. It is given without answers so that it can be duplicated.

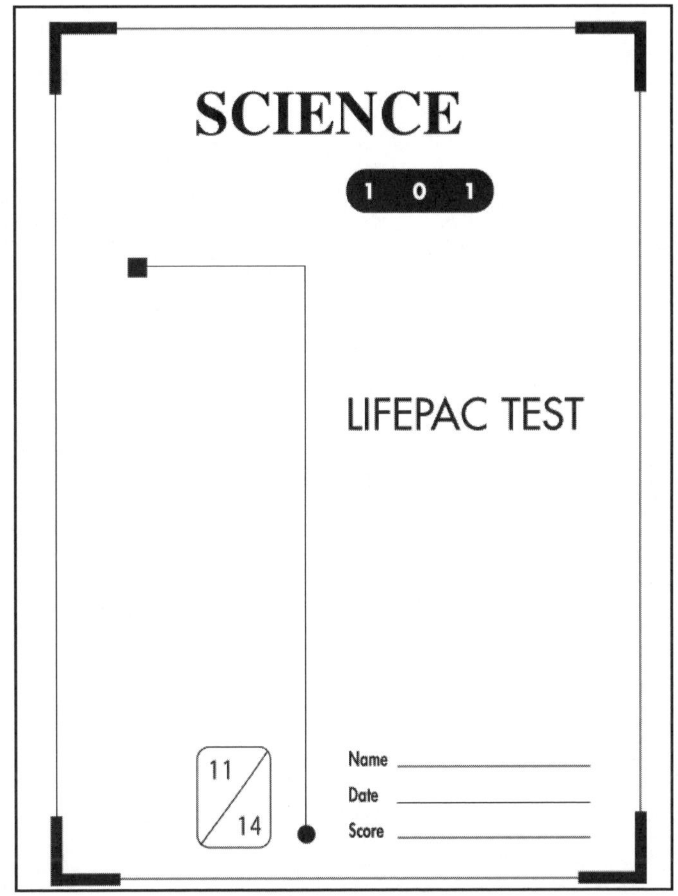

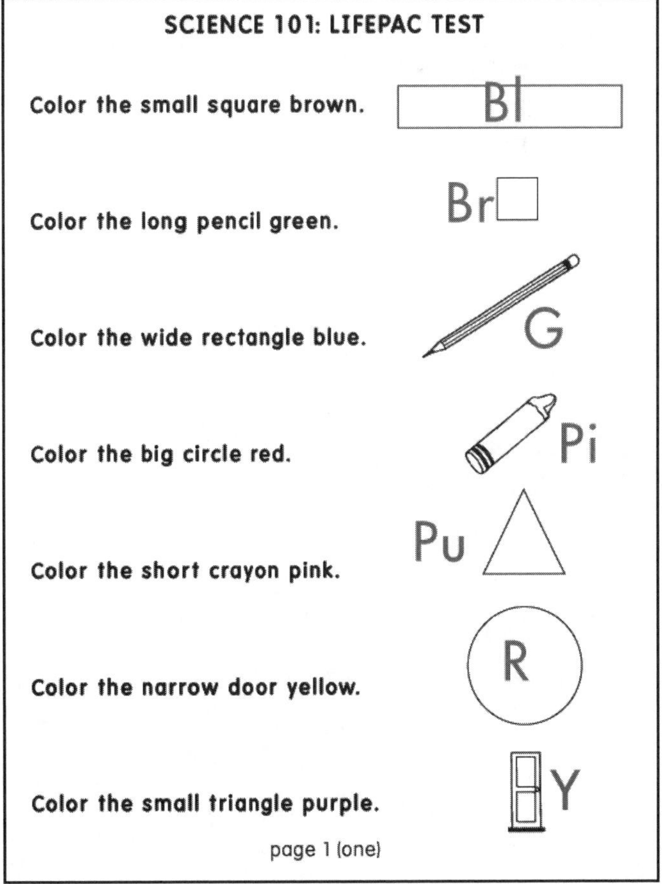
SCIENCE 101: LIFEPAC TEST

Color the small square brown.

Color the long pencil green.

Color the wide rectangle blue.

Color the big circle red.

Color the short crayon pink.

Color the narrow door yellow.

Color the small triangle purple.

page 1 (one)

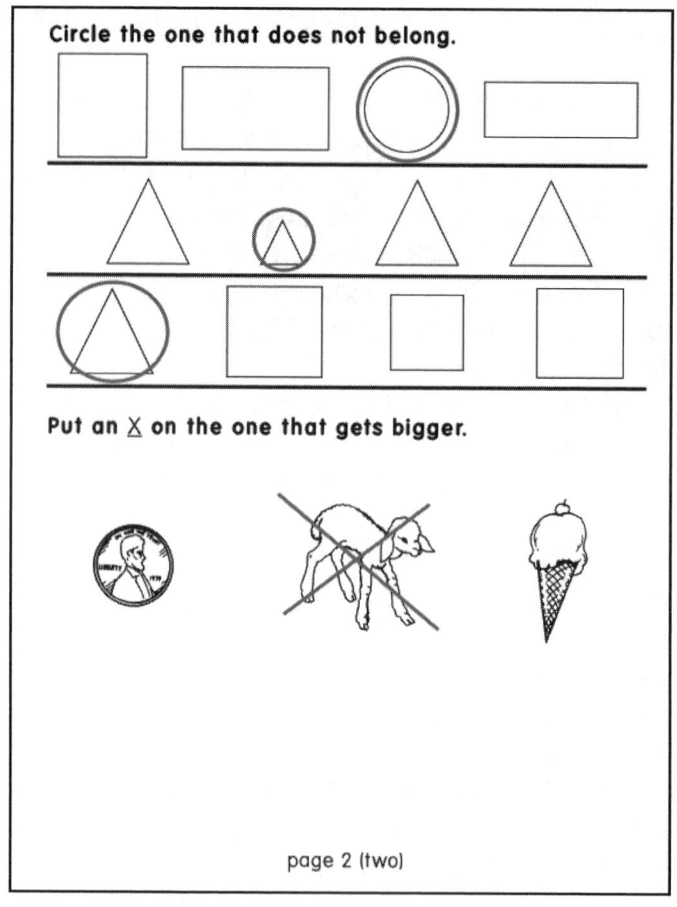
Circle the one that does not belong.
Put an X on the one that gets bigger.
page 2 (two)

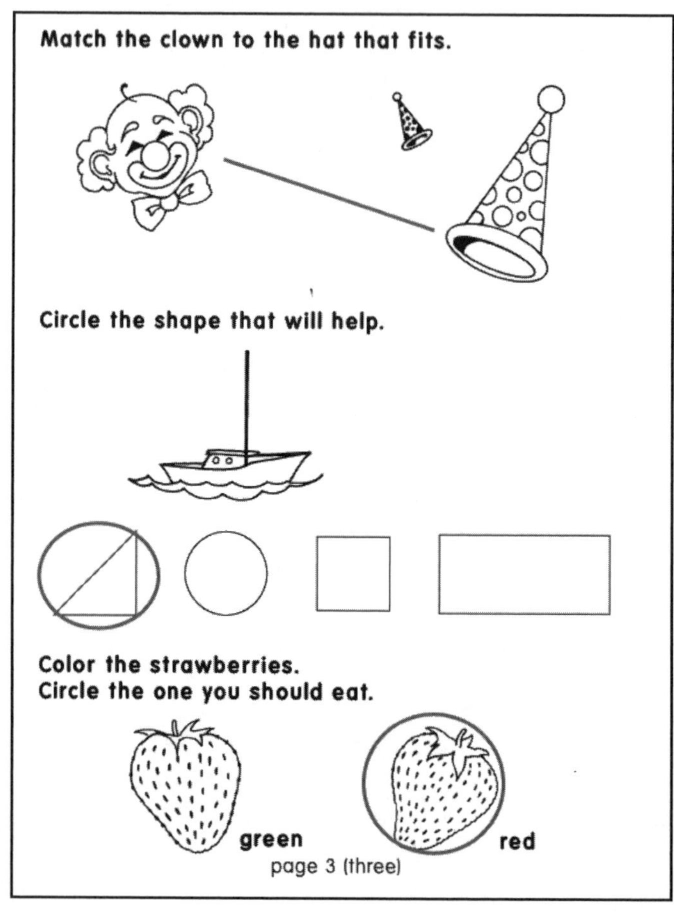
Match the clown to the hat that fits.
Circle the shape that will help.
Color the strawberries.
Circle the one you should eat.
green
red
page 3 (three)

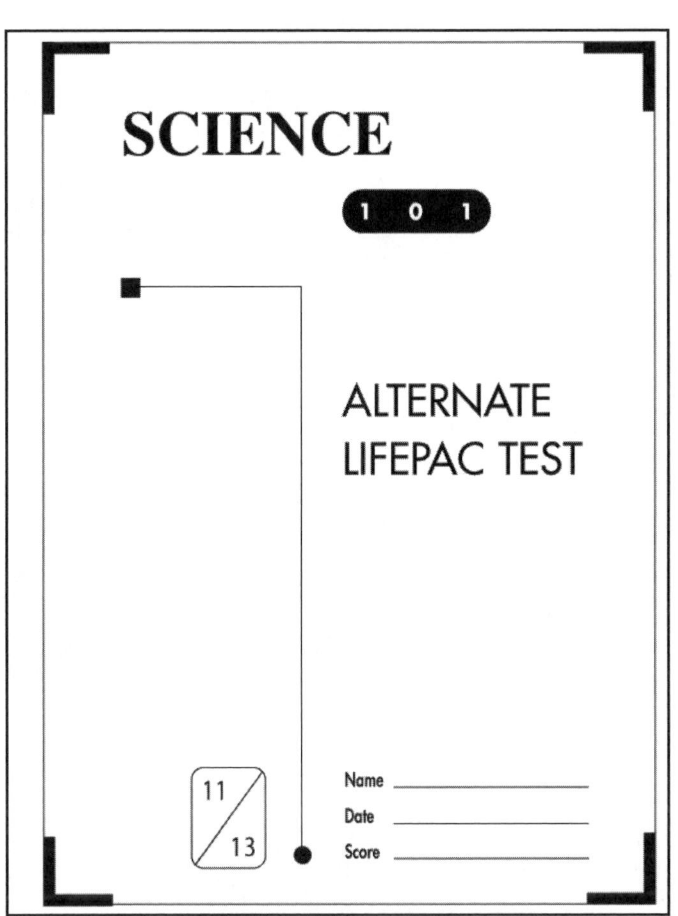
SCIENCE
1 0 1
ALTERNATE
LIFEPAC TEST
11
13
Name
Date
Score

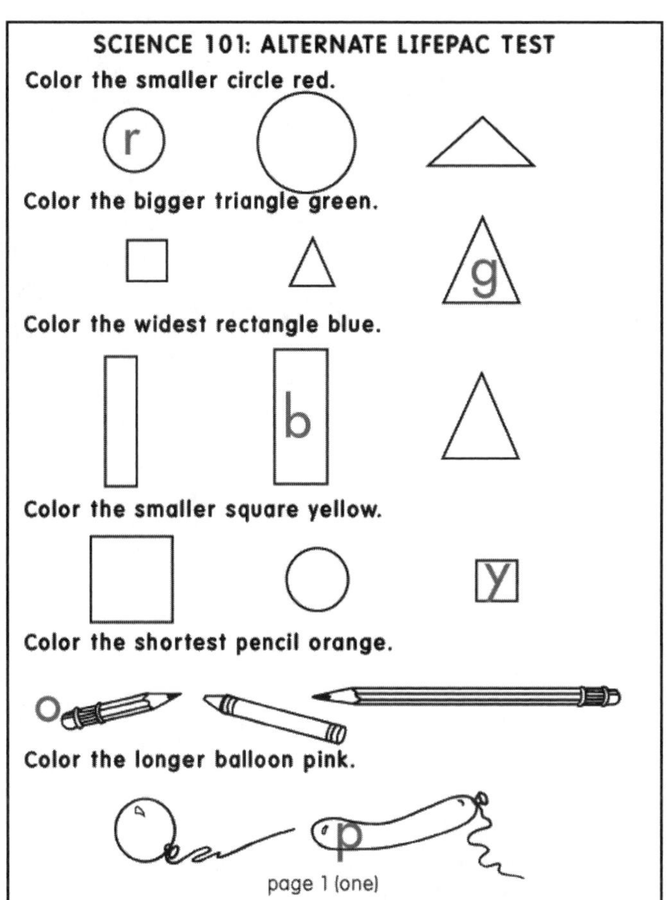
SCIENCE 101: ALTERNATE LIFEPAC TEST
Color the smaller circle red.
r
Color the bigger triangle green.
g
Color the widest rectangle blue.
b
Color the smaller square yellow.
y
Color the shortest pencil orange.
o
Color the longer balloon pink.
p
page 1 (one)

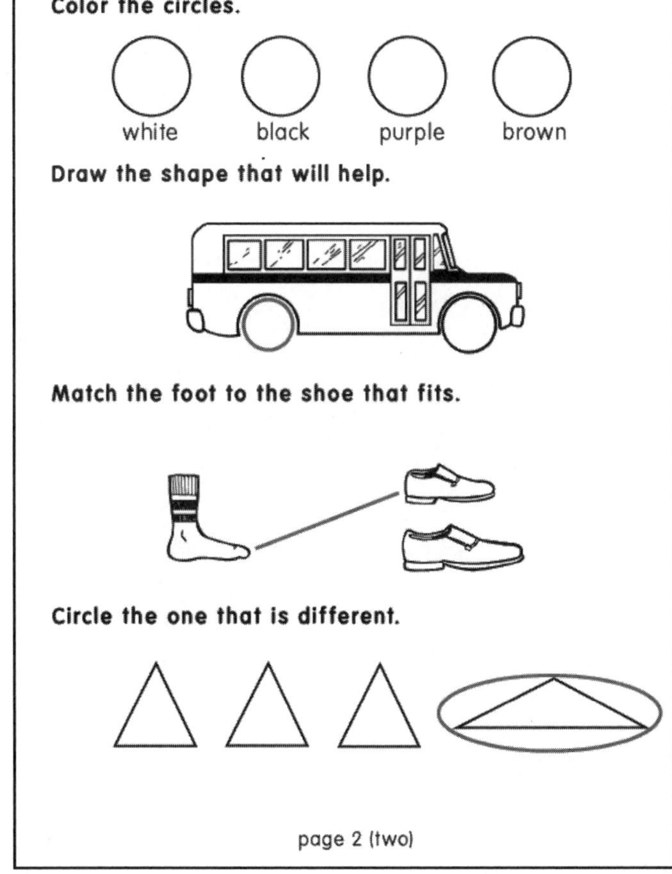
Color the circles.
white
black
purple
brown
Draw the shape that will help.
Match the foot to the shoe that fits.
Circle the one that is different.
page 2 (two)

NOTES
page 3 (three)

Page 1: You Learn With Your Ears

CONCEPT: the value of the sense of hearing to learning

OBJECTIVE: introduction to all objectives for the LIFEPAC

PROCESS: observing, using the sense of hearing

READING INTEGRATION: listening, vocabulary development, sentence recognition, oral directions, left to right

VOCABULARY: ears, hear, sound

MATERIALS NEEDED: pencils; vocabulary word cards; things that make sounds that are distinguishable, such as a large or small bell; science dictionary or chart begun in Science 101; LIFEPAC Tablet

YOU LEARN WITH YOUR EARS

Listen!

You can hear sounds.
You can hear birds sing.
You can hear people talk.
You can make sounds, too.
Sounds can help you learn.
You can learn with your ears.

Objectives

1. I can tell about some sounds I hear.
2. I can read some words about sound.
3. I can tell how sound moves.
4. I can tell how ears catch sounds.
5. I can tell about some sounds I make.

My name is____________________.
I will learn with my ears.

page 1 (one)

TEACHING PAGE 1:

Have all the children cover their eyes at once or one child at a time. Move or shake items selected for children to identify (bells, rattles, crumpled paper, etc.). Ask what they can tell about the objects by the sounds they make. For example, a little bell makes a higher sound than a big bell.

Stress the importance of hearing in learning (for following directions, for identifying, etc.). Use the words *sense* and *observe* orally, "You can *observe* with the *sense* of hearing."

Read the introduction to the class. Repeat one sentence at a time. *Say:* "Put your finger on the first word of the sentence. Follow along as I read from left to right."

Identify the vocabulary words. Have the children point to or circle these words. Discuss each sentence in turn.

Read each objective to the class or have them read by a volunteer. Be sure that the children understand that these objectives are things they will be able to do when they finish the LIFEPAC.

Have the children write their own names. Give help as needed.

ACTIVITIES:

1. Review vocabulary words. Have children use them in sentences orally, write sentences, or make up stories using these words.
2. Write words and sentences in the LIFEPAC Tablet.
3. Continue the science word dictionary or chart begun in Science 101. This science word chart or dictionary should continue throughout LIFEPAC 102 as new vocabulary appears.
4. Reinforce again the idea that the sense of hearing is a gift from God.
5. Refer to science experiment books for activity ideas.

PART 1: YOU HEAR SOUNDS

Page 2

CONCEPT: the value of the sense of hearing to learning

OBJECTIVE: I can tell about some sounds I hear.

PROCESS: observing, using the sense of hearing sections.

READING INTEGRATION: Listening, rhyming, oral vocabulary development.

VOCABULARY: sing, ring (the following words are for discussion only unless the teacher judges a majority of the class to be ready) whistle, rustle, gurgle, splash, chirp, wail, clink, jingle.

MATERIALS NEEDED: pencils, crayons, Worksheets 1 and 2, collection of pictures of things that make distinctive sounds

TEACHING PAGE 2:

Prepare the class for listening and discussion. Explain that they are to listen for words that name a sound (whistle, rustle, gurgle, splash, etc.).

Go over the sound words one at a time asking, "What other things might make these sounds?" *Example:* The wind can whistle and so can a bird, a teakettle, or a person.

Then ask what other sounds some of the things in the poem might make. *Examples:* A bird can chirp, peep, squawk, and so on. Ask what kinds of bells might you hear and how can you tell the difference (a church bell, school bell, dinner bell, sleigh bell, telephone bell, doorbell).

Ask for discussion of other familiar sounds and sound words.

Discuss the sounds shown in the illustrations.

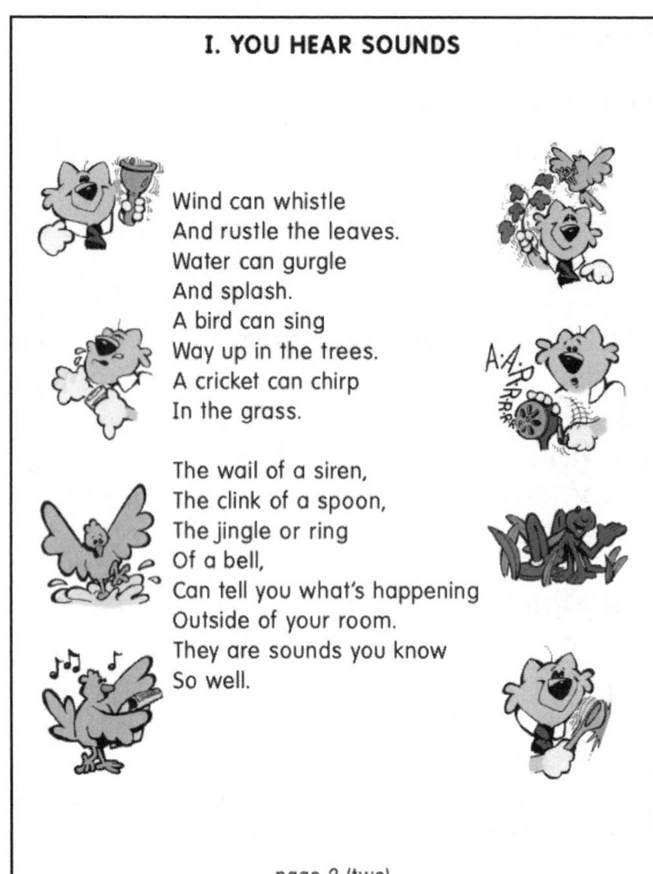

I. YOU HEAR SOUNDS

Wind can whistle
And rustle the leaves.
Water can gurgle
And splash.
A bird can sing
Way up in the trees.
A cricket can chirp
In the grass.

The wail of a siren,
The clink of a spoon,
The jingle or ring
Of a bell,
Can tell you what's happening
Outside of your room.
They are sounds you know
So well.

page 2 (two)

ACTIVITIES:

1. Add sound words to the class dictionary.
2. Do Worksheets 1 and 2.

Read the directions to and with the class. Emphasize direction words *circle* and *color* and sound words *ring* and *whistle.*

Name ______________

Circle the ones that ring.
Color the pictures.

Science: 102
Worksheet 1
with page 2

Teacher check ______________
Initial Date

Name ______________

Circle the ones that whistle.
Color the pictures.

Science 102
Worksheet 2
with page 2

Teacher check ______________
Initial Date

Page 3: Sounds of Nature

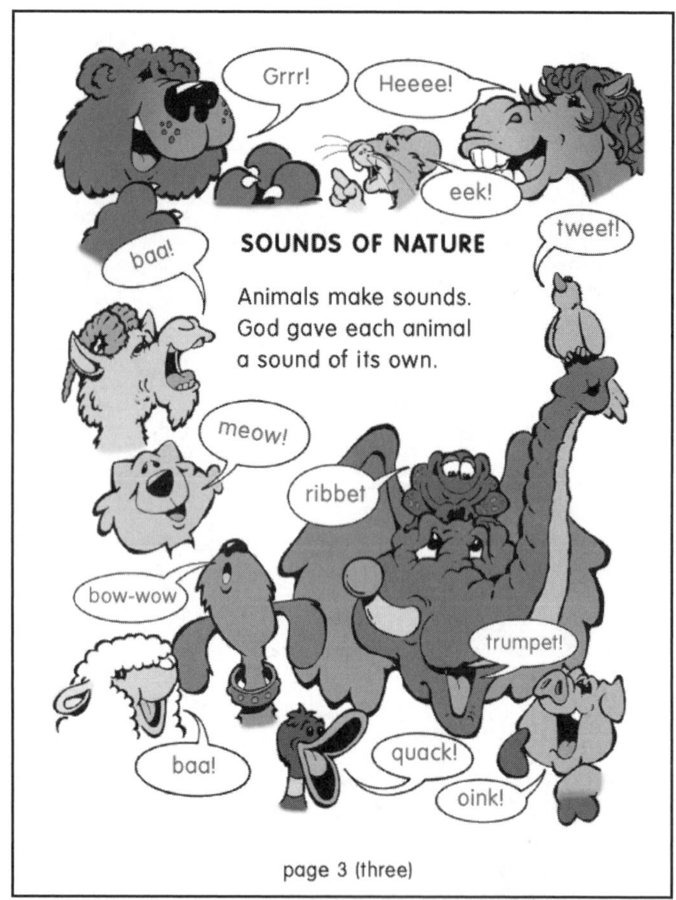

CONCEPT: Animals have sounds of their own.

OBJECTIVE: I can tell about some sounds I hear.

PROCESS: observing, using the sense of hearing

READING INTEGRATION: listening, group discussion, sentence recognition

MATERIALS NEEDED: pictures of familiar animals; record or tape of animal sounds, if available, for discussion

TEACHING PAGE 3:

Display pictures of familiar animals. Have volunteers imitate the sounds that animals make. Reverse the procedure and play a recording or imitate an animal sound. Have the children name or find a picture of the animal that makes the sound. You may want to vary the sounds. *Example: purr* or *meow* for a cat, *whine, bark,* or *pant* for a dog.

Read the page. Have the children name the animals in the picture. Explain the cartoon balloon to them telling them that this "balloon" is used in a picture whenever we want to show a sound made by an animal or the words said by a person.

Have the children tell what sound each animal makes. Fill in the balloons for those that are possible to translate into letters.

ACTIVITIES:

1. Extend the concept of animal sounds by introducing the idea that all sounds are not made by the animal's voice. The clip-clop of a horse's hooves and the flap of a bird's wings are examples of sound made in other ways. Suggested read aloud: *The Three Billy Goats Gruff.* (Note: fact/fantasy reading integration)
2. Read stories about animals that deal with animal sounds.

Page 4: Activity Page

READING INTEGRATION: listening, group discussion, sentence recognition, form (quotation marks)

VOCABULARY: sheep, dog, cow, cat

MATERIALS NEEDED: crayons

TEACHING PAGE 4:

Read the introductory statement to the class. Draw attention to the direction arrow. Note that when they see such an arrow, they will find a sentence telling them what to do. Read the direction to and with the students. Read the sentences under the picture squares. Call attention to the vocabulary words: *sheep, dog, cat,* and *cow.* Draw attention to quotation marks. Emphasize that such marks always enclose something that is said. One approach is to liken quotes to the corners of the mouth. What comes out of the mouth is enclosed. Let the children complete the activity, giving additional help as needed.

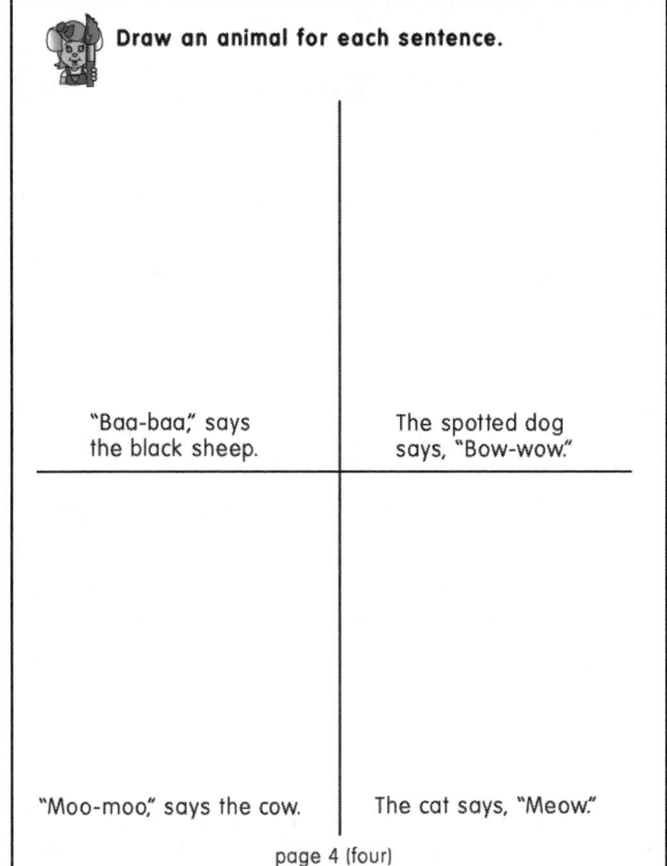

Page 5: Activity Page

READING INTEGRATION: written and oral directions, left to right

VOCABULARY: animal, sound, match

MATERIALS NEEDED: materials from page 3, Worksheet 3

TEACHING PAGE 5:

Review the animal pictures and sounds.

Practice the vocabulary words.

Read the direction sentence to and with the class or have it read aloud by a volunteer. Ask what one word in the sentence tells what to do (match). Let children complete the page independently.

ACTIVITIES:

1. Introduce concept of warning sounds animals make. *Example:* rattle of the rattlesnake, growl of the dog. Ask how these sounds can help.
2. Promote discussion of safety around animals.
3. Add animal-sound words to science chart or dictionary.
4. Have children write animal-sound stories as a group, dictate them to a helper, and illustrate them to display on the bulletin board.
5. Do Worksheet 3.

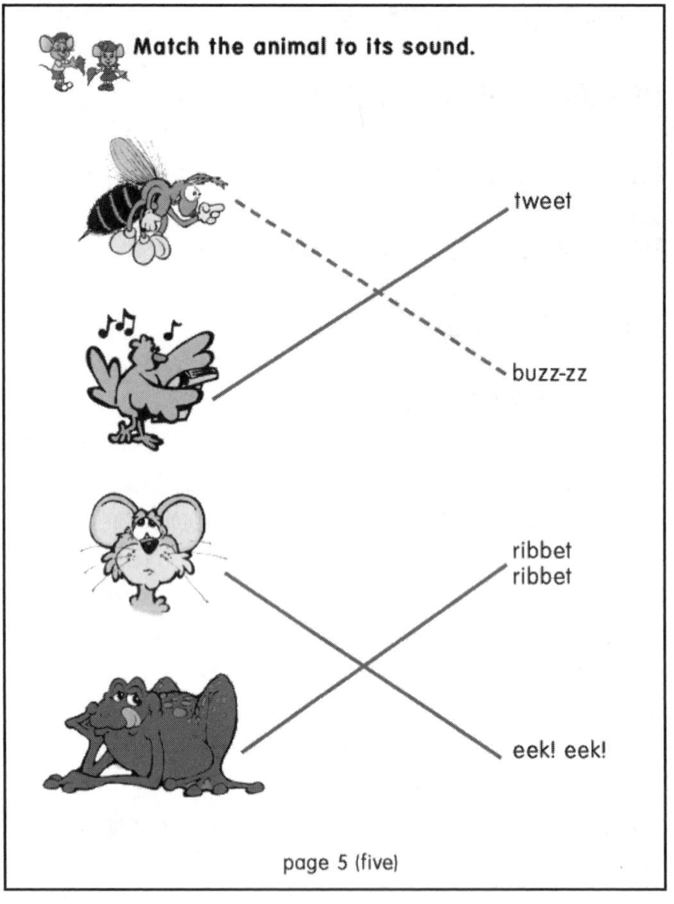

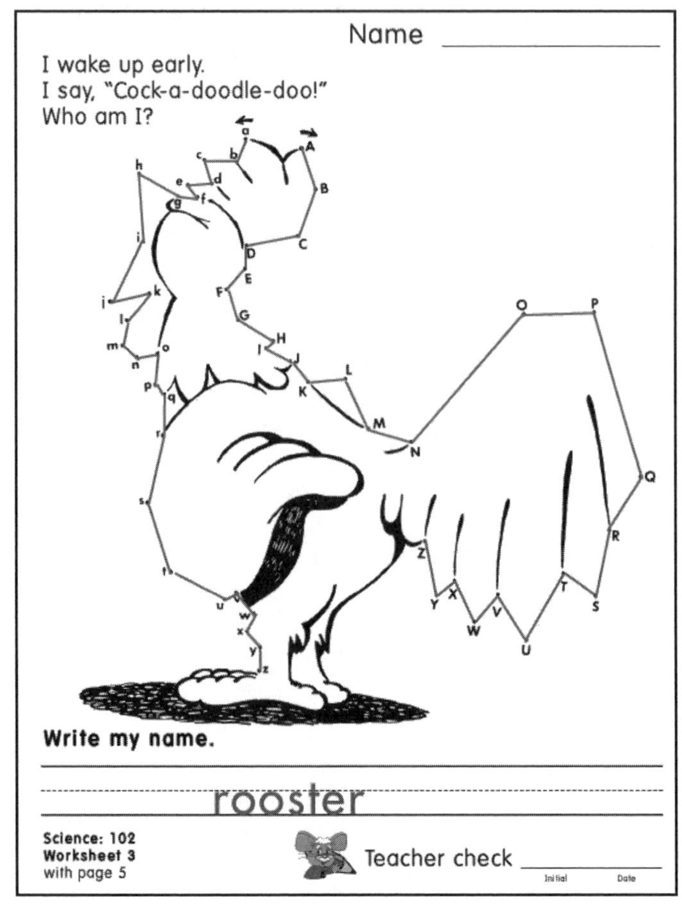

Match the animal to its sound.

ribbet ribbet

Name
I wake up early.
I say, "Cock-a-doodle-doo!"
Who am I?
Write my name.
rooster
Science: 102
Worksheet 3
with page 5
Teacher check
Initial
Date

Page 6: Weather Sounds

CONCEPT: Some kinds of weather can be identified by sound.

OBJECTIVE: I can tell about some sounds I hear.

PROCESS: observing, using the sense of hearing

READING INTEGRATION: listening, sentence form (quotation marks), taking part in group discussion

VOCABULARY: weather, wind, rain, thunder (not for writing or spelling)

MATERIALS NEEDED: weather pictures, recording of weather sounds, stories about weather

Sound can tell about the weather.
"Pitter-patter," says the rain.
"Whoo-oo," says the wind.
"Crash," goes the thunder.
"Splish-splash," say the puddles as you play.
page 6 (six)

TEACHING PAGE 6:

Display weather pictures. Discuss sounds that might be heard. Note that some weather conditions make no sound at all.

Have the children respond to suggested conditions heard outside their window in the night. *Examples:* tap, tap, tap on the window or roof. What kind of weather?

Use the pictures on the page as the display pictures. Call attention to quotation marks. Note that even though wind, rain, thunder, and so on do not have mouths, we use quotes to enclose the sounds they make as if they did. Ask children to try to think of or to imitate other sounds the wind, rain, and so on might make.

Ask what goes with thunder (lightning). Ask if lightning makes noise. (Thunder is the noise made by the expansion of suddenly heated air. It is caused by lightning.)

Page 7: Quiet Weather

CONCEPT: Some kinds of weather make no sounds.

OBJECTIVE: I can tell about some sounds I hear.

PROCESSES: observing, using the sense of hearing; classifying, by sound

READING INTEGRATION: listening, discussion of directions

VOCABULARY: quiet, cannot, weather

MATERIALS NEEDED: pencils, crayons, LIFEPAC Tablet, Worksheet 4, weather pictures used for page 6

Some weather is quiet.
Circle the weather you cannot hear.
wind
sunshine
clouds
rain
page 7 (seven)

TEACHING PAGE 7:

Using the same weather pictures as page 6, have the children identify the condition that cannot be heard.

Read the introductory sentence. Emphasize the vocabulary words *quiet* and *weather.* Read the directions to and with the children. Emphasize the vocabulary word *cannot* and direction words *circle* and *color.*

The page can be completed independently.

ACTIVITIES:

1. Begin a sound scrapbook. Divide it into sections for animals, weather, people, machines, and so on. The animal section can have one or more animals per page either drawn or cut from magazines. On the page list or illustrate as many sounds as possible for each animal. A dog, for example, can howl, bark, whine, cry, lap water, and so on.

   The weather section can contain a page for each type of weather. List, illustrate, or find a picture for the things that happen and the types of activity that can be done on a day that has the kind of weather illustrated. On a rainy day, for example, pictures of someone walking with an umbrella or raincoat would be appropriate or a picture of someone doing something inside while it rains outside.
2. Have the more advanced students make up stories for each page in the scrapbook. They can dictate the stories to an aide or print them neatly if they are able.
3. Do Worksheet 4.
4. Continue science dictionary.
5. Practice vocabulary words or sentences in Tablet.

Name ______________

Cut out the sentences.
Glue each sentence under its picture.
Color the pictures.
Write the sentences in your Tablet.

I can hear wind and rain.

Some weather is quiet.

Science: 102
Worksheet 4
with page 7

Teacher check ____________
Initial Date

Page 8: Sounds of People

CONCEPT: People make sounds in different ways, such as voice, movement, and machines.

OBJECTIVE: I can tell about some sounds I hear.

PROCESS: observing, using the sense of hearing

READING INTEGRATION: discussion, listening

VOCABULARY: listen, hear, sound, ear

MATERIALS NEEDED: pictures of people doing various activities, LIFEPAC Tablet, word cards, pencils

TEACHING PAGE 8:

Have children close their eyes and use only their ears to identify what you do. Ask for volunteers to tell what they think you are doing as you do one or all of the following activities.

Examples: write on the chalkboard
move a piece of furniture
open and close the door
open and close the window
whistle, speak, sing

Have the children study each picture in turn. Lead discussion to the sound or sounds the picture represents. Ask what they know by just hearing the sound.

Example: the crying child
sound: crying
to learn: Something is wrong with the child.
question: What could be wrong?
response: The child is sad (for various reasons).
why?: The cat ate her ice cream.

Follow the same line of questioning for each picture.

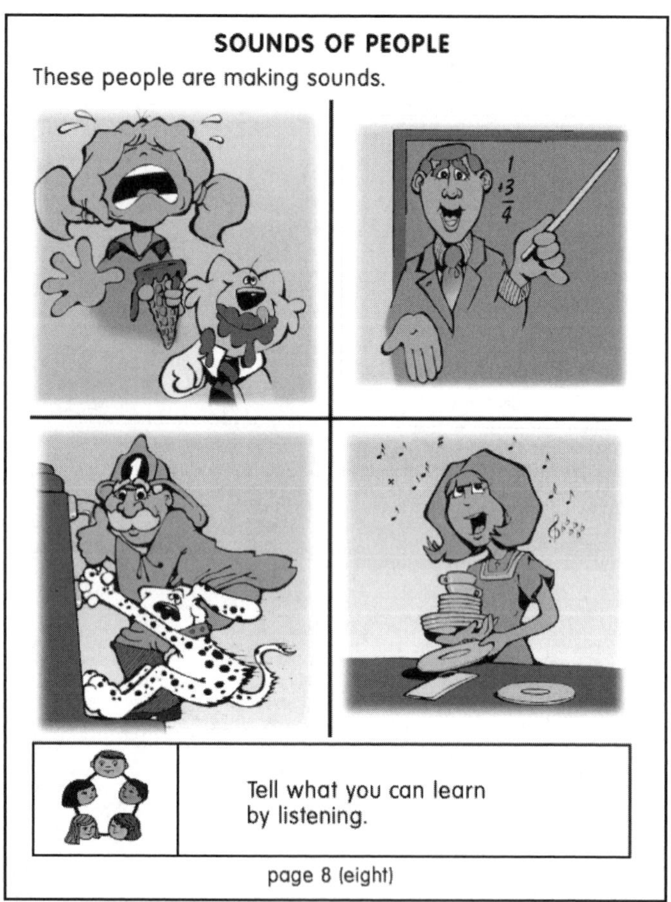

SOUNDS OF PEOPLE
These people are making sounds.
Tell what you can learn by listening.
page 8 (eight)

ACTIVITIES:

1. Use the Tablet. Have the children write sound words they know so far. If class or individuals are able, have them write a sentence with the words. *Examples:* I listen with my ears. I can hear sounds.
2. Continue the sound scrapbook.

Page 9: Activity Page

CONCEPT: We do not always listen to what we should.

OBJECTIVE: I can tell about sounds I hear.

PROCESS: observing, using the sense of hearing

READING INTEGRATION: listening, rhyming, main idea

VOCABULARY: trace, write

MATERIALS NEEDED: LIFEPAC Tablet, word cards, pencils, crayons, Worksheet 5

TEACHING PAGE 9:

To prepare the children for this page, read this poem aloud to the class. Ask them to listen carefully so they might tell the main idea in their own words.

LISTEN

"Listen, listen," Mother says.
Teacher says it, too.
"Use your ears so you will know
Just what you are to do."

Your ears are busy all the time.
The sounds come rushing through.
Sometimes you do not listen
To the ones they want you to.

A bird song and the pat of rain
Are sounds you like to hear.
A barking dog, a whistling train
Come creeping in your ear.

"Are you listening?" Mother says.
Teacher says it, too.
"Pay attention, so you'll know
What you're supposed to do."

Phyllis A. MacDonald

Ask for volunteers to give the main idea.

Discuss the presence of distracting sounds that tend to draw attention away from the lessons, instructions, and so on.

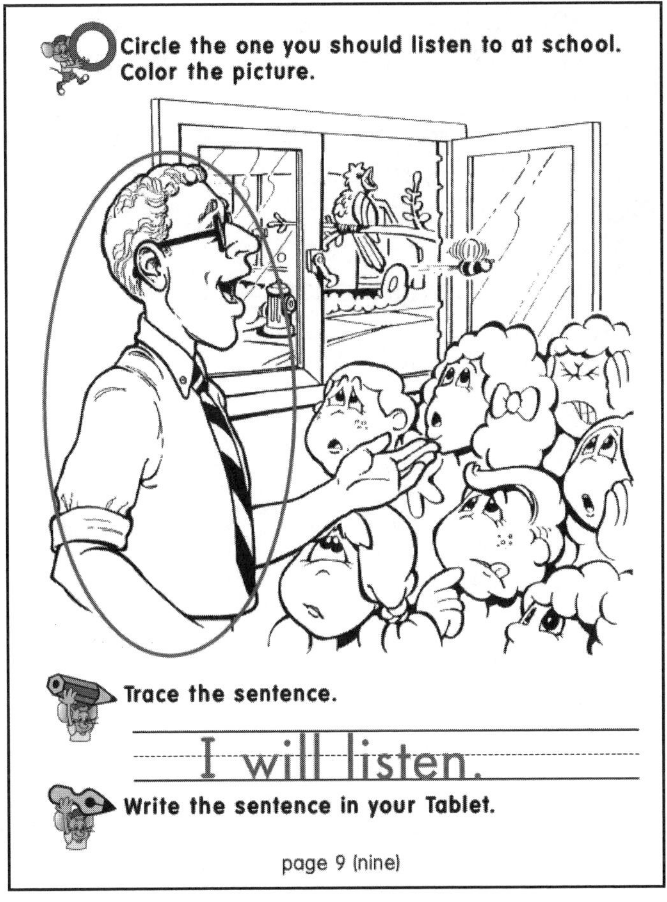

Circle the one you should listen to at school.
Color the picture.
Trace the sentence.
I will listen.
Write the sentence in your Tablet.
page 9 (nine)

Discuss how sounds are around all the time and how to concentrate on the sounds that should be heard at certain times.

Introduce direction words *trace* and *write*. Use word cards. Demonstrate *trace* on the board.

Discuss the picture.

What sounds can the children in the picture hear? (bee, truck, bird, teacher)

Which sound should they be listening to? (teacher)

Read the directions to and with the class.

Have the page completed independently.

ACTIVITIES

1. Discuss other situations where the children must listen. In church, for example,

they should listen to the Word of God and not to other noises or distractions around them.

2. Have more advanced students expand the sentence in their Tablets. *Example:* I will listen to my teacher.

3. Continue sound scrapbook. Add pages that show situations where listening is important.

4. Do Worksheet 5.

Name ______________

Circle the one you should listen to at home.

Color the picture.

Science: 102
Worksheet 5
with page 9

Teacher check ______________
Initial Date

Page 10: Praise

CONCEPTS: God created sound and our ability to hear it and learn from it. He likes for us to use sound to praise Him.

OBJECTIVES:
I can tell about sounds I hear.
I can read some words about sound.

BIBLE REFERENCES: Proverbs 20:12; Matthew 10:27, 13:16, 17:5; Luke 8:21

PROCESSES: observing, using the sense of hearing; classifying, sounds we use to praise God

READING INTEGRATION: left to right, main idea, memorization

VOCABULARY: praise, noise, singing

MATERIALS NEEDED: Bible, word cards, LIFEPAC Tablet, drawing paper, copies of Psalm 100:1 and 2

TEACHING PAGE 10:

The Bible makes many references to hearing, ears, and sound.

Use the Bible verses to emphasize the Creation and wise use of the sense of hearing.

Use the LIFEPAC page for Psalm 100:1 and 2, Read or have read the introductory sentences and the Bible verse. Give each child a copy or have the children copy it themselves, checking carefully that it is done correctly. (Children may take the verse home to memorize.)

Read the sentence in the box and discuss. Ask how children can make a joyful noise. Help the children to learn their verses.

ACTIVITIES:

1. Have the children choose one of the Bible verses to memorize and recite for the class.
2. Have the children copy one of the verses in their Tablets.

People make sounds to praise God.

The Bible tells us:

"Make a joyful noise unto the Lord, all ye lands.
Serve the LORD with gladness: come before his presence with singing."
Psalm 100:1 and 2

Learn the verses. Say them to your teacher.

Teacher Check ______ Initial ______ Date

Talk about other ways to praise God.

page 10 (ten)

3. Give each child a sheet of drawing paper. Tell the children to draw a picture to go with the Bible verses. Make a bulletin board display. Put the verses in the middle and surround them with the children's pictures.
4. Sing a song of praise.

Page 11 : Machines

CONCEPT: Machines make sounds.

OBJECTIVE: I can tell about sounds I hear.

PROCESSES: observing, using the sense of hearing; classifying, machines that work, machines that move, machines that signal

READING INTEGRATION: left to right, sentence recognition, vocabulary development, following directions

VOCABULARY: machine, signal, move, work

MATERIALS NEEDED: word cards, pictures of machines for discussion, drawing paper, LIFEPAC Tablet, pencils

People use machines to do **work**.
People use machines to **move**.
People use machines to **signal**.
Write W, M, or S if the machine helps people work, move, or give a signal.
Some pictures use more than one letter.
W
M
W
S
W
M
page 11 (eleven)

TEACHING PAGE 11:

Use word cards to develop vocabulary. Have the children use these words in sentences. Display pictures of machines. Have the children discuss how machines are used.

Read the introductory sentences to or with the class. Have the children look at the pictures of machines and match them with each sentence. Read directions. Be sure the children tell what they are to do and what each picture is. The page may be completed independently. Pictures may be colored when the task is complete.

ACTIVITIES:

1. Provide paper for the children to "invent" a machine to do a job and draw a picture of it. Have each child write or dictate two sentences telling what the machine does and what sound it makes. Accept "made-up" sounds. *Examples:* buckety buckety, ger-uch-ger-uch.
2. Have the children copy the three introductory sentences from the LIFEPAC page in their Tablets.
3. Continue the sound scrapbook. Add pages for machines that *work, move,* and *signal* or put the picture of a machine on the page and list or illustrate all the ways in which the machine can be used.

Pages 12 and 13: Self Test 1

CONCEPT: Review child's progress.

OBJECTIVES:

I can tell about some sounds I hear.
I can read some words about sound.

BIBLE REFERENCE: Psalm 100:1 and 2

MATERIALS NEEDED: pencils, crayons, Worksheets 6 and 7

TEACHING PAGES 12 AND 13:

Review the vocabulary words for Section One.

Practice with the word cards and sentences.

Review classifying sounds: Word cards can be used to classify sounds of animals, sounds of weather, sounds of machines, and sounds of praise. Review direction words: *Match, Circle,* and *Put an X on.*

The ability of your group should dictate whether you choose to direct the self test or to allow the children to proceed independently once directions are given.

Evaluate the test and discuss the results with the child. If a child does poorly in a section, review those pages and activities that stress the concepts missed .

ACTIVITIES:

1. Do Worksheet 6. This worksheet can be used for review or for enrichment as needed. Read the directions. Let the child complete the page independently
2. Do Worksheet 7. Read the directions. Help those children who need help.

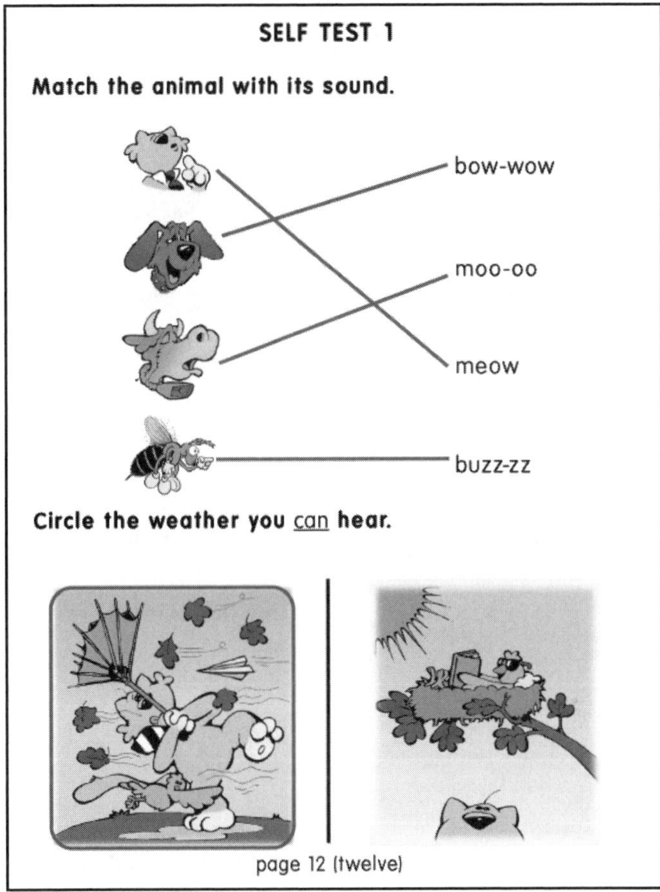

SELF TEST 1
Match the animal with its sound.
bow-wow
moo-oo
meow
buzz-zz
Circle the weather you can hear.
page 12 (twelve)

Put an X on each sound people can make.
Circle the machine that gives signals.
Say the Bible verses you learned (Psalm 100:1 and 2).
EACH ANSWER, 1 POINT
7/9
Teacher Check
Initial
Date
My Score
page 13 (thirteen)

Name ______________

Draw a picture for each sound.

Buzz

Ding-dong

Tweet

Science: 102
Worksheet 6
with page 13

Teacher check ______________
Initial Date

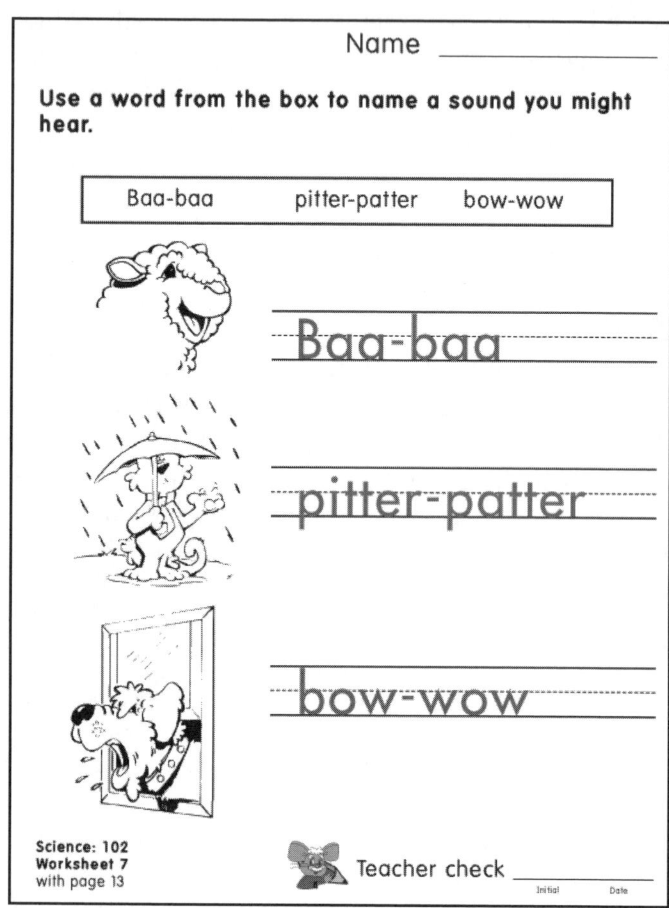

Name ______________

Use a word from the box to name a sound you might hear.

Baa-baa	pitter-patter	bow-wow

Baa-baa

pitter-patter

bow-wow

Science: 102
Worksheet 7
with page 13

Teacher check ______________
Initial Date

Section II: YOU LEARN ABOUT SOUND

Page 14

CONCEPT: overview of the way in which sound works

OBJECTIVES:

I can tell how sound moves.
I can tell how ears catch sound.

PROCESS: observing, using the senses of sight and hearing

READING INTEGRATION: listening, rhyming, recalling detail

VOCABULARY: waves, brain

MATERIALS NEEDED: word cards, pencils, LIFEPAC Tablet

TEACHING PAGE 14:

Clap your hands.

Ask: "Did you hear the sound? Where did the sound come from? How did it get from my hands to your ears?"

Read the poem aloud to the class. Read again, with the children following along.

Ask the children to identify the rhyming words, the words that tell ways we can observe (see, hear), the words that name sounds, and the vocabulary words waves and brain.

ACTIVITIES:

1. Continue science dictionary.
2. Discuss the sounds they hear that hurt their ears or those that sound pleasant to their ears.
3. Use the Tablet to write sentences about sounds.

II. YOU LEARN ABOUT SOUND

If you drop some pebbles in a pond,
You see the circles spread.
Sound is like pebbles in the air.
But you hear the waves instead.

You pluck a string to make a sound,
Or bang upon a pan.
You talk or whistle, cry or sing.
Just try, I know you can.

Waves of sound move
through the air,
And go into your ear,
Which sends a message
to your brain.
It tells you what you hear.

page 14 (fourteen)

Page 15: Sound Is Vibration

CONCEPT: Sound is vibration.

OBJECTIVE: I can tell how sound moves.

PROCESS: observing, using the senses of sight, hearing, and touch

READING INTEGRATION: speaking in a group

VOCABULARY: vibrate, vibration

MATERIALS NEEDED: stringed instrument, triangle, drum, horn, or other wind instruments (if available), crayons, bottles, combs, LIFEPAC Tablet

SOUND IS VIBRATION
Sound is made
when something moves.
Tell what is moving.
page 15 (fifteen)

TEACHING PAGE 15:

Ask for two volunteers to come up to the teacher.

As you make sounds, have the volunteers feel your throat. The children should be able to feel the vibrations change as you make high and low sounds with your voice.

Have the rest of the group feel their own, or each other's, throats as they make high and low sounds.

Ask: "Something moves when your voice makes sounds. What is it?"

Tell: "This moving is called *vibration.* Your voice makes your throat vibrate.

Have the children write *vibrate* and *vibration* in their Tablets. Have them use these words in sentences. Read them or have the sentences read.

Use the pictures for discussion of vibration and sound. Have the children tell what is vibrating in each picture, what is causing the vibration, and what kind of sound is being made.

ACTIVITIES:

1. Set up a discovery center with sound-making materials: bottles-water-stick, comb-tissue, oatmeal box or coffee can, other simple sound devices, and pictures showing methods to produce sound with these and other materials.
2. Allow children to experiment with the materials in the discovery center. Have them write or dictate sentences about what they learn. Use this discovery center throughout Section II until all children have at least one opportunity to experiment.

Page 16: Activity Page

CONCEPT: Sound moves through air waves moving in all directions from a source as water moves from the source of disturbance.

OBJECTIVE: I can tell how sound moves.

PROCESSES: observing, using the sense of sight; predicting

READING INTEGRATION: reading simple directions, predicting outcome

VOCABULARY: first, next

MATERIALS NEEDED: pan of water, several small pebbles, crayons, Worksheets 8 and 9, scissors, paste or glue, pencils, LIFEPAC Tablet

TEACHING PAGE 16:

Set up pan of water and pebbles for group demonstration. Have the children stand in a circle with the pan below their eye level so that all may see clearly.

As children watch, drop a pebble into the pan.

Ask: "What did you see?" or "What happened to the water?"

Give the children a chance to speculate about what happened.

Give the children an opportunity to try the experiment. Be sure the water is calm before each new try.

Have volunteers read the title and the direction. Be sure all the children understand what they are to do. Note that they are to draw what they saw happen to the water in the demonstration.

ACTIVITIES:

1. Do Worksheets 8 and 9. Read the directions to the children. Let them work in steps so that they understand exactly what they are to do.
2. Have more advanced students write a story in their Tablets for Worksheets 8 and 9.

Look at the first picture. In the second picture, draw what happens next.
page 16 (sixteen)

Name
Color the pictures.
Cut them apart.
Glue them onto Worksheet 9 in the right order.
Science: 102
Worksheet 8
with page 16
Teacher check
Initial
Date

Name

The Hungry Frog

Write a sentence about the hungry frog.

The frog was hungry.

Science: 102
Worksheet 9
with page 16

Teacher check
Initial Date

Page 17: Sound Moves

CONCEPTS: Sound moves through the air and water in all directions from the source. Sound moves through solids even better.

OBJECTIVE: I can tell how sound moves.

PROCESS: observing

READING INTEGRATION: group speaking

VOCABULARY: air, water, solids, through

MATERIALS NEEDED: two aluminum or tin cans, string, drum or triangle, tuning fork, a glass of water

SOUND MOVES
Sound moves through the air.
Sound moves through water.
Sound moves through solids.
page 17 (seventeen)

TEACHING PAGE 17:

Tell the class that you are going to use the page in the book to show how sound can move through different kinds of things. Practice vocabulary with word cards and sentences. Have the children open their books.

Read the sentence, "Sound moves through the air," or have a student read it aloud.

Demonstration: Have a volunteer move to various parts of the room as you play the triangle or the drum. Do not change the loudness.

Ask: "Can you hear just as well everywhere in the room?" (If the room is large, the note will sound softer as the distance increases.)

Try it next with your voice. First say something facing the class. Then repeat it in the same tone with your back to the class.

Ask: "Which way can you hear the sound better?"

Note: Sound waves decrease in intensity as distance from the sound source increases.

Read the sentence, "Sound moves through water," or have a student read it aloud.

Demonstration: Have class gathered around for viewing.

Strike tuning fork and dip it carefully into glass of still water. Water should visibly vibrate and set up a wave pattern.

or

Fill a crystal goblet with water. Strike the edge of the goblet. Water will vibrate. Change the amount of water in the glass. The tone will be different.

Read the sentence, "Sound moves through solids."

Demonstration: Use volunteers. Have the child place his ear next to the chalkboard tray. Tap the tray softly on the other end.

Ask the class if they could hear the tap. Most will not.

Ask the child whose ear was on the tray if he heard it. It should have been heard quite plainly.

Let the children try this demonstration on their own desks. Ask them to tap so softly that you cannot hear it. Let the children discuss this experience and tell you what they learned.

Discuss the tin can telephone picture in the student book.

Children may want to make one of their own. They can do this project at home.

Page 18 : Activity Page

MATERIALS NEEDED: pencils, crayons, LIFEPAC Tablet

TEACHING PAGE 18 :

Review the words *air, water,* and *solid.*

Read the direction.

Let the children complete the page independently.

ACTIVITIES:

1. Continue sound experiments in discovery center.
2. Have the children write these sentences in their Tablets. Sound moves through water. Sound moves through air. Sound moves through solids.
3. Make collages of how sounds move: one for air, one for water, and one for solids.

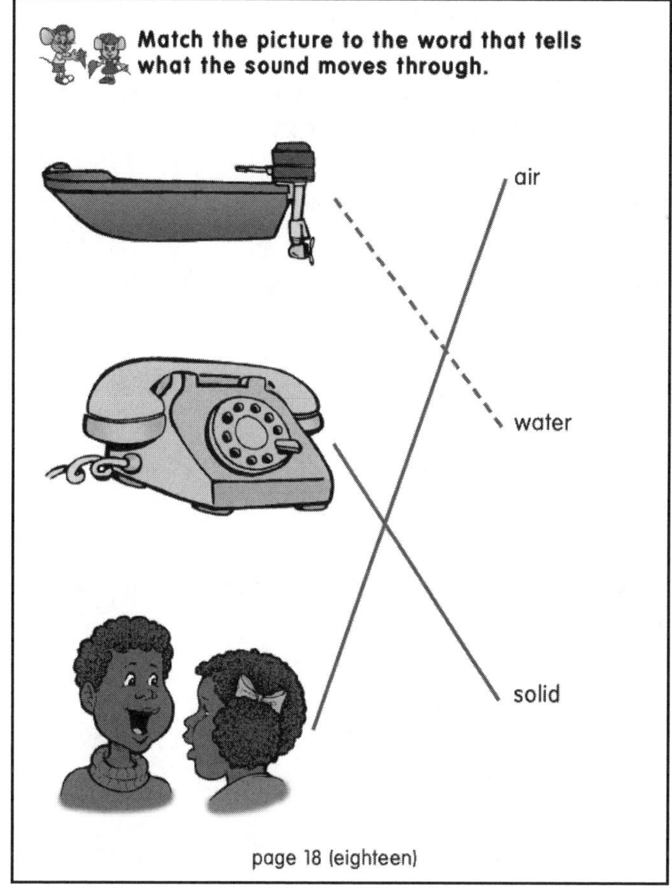
Match the picture to the word that tells what the sound moves through.
air
water
solid
page 18 (eighteen)

Page 19: Ears Catch Sound

CONCEPT: Sounds are caught by your ears and interpreted by your brain.

OBJECTIVE: I can tell how ears catch sound.

PROCESS: observing, by using the sense of hearing

READING INTEGRATION: speaking in a group

VOCABULARY: middle, outer, ears, brain, vibrate, vibration

MATERIALS NEEDED: vocabulary-word cards, LIFEPAC Tablet, pencils

TEACHING PAGE 19:

Ask: "What part of your body do you use to hear? What happens when you block your ears?"

Have the children note the difference in how they hear sounds with their ears open and blocked.

Read the page title and the first sentence or ask a volunteer to read them.

Call attention to the diagram. Use the word cards to identify the parts.

Note to teacher: The outer ear is the collector of sound waves. The sound waves create a vibration of the eardrum. This vibration passes through the parts of the middle ear and on into the brain where it is interpreted as sound.

Read and discuss the sentences about the parts of the ear.

ACTIVITIES:

1. Have the children use their Tablets to write any or all of the sentences on the student page. You may wish to have them make up their own sentences.
2. Continue sound scrapbook.

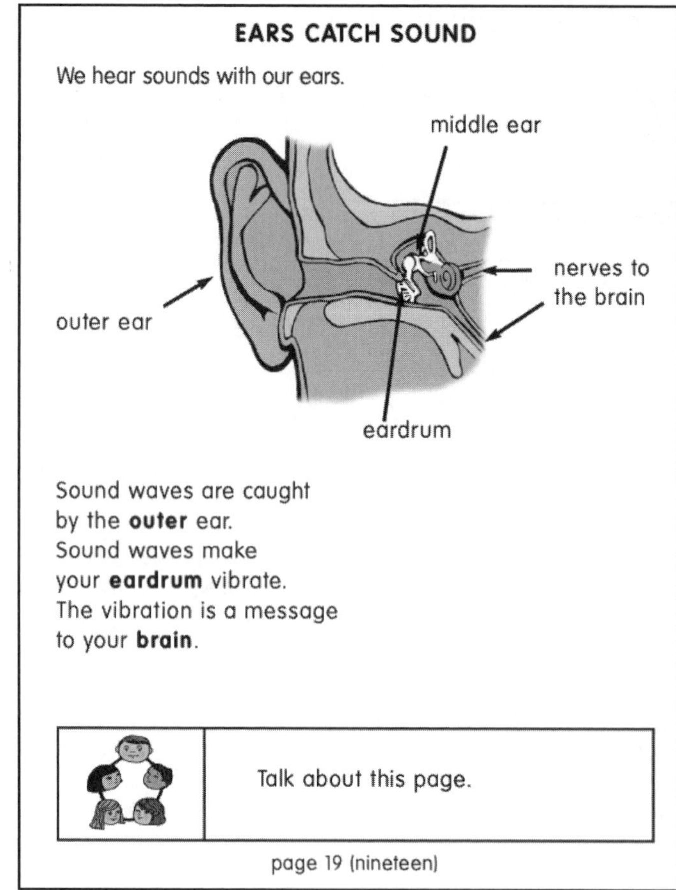

EARS CATCH SOUND

We hear sounds with our ears.

Sound waves are caught
by the **outer** ear.
Sound waves make
your **eardrum** vibrate.
The vibration is a message
to your **brain**.

Talk about this page.

page 19 (nineteen)

Page 20: Animals Have Ears

CONCEPT: Animal ears are different to fit special needs.

OBJECTIVE: I can tell how ears catch sound.

PROCESSES: observing, by using the sense of sight; comparing

READING INTEGRATION: speaking in a group, following written directions

VOCABULARY: owner

MATERIALS NEEDED: pictures of various animals (other than those in LIFEPAC), Worksheet 10, LIFEPAC Tablet

TEACHING PAGE 20:

Display the pictures. Ask the children to compare the ears of the animals. Encourage them to use words that describe the physical attributes of the various ears (tall, wide, pointed, floppy, etc.).

Write the words used on a chart or chalkboard with the animal names.

Example:

Animal	Ears
mouse	round

Read the sentences to the class or have a volunteer read them. Proceed with the animals pictured on the page as you did with the pictures in the display.

Ask: "Which animals do you think might have the best hearing? Why do some animals need to hear better than others?"

Teach vocabulary word *owner.* Have a child use the word in a sentence on the board. Have the children write the sentence in their Tablets.

Read the directions to the students. Have the page completed independently.

ACTIVITIES:

1. Be sure that all the children have had a chance to experiment with sound in the discovery center.

2. Review the LIFEPAC pages to prepare for the self test.
3. Make an "ear collage" with pictures cut from magazines.
4. Do Worksheet 10. After the sheets have been distributed discuss the problems the animals might have with the wrong ears. Have children color the pictures and give the silly looking animals new names. Give help for spelling the names.

Name

How can these animals hear?

Color them.

Name them.

deerephant

elecat

froggit

rog

Science: 102

Worksheet 10

with page 20

Teacher check

Initial Date

Page 21: Activity Page

CONCEPT: An ear horn can magnify sound.

OBJECTIVE: I can tell how ears catch sound.

PROCESSES: observing, by using the sense of hearing; comparing

READING INTEGRATION: following written directions

VOCABULARY: louder, softer

MATERIALS NEEDED: construction paper or tag board (9" x 12"), tape, LIFEPAC Tablet, pencils

TEACHING PAGE 21:

Prepare an "ear horn" like those the children will make.

Ask: "Do you think something like this ear horn could help you hear?" Allow the children to discuss reasons why it might. Proceed to the page.

Read or have a child read the directions at the top of the page. Pass out the materials to the class (paper, tape). Demonstrate how the children are to roll the paper into an open-ended cone and tape the edges.

Allow the children to make their own "ear horns."

Give them time to use them and compare sounds heard with and without the horn.

When the experience time is up, have the children do the activities at the bottom of the page. Go over the directions with them.

ACTIVITIES:

1. To extend the concept, discuss how hearing aids, like ear horns, make sounds louder. They are used to help people with hearing problems.
2. The ear horn can also be a megaphone. When you speak through the ear horn, the sound is magnified and can be directed.

Make a cone.
a piece
of paper
Hold it to your ear and listen.
Draw a line under the sentence that tells what happens.
The sound seems louder.
The sound seems softer.
Write the sentence in your Tablet.
Teacher Check
Initial
Date
page 21 (twenty-one)

Pages 22 and 23: Self Test 2

CONCEPT: Review child's progress.

MATERIALS NEEDED: pencils, crayons, Worksheet 11

TEACHING PAGES 22 and 23:

Review the vocabulary words for the first two sections and the direction words *Circle, Match,* and *Put an X.*

The proficiency of your class should determine whether you will do the self test as a group or allow the children to proceed independently once the directions are given. If you choose to do it as a group, read each direction, answer any questions, then allow time for every child to complete the activity.

If your group is working independently, be sure that you are available for individual questions.

For those children who did not score well on the self test, have them make corrections in the LIFEPAC and then give them Worksheet 11 for reinforcement.

This worksheet may also be used as a supplementary activity for the whole class.

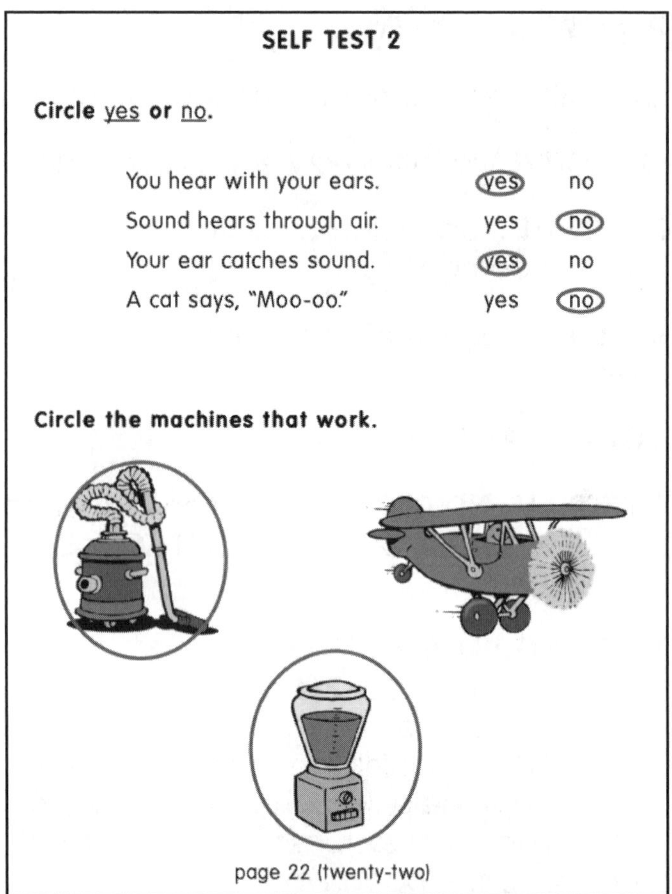

SELF TEST 2

Circle yes or no.

You hear with your ears.	(yes)	no
Sound hears through air.	yes	(no)
Your ear catches sound.	(yes)	no
A cat says, "Moo-oo."	yes	(no)

Circle the machines that work.

page 22 (twenty-two)

Match the ears with their owners.

Put an X on something that helps you hear.

Say the Bible verses you learned (Psalm 100: 1 and 2).

EACH ANSWER, 1 POINT

9/11 Teacher Check ______ Initial Date

My Score

page 23 (twenty-three)

Name ______________

Write the word that fits.

Animals	**hear**	**vibrate**

You hear with your ears.

Animals have special ears.

Sound makes your eardrums vibrate.

Draw the ears on this animal.
Color it.

Science: 102
Worksheet 11
with page 23

Teacher check ______________
Initial Date

PART III: YOU MAKE SOUNDS

Page 24

CONCEPT: People can make different kinds of sounds.

OBJECTIVE: I can tell about sounds I make.

BIBLE REFERENCES: Psalms 100:1 and 2, 150

PROCESS: observing, by using the sense of hearing

READING INTEGRATION: listening, rhyming, vocabulary development, recalling detail

VOCABULARY: voice, hands, feet

MATERIALS NEEDED: word cards, Worksheet 12

TEACHING PAGE 24:

Teach the vocabulary words. Have the children use them in sentences. Prepare the class for listening and discussion. Explain that they are to listen for words that tell what you might use to make sounds, sound words, and rhyming words.

Read the poem aloud with feeling.

Read again slower with children following along.

Ask children to identify the vocabulary words, the rhyming words, and the sound words.

Try to have the children memorize the poem so it can be used as a choral reading.

ACTIVITIES:

1. Read Psalm 100:1 and 2 and Psalm 150.

   Ask the children to pick out sound words. Illustrate Psalm 150. Have the children learn parts of it from memory.
2. Do Worksheet 12. Go over the directions and the pictures with the children. Help those who need it. Let the others complete the page independently.
3. Add to the sound scrapbook.

III. YOU MAKE SOUNDS

You use your voice
to talk and shout,
To whisper, laugh, and sing.
With your hands you beat a drum
Or cause a bell to ring.

As you walk, your feet make sounds.
They bump upon the floor
Or tiptoe softly 'cross a room,
Then scuffle through a door.

Of all the sounds that you can make
The nicest ones to hear
Are the songs you sing
to praise the LORD.
And the words you use in prayer.

page 24 (twenty-four)

Name ______________

Write voice, hands, or feet to name what you might use to make these sounds.

hands — feet

voice — hands

Science: 102
Worksheet 12
with page 24

Teacher check ______________
Initial Date

Page 25: Activity Page

MATERIALS NEEDED: crayons, pencils, LIFEPAC Tablet

TEACHING PAGE 24:

Read and discuss the directions for the two pictures. Let the children draw the pictures on their own.

After they have finished, each child should explain his two pictures to the class.

Have children write a sentence or two in their Tablets about each picture.

Draw a picture of a place where you use a loud voice.

Draw a picture of a place where you use a soft voice.

page 25 (twenty-five)

Page 26: You Use Your Voice—Tone

CONCEPT: A voice can vary in tone to portray feelings.

OBJECTIVE: I can tell about sounds I make.

PROCESSES: observing, by using the senses of hearing and sight; comparing

READING INTEGRATION: reading a paragraph, speaking in a group

VOCABULARY: tone (happy, loud, sad, soft voice)

MATERIALS NEEDED: word cards, LIFEPAC Tablet, paper, crayons, magazines, scissors, glue or paste

YOU USE YOUR VOICE
Listen to your friend's voice. It can be loud. It can be soft.
Loud and soft are different **tones**. Your voice has tones.
Tone can tell someone how you feel. Your tone of voice can be happy or sad.
Tell some ways that the tone of your voice can let others know how you feel.
page 26 (twenty-six)

TEACHING PAGE 26:

Teach the vocabulary words. Have the children use them in sentences. Use the word cards *loud* and *soft* to demonstrate various tones of voice. Ask the children to pick the card that names the tone you use, loud or soft.

Have the children demonstrate how they might look when they feel happy or sad and how they might sound.

Read the introductory paragraph to the group. Ask how many sentences are in the paragraph. Make note of the fact that sometimes more than one paragraph is required to get an idea across.

Read the remaining paragraphs.

Read the sentence in the box and discuss with the children. Ask them to say something in a happy tone of voice, a sad tone, an excited tone, and so on. Let one child say something and have the others guess from his tone of voice how he feels.

ACTIVITY:

Begin a class mural that will show sounds being made in many different ways. This mural may be done with paint, crayon, or cut-out magazine pictures. Each child should be allowed to participate in this project, which can continue throughout the remaining time it takes to complete the LIFEPAC.

Page 27: You Use Your Voice—Pitch

CONCEPT: A voice varies in pitch as a person speaks.

OBJECTIVE: I can tell about sounds I make.

PROCESSES: observing, by using the sense of hearing; comparing

READING INTEGRATION: reading a paragraph, identifying sentences

VOCABULARY: high, low, pitch, down

MATERIALS NEEDED: word cards, Worksheet 13, pencils, crayons

TEACHING PAGE 27:

Teach the vocabulary. Let the children listen to you read a poem or a part of a story, keeping your voice flat, do not change the pitch. Then, reread it with feeling and inflection. Ask the children if they hear the difference. *Ask:* "What made the poem or story sound better the second time?"

The change in pitch as you speak or read conveys the meaning and the feeling of what your voice is saying.

Read the paragraphs and the direction sentences. Ask another volunteer to do what the direction says. Give several or all of the children a chance to experiment with the change of pitch. Have some of them start low and let the voice slide up.

Read the next sentence and the direction. Let several children read the sentences following the moving lines, indicating pitch with their voices.

Make sure they know what the words are. Read the final direction. Tell the children what they are to do and let them do it on their own.

ACTIVITIES:

1. Have the children recite their Bible verses first without any tone or pitch, then using tone and pitch.

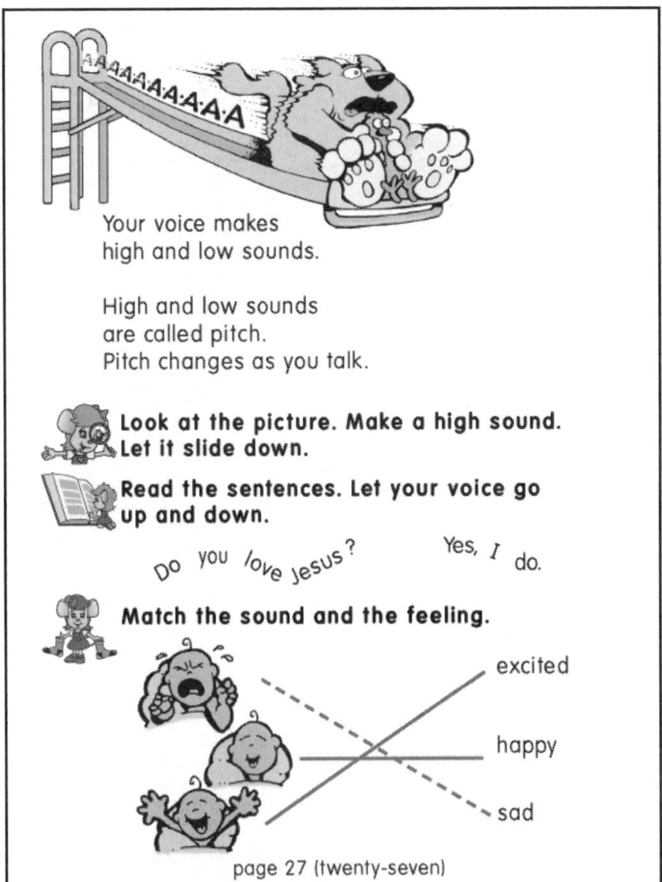

AAAAAAAAAA
Your voice makes
high and low sounds.
High and low sounds
are called pitch.
Pitch changes as you talk.
Look at the picture. Make a high sound.
Let it slide down.
Read the sentences. Let your voice go
up and down.
Do you love Jesus?
Yes, I do.
Match the sound and the feeling.
excited
happy
sad
page 27 (twenty-seven)

2. Do Worksheet 13.
3. Read books on sound to the children.

Name ____________

Write tone **or** pitch.

Your voice changes pitch when you talk or read.

The tone of your voice tells your feelings.

Write high **or** low.

Patches voice has a low pitch.

Color Patches.
He has brown spots.

Science: 102
Worksheet 13
with page 27

Teacher check ____________
Initial Date

Page 28: You Move

CONCEPTS: A person makes sounds when he moves. These sounds have different tone and pitch.

OBJECTIVE: I can tell about sounds I make.

PROCESSES: observing, by using the senses of hearing; comparing

VOCABULARY: beat, rhythm, walk, move, sounds, tone, pitch, feet, hands

MATERIALS NEEDED: LIFEPAC Tablets, pencils

TEACHING PAGE 28:

Tell the children that they will make some sounds by moving. Some sounds will be easy to hear and some will not.

Rub your fingers together. Ask, "Can anyone hear the sound I am making?" Most likely, no one will. Then ask the children to do the same thing, moving their hands closer to their ears until they can hear the sound made by the rubbing.

Snap your fingers. Ask, "Can anyone hear the sound I am making?" Most will be able to hear it.

Ask, "What was different, the tone or the pitch of the sound?" (tone)

Read the sentences or have them read. Continue with the sections of the page as you did in the demonstrations just completed. Give the children plenty of opportunity to experiment with ways of making sounds by moving.

ACTIVITIES:

1. Use the Tablets to have the children record the kinds of sounds they can make by moving. Encourage them to use complete sentences.
2. Add pages on moving and sound to the sound scrapbook. Make a page for hands, for example, and write or illustrate all the sounds you can make by moving you hands.

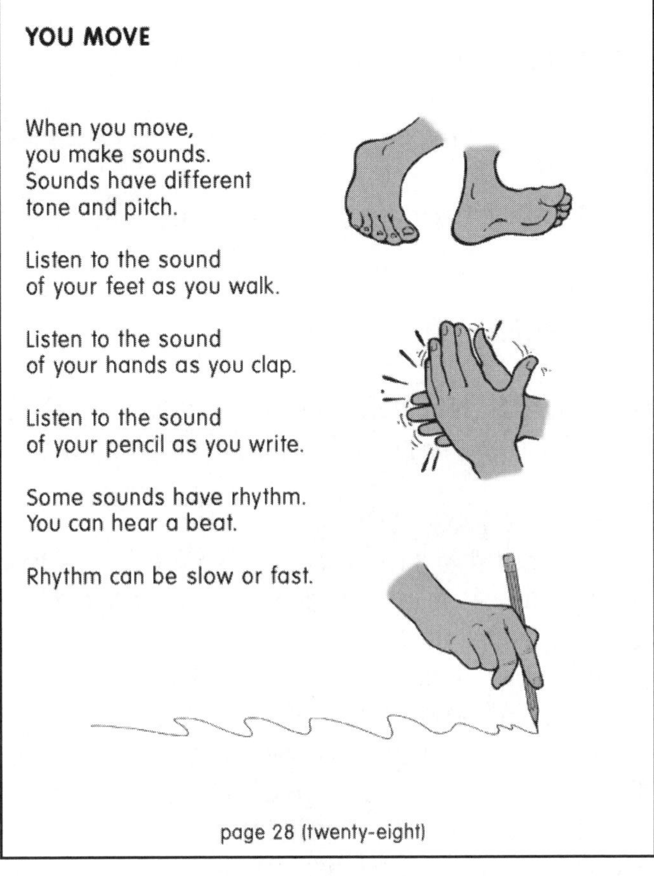

YOU MOVE
When you move,
you make sounds.
Sounds have different
tone and pitch.
Listen to the sound
of your feet as you walk.
Listen to the sound
of your hands as you clap.
Listen to the sound
of your pencil as you write.
Some sounds have rhythm.
You can hear a beat.
Rhythm can be slow or fast.
page 28 (twenty-eight)

3. Do some rhythm practice. Clap your hands in a straight 4/4 rhythm- X X X X. Clap your hands in a different rhythm- XX X XX. Ask the children what difference they heard in the beat (first-slow; second-fast, slow, fast). Have the children name other things that have a beat (walking, tapping, etc.).
4. Clap or tap name rhythms.

example:

John	Robert
X	X x
Julia	Catherine
X x x	X x x

Page 29: You Move—Rhythm

CONCEPT: Sounds have rhythm.

OBJECTIVE: I can tell about sounds I make.

PROCESS: observing, by using the sense of hearing

VOCABULARY: rhythm, beat

MATERIALS NEEDED: word cards, LIFEPAC Tablet, crayons, pencils, rhythm instruments

TEACHING PAGE 29:

Reread the poem on page 24. Stress the beat. Have the children clap along to reinforce the rhythm.

Ask for other suggestions of sounds that have a rhythm. Allow time for discussion.

Read the direction sentence and have the children name the pictures. Let them complete the first activity then check it together. Ask volunteers to tell which pictures they circled and tell why they chose them. Have children imitate or demonstrate the beat of the circled pictures.

Read the statement, *rhythm can be slow or fast.* Ask a child to demonstrate by clapping a fast rhythm. Ask another child to demonstrate a slow rhythm.

Have the children read and follow the directions for the rest of the page.

Circle the pictures that show rhythm.
Write this sentence in your Tablet.
Rhythm can be slow or fast.
Write slow. slow
Write fast. fast
page 29 (twenty-nine)

ACTIVITIES:

1. To reinforce the concept of rhythm, play some music with various beats (for example, hymns, marches, ballads, etc.) and various speeds (tempos). Make note of the fact that the rhythm and tempo of music can convey different moods or feelings.
2. Add to sound scrapbook pages on rhythm.
3. Have more advanced children expand the sentence written in the Tablet to an example or short story.
4. Have rhythm sticks, drum, or other rhythm instruments available in the discovery center. Have children work together or with an aide to practice rhythm patterns and imitation of these patterns. One child, for example, can tap a short, simple rhythm pattern. A second child can repeat the pattern.

Page 30: You Make Music

CONCEPT: Music has tone, pitch, and rhythm.

OBJECTIVE: I can tell about sounds I make.

PROCESS: observing, by using the sense of hearing

READING INTEGRATION: following directions, listening

VOCABULARY: pitch, rhythm, tone

MATERIALS NEEDED: recordings or tapes of several kinds of music for listening (marches, lullabies, songs, loud music, soft music, etc.), record player or tape recorder, LIFEPAC Tablet, pencils

TEACHING PAGE 30:

Play a recording or two. Have children discuss the music they hear. Try to convey the idea that music can set a mood or make people feel a certain way. *Example:* A marching band makes you feel like marching, a lullaby makes you feel sleepy, a song of praise to God makes you feel joyful.

Read title and introductory sentences to the children or have them read by a volunteer.

Demonstrate each pair of sentences with a recording.

ACTIVITIES:

1. If possible, set up a listening area where children may enjoy recorded music. The choices are wide. Your library may have a selection from which to choose.
2. Have the children write a sentence in their Tablets to tell how the music they chose made them feel.
3. Continue the sound scrapbook.

YOU MAKE MUSIC

Music has tone.
It can be loud or soft.

Music has pitch.
It can go high or low.

Music has rhythm.
You can march to the rhythm of a band.

page 30 (thirty)

Page 31: Activity Page

CONCEPT: Music has rhythm, pitch, and tone.

OBJECTIVE: I can tell about sounds I make.

PROCESS: observing, by using the senses of hearing and sight

READING INTEGRATION: listening, reading sentences, memorizing

VOCABULARY: march, sing, play; enrichment: note, staff

MATERIALS NEEDED: word cards, crayons, pencils, piano (if available)

TEACHING PAGE 31:

Read the first direction and discuss the pictures. Let the children write the appropriate word under the picture. Read the second direction. Help the children complete this activity. Sing or play the scale for the children so that they hear the difference in pitch.

Tell the children that they will learn a little song that tells about music. It has pitch, tone, and rhythm. The words and music will tell them what to do.

Read the introduction to the song. Play and sing the music for the children. If you do not have a piano or other instrument to play the notes, you might have it taped by a volunteer parent so that it will be easier to teach. Give the children an opportunity to learn the song. You could have them march to it as they sing.

ACTIVITIES:

1. Make a rhythm band. An empty oatmeal box makes a good drum. Two hardwood sticks tapped together add to the rhythm. A triangle, a juice can filled with a few beans and covered, and a tissue-covered comb make interesting sounds.
2. Teach simple, music-reading skills. The five lines are the staff. The dots with stems are the notes. The notes go up, down, and across the staff.
3. The children could make musical instruments in the discovery center as a whole-group project or as a take-home activity.
4. If any child plays a musical instrument, he could demonstrate for the class.
5. Have the group review the last section of the LIFEPAC in preparation for the last self test.
6. Finish the sound scrapbook. Go through all the pages as a review of the LIFEPAC. Keep it in a place where children can refer to it.

Page 32: Self Test 3

MATERIALS NEEDED: pencils

TEACHING PAGE 32:

Review the vocabulary words for the LIFEPAC. Play a flash card game with the words—- have the children pick a word, say it, and make up a sentence using the word. Give the children an opportunity to review the pages of the LIFEPAC before doing the self test.

The proficiency of your class should dictate whether you will direct the self test or allow the children to proceed independently once directions are given. If you choose to direct the test, read each direction, answer any questions, and then allow enough time for every child to complete the activity.

If your group is working independently, be sure you are available to answer individual questions.

Review the direction words *Match, Circle, Put an X,* and *Write.*

Help anyone who needs help with words in the first two activities. The first activity may be done orally by the very slow student. If a student does poorly in any of the activities on page 32, review the pages and activities that stress the concepts.

Activity 1: Review Part III.
Activity 2: Review Part II.
Activity 3: Review Part I.

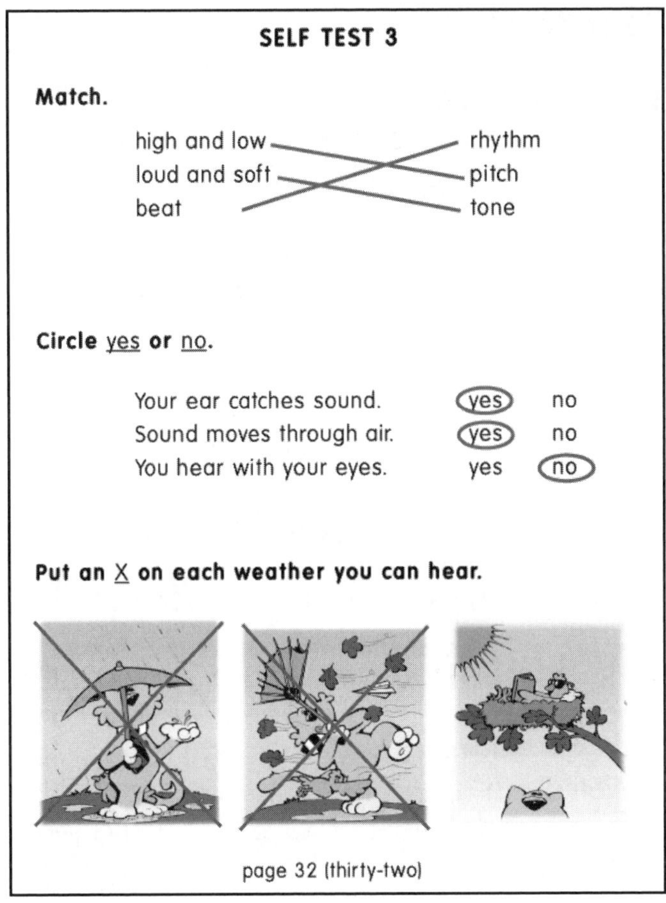

SELF TEST 3
Match.
high and low
loud and soft
beat
rhythm
pitch
tone
Circle yes or no.
Your ear catches sound. yes no
Sound moves through air. yes no
You hear with your eyes. yes no
Put an X on each weather you can hear.
page 32 (thirty-two)

Page 33: Self Test 3

TEACHING PAGE 33:

Read the directions. Give some samples on the board for Activity 2.

Example:	sou_d	(a e n r)
	pitc_	(b h e d)

Ask the children to finish the word.

If children do poorly on this page, review the pages and activities that stress the concepts.

Activity 1: Review Section 1.
Activity 2: Review vocabulary word cards.

If some students score under the accepted level, have them review and correct errors made in completing the activities in the LIFEPAC. You might also provide additional copies of the worksheets for further review.

All students should do a little reviewing before taking the LIFEPAC Test.

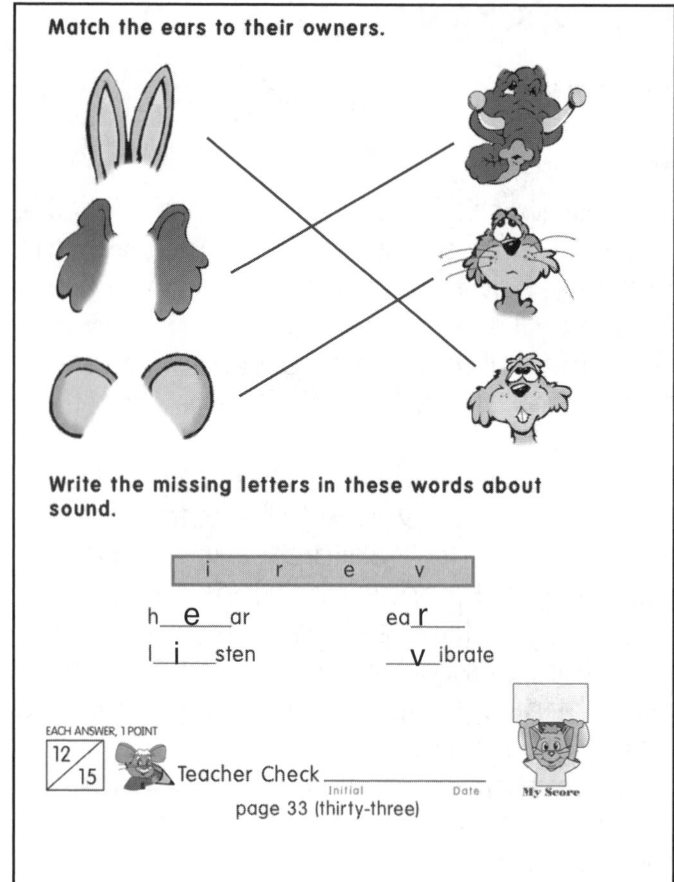

Match the ears to their owners.
Write the missing letters in these words about sound.
i r e v
h e ar
ea r
l i sten
v ibrate
EACH ANSWER, 1 POINT
12
15
Teacher Check
Initial
Date
My Score
page 33 (thirty-three)

LIFEPAC TEST AND ALTERNATE LIFEPAC TEST

Administer the test to the class as a group. Ask to have directions read or read them to the group. In either case, be sure that the children clearly understand the directions. Put examples on the board if it seems necessary.

Give sufficient time for each activity to be completed before going on to the next.

When the entire test is complete, collect and score. Go over the test with each child. For those children who do not achieve the acceptable score, review the LIFEPAC. This final review may be supervised by a parent or a volunteer helper. If none are available, allow the child to take the material home for study. Provide a list of vocabulary words. When you are convinced the child is prepared, administer the Alternate LIFEPAC Test.

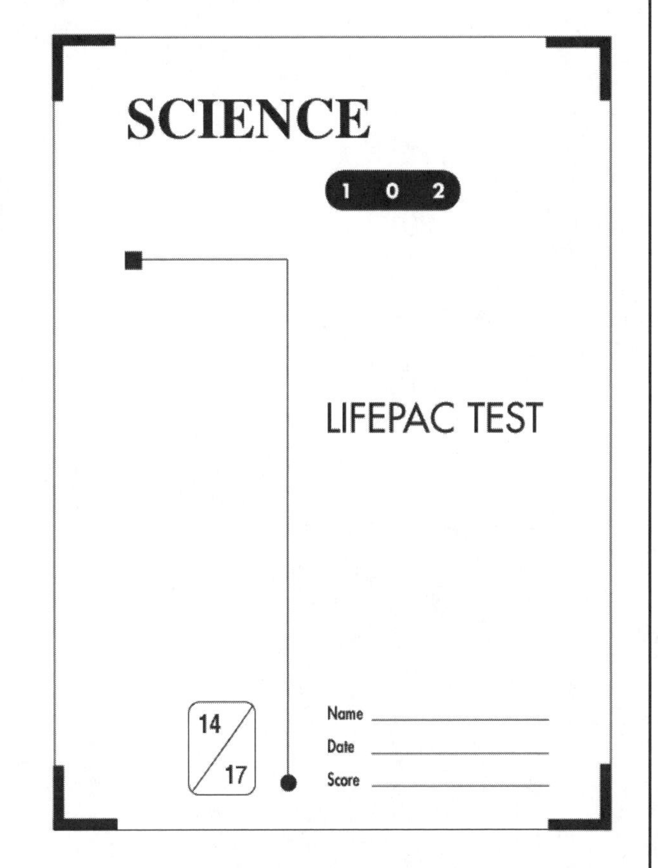

SCIENCE
1 0 2
LIFEPAC TEST
14
17
Name
Date
Score

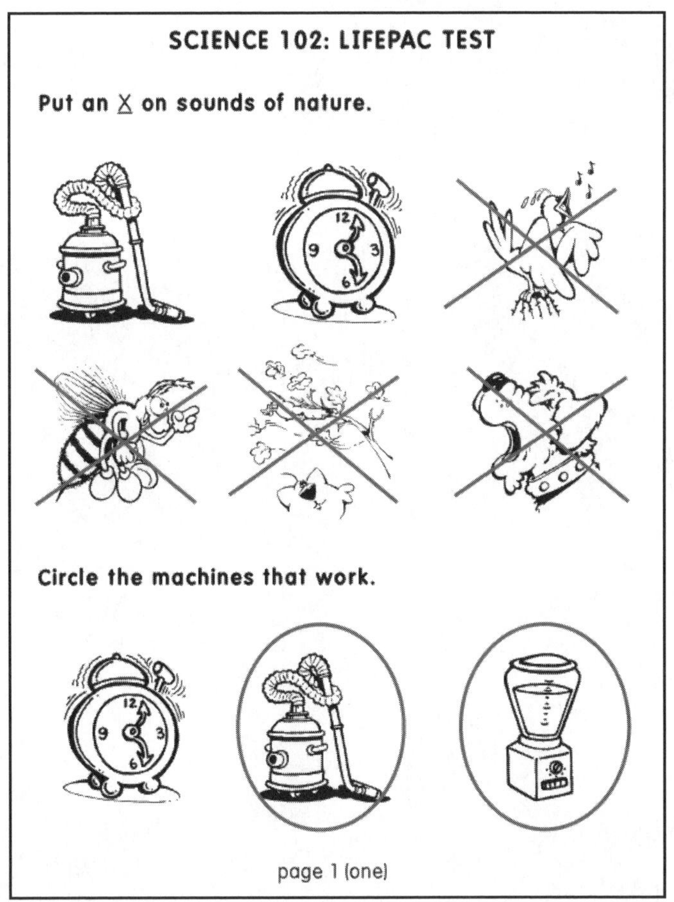

SCIENCE 102: LIFEPAC TEST
Put an X on sounds of nature.
Circle the machines that work.
page 1 (one)

Circle yes or no.

You make sound when you move.	(yes)	no
God gave animals special ears.	(yes)	no
You see with your ears.	yes	(no)
You listen to your teacher in school.	(yes)	no
Sound waves make your eardrums vibrate.	(yes)	no

Put an X on sounds you hear in school.

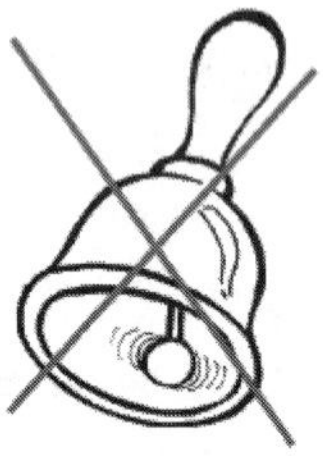

page 2 (two)

Write the word that fits.

A song has pitch (shout/pitch). It can go high or low.

Music has **rhythm** (air/rhythm). You can hear a beat.

Your voice has **tone** (tone/clouds). It can be loud or soft.

Say your Bible verses (Psalm 100: 1 and 2).

page 3 (three)

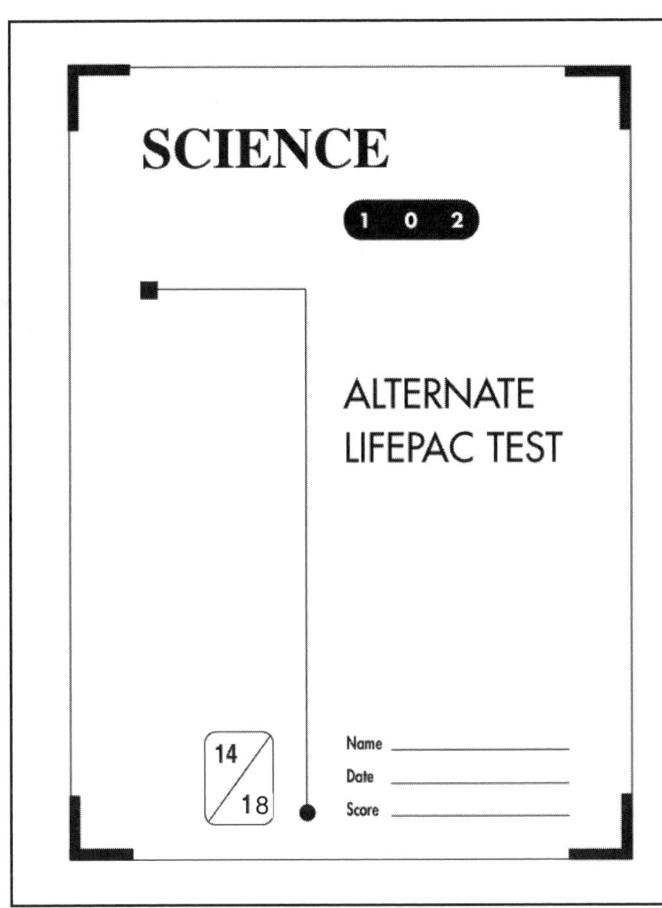

SCIENCE

1 0 2

ALTERNATE LIFEPAC TEST

14/18

Name ______
Date ______
Score ______

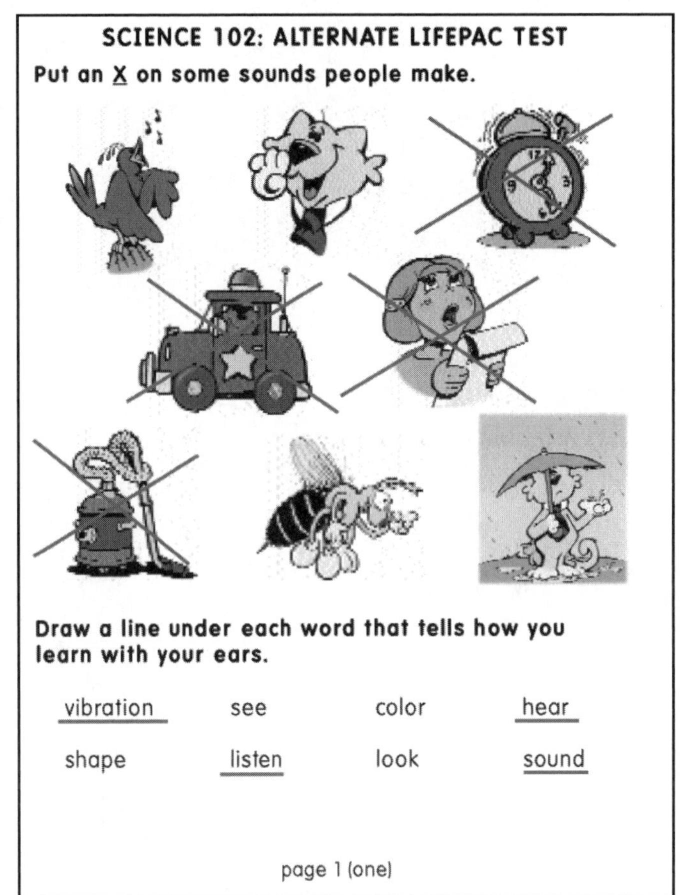

SCIENCE 102: ALTERNATE LIFEPAC TEST

Put an X on some sounds people make.

Draw a line under each word that tells how you learn with your ears.

vibration	see	color	hear
shape	listen	look	sound

page 1 (one)

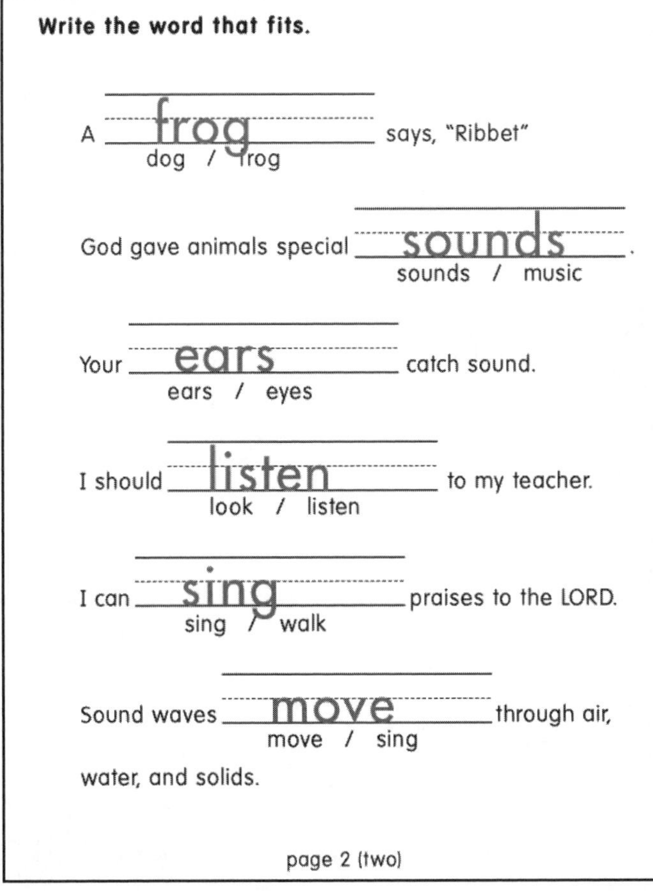

Write the word that fits.

A __frog__ says, "Ribbet"
dog / frog

God gave animals special __sounds__.
sounds / music

Your __ears__ catch sound.
ears / eyes

I should __listen__ to my teacher.
look / listen

I can __sing__ praises to the LORD.
sing / walk

Sound waves __move__ through air, water, and solids.
move / sing

page 2 (two)

Write the word that fits.

Your voice has __tone__. It can be loud or soft.
tone/clouds

A song has __pitch__. It can go high or low.
shout/pitch

Music has __rhythm__. You can hear a beat.
air/rhythm

Say your Bible verses (Psalm 100: 1 and 2).

page 3 (three)

Page 1: MORE ABOUT YOUR SENSES

CONCEPT: introduction to the concepts to be taught in the LIFEPAC

OBJECTIVE: introduction to the objectives to be met in the LIFEPAC

PROCESS: introduction to the processes, mainly observation, that will be used in the LIFEPAC

READING INTEGRATION: listening, rhyming, recalling detail

VOCABULARY: smell, taste, touch, nose, tongue, skin, feeling

MATERIALS NEEDED: word cards, display listing and illustrating the senses

TEACHING PAGE 1:

Give the children a chance to look through the LIFEPAC without marking in it. When they have had enough time, have them go to the table of contents. As you read through the list of the contents of the LIFEPAC, have the children follow along.

Ask: "Can you name the three senses we will study in this LIFEPAC? (smell, taste and touch) Can you name the senses we studied in Science LIFEPACs 101 and 102?" (sight and hearing)

Read the title aloud to the class.

Have the children listen carefully to the poem. Ask them to listen for the names of the senses they will study, for the parts of the body that they use for these senses, and for the rhyming words.

Read the objectives. Remind the children that they will be able to do these things when the LIFEPAC is finished.

Repeat the poem. Have the children follow along. Perhaps a child or two would like to read the poem aloud.

MORE ABOUT YOUR SENSES

My eyes and ears can tell a lot.
But, I can learn so much,
If I use my other senses, too –
Smell and taste and touch.

To smell, I have to use my nose.
To taste, I use my tongue.
Touch is feeling with my skin.
God gave me every one.

So, thank you, God, for senses.
They really help me out.
I see, hear, touch, taste, and smell
What my world's all about.

1. I can tell about the sense of smell.
2. I can tell about the sense of taste.
3. I can tell about the sense of touch.
4. I can tell how my senses can work together.

page 1 (one)

ACTIVITY:

Set up a discovery center to be used throughout the section. Include spices, vinegar, sliced fruits and vegetables with distinctive odors (these items will have to be replaced frequently because they lose their fragrance when exposed to air), and any other items with distinctive smells. Have the children takes turns in the center and have them write or dictate sentences about what they learn. Caution the children to *smell*, not *taste*!

PART 1: SMELL AND TASTE

Page 2

CONCEPT: Smell and taste work together.

OBJECTIVES:
I can tell about the sense of smell.
I can tell about the sense of taste.

PROCESS: observing, using the sense of smell

READING INTEGRATION: sentence structure (question)

VOCABULARY: lemon, sugar, water, lemonade

MATERIALS NEEDED: lemons (enough for lemonade for the class), sugar, pitcher, cups, knife, juicer, spoon

I. SMELL AND TASTE
Smell and taste are important senses.
They tell you a lot of things.
Smell and taste work together.
SUGAR
lemon + sugar = lemonade
What do you smell?
page 2 (two)

TEACHING PAGE 2:

Ask the children to raise their hands to show that they have smelled a lemon. Ask a volunteer to describe how it smelled.

Cut a lemon or two in halves. Pass the cut lemon throughout the class and ask the children to smell it.

Ask: "How did it smell? What happened to your mouth when you smelled the lemon?"

Note to teacher: The saliva increase in the mouth when you smell a lemon is an indication that the taste buds on the tongue are working, too. Taste and smell are working together.

Read or have a child read the introductory sentences.

Ask for a volunteer to find and read the question on the page. Have the child tell how he knew that the sentence was a question (the ?).

Tell the children to look at the picture.

Ask: "What does the girl smell? (lemon) What else do you see in the picture? (sugar) Can the girl smell the sugar?"

Give the children an opportunity to smell some sugar. It has no smell or very little. The mouth does not salivate.

ACTIVITY:

Make some lemonade for the class. Let the children help.

Page 3: Activity Page

MATERIALS NEEDED: pencils, crayons

TEACHING PAGE 3:

Discuss all aspects of the picture with the children before reading the directions. Read the direction or have it read by a volunteer.

Check the page by having the children name the thing and try to describe the smell.

Put an X on each thing you might smell outdoors.
page 3 (three)

Pages 4 and 5: I Use My Nose to Smell

CONCEPT: You use your nose to smell.

OBJECTIVE: I can tell about the sense of smell.

PROCESS: observing, using the sense of smell

READING INTEGRATION: reading and writing sentences, following directions

VOCABULARY: breakfast, morning, outside, school

MATERIALS NEEDED: word cards, LIFEPAC Tablet, Worksheet 1

TEACHING PAGES 4 and 5:

Discuss the illustration. Read the title or have a child read it.

Read the text and discuss each sentence with the children. Encourage all the children to contribute to the discussion. Introduce vocabulary words in context.

Read the directions. Have the children complete the page independently. Check by discussing their answers.

ACTIVITIES:

1. Do Worksheet 1.

Read the sentence and the direction.

Discuss the partial illustration.

Have pictures of happy faces around for the children to see. Tell them to finish the face.

2. Set up an independent reading table with as many books as you can find about the senses. These books can be used in many ways: to look up additional information, to write short reports, to provide productive time use for those children who finish their work ahead of others, and to provide additional reading practice for those who need it.

I USE MY NOSE TO SMELL

In the morning
I smell breakfast.
I can smell things outside, too.
I can smell things at school.
Some smells are nice.
Some smells are not so nice.

page 4 (four)

Circle the things you might smell from your room.
MILK
page 5 (five)

Name ______________

Here is a nose smelling something nice.

Draw the rest of the face.

Science: 103
Worksheet 1
with page 5

Teacher check ______________
Initial Date

Pages 6 and 7: Activity Page

MATERIALS NEEDED: LIFEPAC Tablet, pencils, crayons, alphabet charts, Worksheet 2

TEACHING PAGE 6:

Read the directions for the first activity.

Make sure the children have their alphabet charts for reference. Instruct them to begin with the capital letters. Then have them finish the drawing by connecting the small letters. Less capable students may need help with the small letters.

Ask the children what animal they have made (skunk). Ask them why people do not always like skunks. Ask them what color a skunk is (black and white). Have them color the skunk.

Read the second direction. Allow the children time to draw their pictures. When they have finished, let each child talk about his picture.

TEACHING PAGE 7:

Read the directions. Instruct the children to draw the picture and to copy the sentence into their Tablets.

When they have finished, let them explain their pictures.

ACTIVITIES:

1. Do Worksheet 2.

Discuss the partial illustration.

Read the sentence and direction.

Tell the children that they are to complete the face of the person smelling the pig.

Let them discuss their drawing when they have finished.

2. Have the children write two or three sentences in their Tablets about one of the pictures they have just drawn. Slower children may dictate their sentences and then copy them into their Tablets.

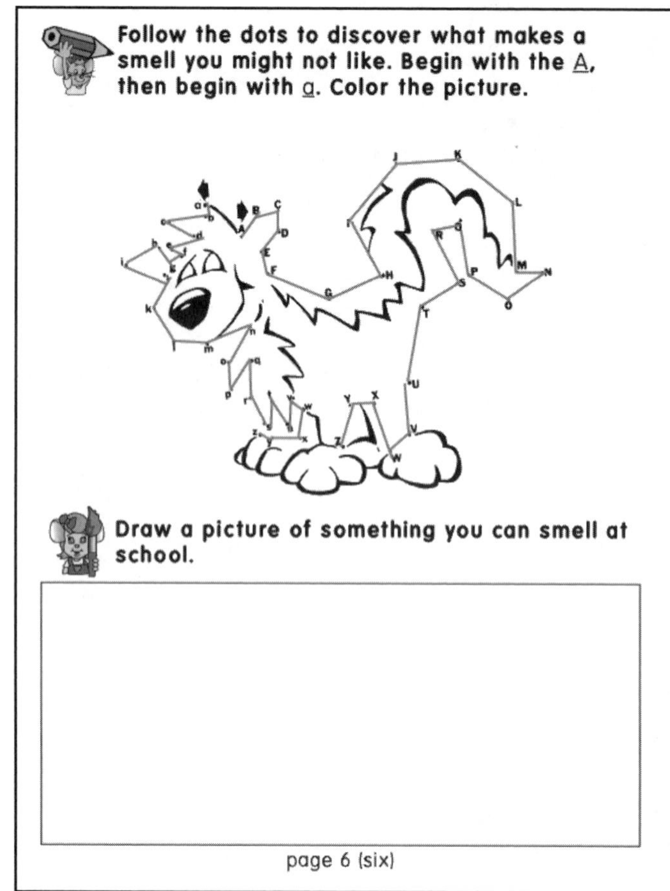

Follow the dots to discover what makes a smell you might not like. Begin with the A, then begin with a. Color the picture.

Draw a picture of something you can smell at school.

page 6 (six)

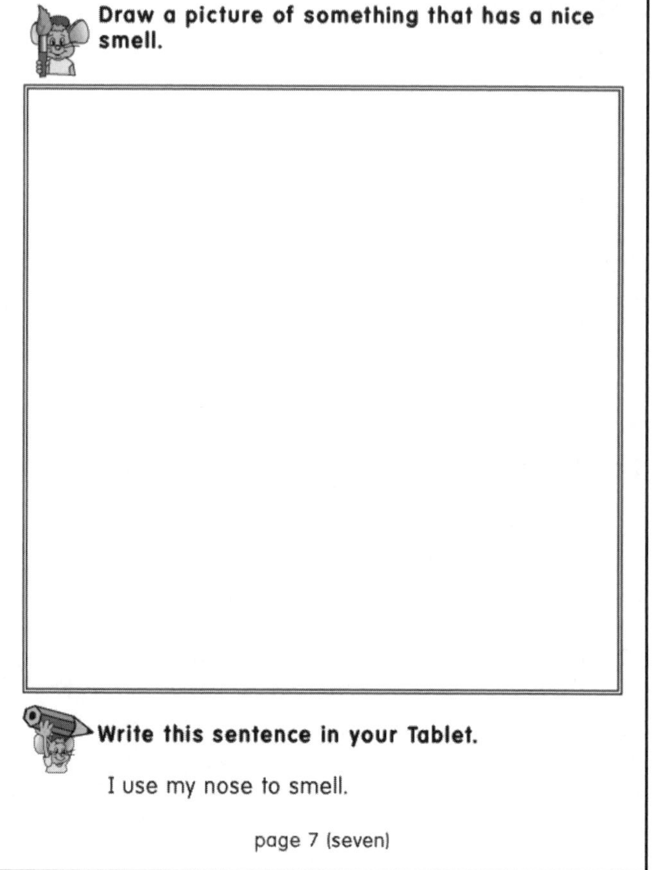

Draw a picture of something that has a nice smell.

Write this sentence in your Tablet.

I use my nose to smell.

page 7 (seven)

Name _______________

This nose is smelling something it does not like.

Draw the rest of the face.

Science: 103
Worksheet 2
with page 7

Teacher check _______________
Initial Date

Page 8: I Use My Tongue to Taste

CONCEPTS: Taste buds on the tongue help the sense of taste. They can taste sweet, salt, sour, and bitter.

OBJECTIVE: I can tell about the sense of taste.

PROCESS: observing, using the sense of taste

READING INTEGRATION: sentence structure (statement), vocabulary development

VOCABULARY: buds, sweet, sour, bitter, salty, (tongue)

MATERIALS NEEDED: word cards, mirrors (small pocket mirrors will do, as many as you can find), LIFEPAC Tablet, magnifying glass (if available), Worksheet 3

I USE MY TONGUE TO TASTE
I have taste buds
on my tongue.
My tongue tastes sweet things.
My tongue tastes sour things.
My tongue tastes salty things.
My tongue tastes bitter things.
Write this sentence in your Tablet.
I use my tongue to taste.
Talk about things that
taste sweet, sour, salty,
and bitter.
page 8 (eight)

TEACHING PAGE 8:

Put a diagram of a tongue on the board. It might look something like this one.

a) bitter
b) sweet
c) sour
d) salt

Introduce the vocabulary words in conjunction with the diagram.

Tell the children that the taste buds on the tongue have special jobs to do. The taste buds on the tip of the tongue taste sweet things. Those buds along the sides of the tongue taste salty and sour things. In the middle of the back are taste buds that taste things that are bitter.

The next three pages will help the children remember that the tongue tastes only these things. All other refinements of taste are a function of the sense of smell.

Have a child read the title and introductory sentence. Give each child a mirror or have children share the mirrors that are available. Ask them to try to see the taste buds on their own tongues. If you have magnifying glasses, let them get a better look. Discuss what the children see.

Finish reading the sentences on the page. Let the children complete the Tablet activity. Drill vocabulary words in context.

Discuss the sentence in the box.

List the things that the children name for each category on the board or on a "Taste Chart." Note that not all things taste the same way to all people.

ACTIVITY:

Do Worksheet 3.

Read the directions.

Let the children do the page independently using the diagram on the board for reference.

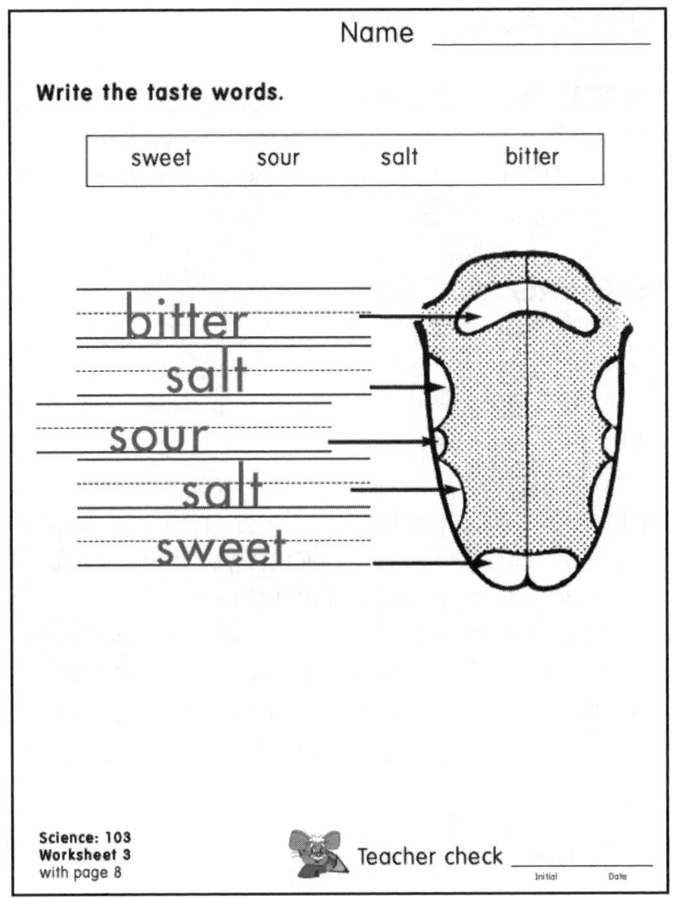
Name

Write the taste words.

sweet	sour	salt	bitter

Science: 103
Worksheet 3
with page 8

Teacher check
Initial Date

Page 9: Activity Page

MATERIALS NEEDED: crayons; pictures of some things that would taste sweet, sour, salty, and bitter; magazines; banner paper for posters

TEACHING PAGE 9:

Ask the children to think of some foods that have the taste of each word.

Note to teacher: Remind the children about the importance of not tasting something with which they are not familiar unless an adult says that it is all right. Many children are poisoned each year as a result of tasting things they should not.

Have someone read the directions. When the children understand what they are to do, they may complete the page independently. Check and share the work together.

ACTIVITIES:

1. Make a paste-up poster or a collage for each taste. Use old magazines to find pictures of foods.
2. Have the children write sentences about their favorite tastes. They may use their Tablets.

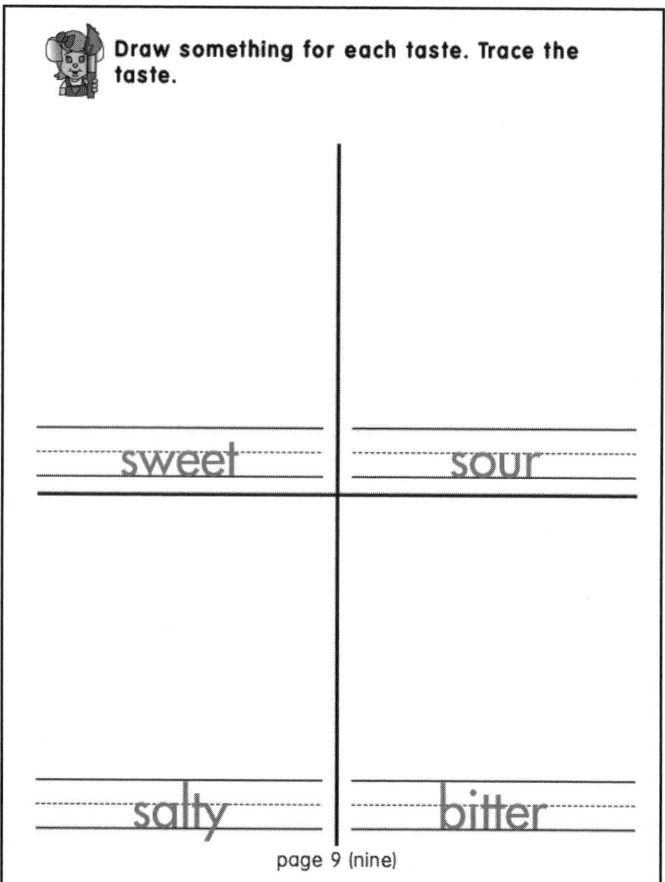

Draw something for each taste. Trace the taste.
sweet
sour
salty
bitter
page 9 (nine)

Page 10: Smell and Taste Go Together

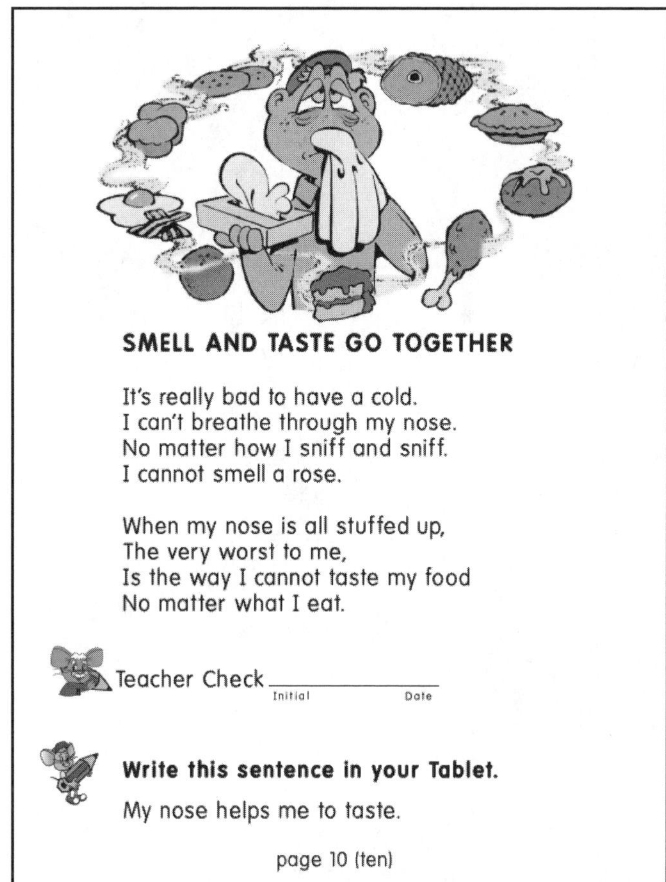

SMELL AND TASTE GO TOGETHER

It's really bad to have a cold.
I can't breathe through my nose.
No matter how I sniff and sniff.
I cannot smell a rose.

When my nose is all stuffed up,
The very worst to me,
Is the way I cannot taste my food
No matter what I eat.

Teacher Check ____________ Initial Date

Write this sentence in your Tablet.

My nose helps me to taste.

page 10 (ten)

CONCEPT: Taste and smell work together.

OBJECTIVES:

I can tell about the sense of smell.
I can tell about the sense of taste.

PROCESSES: observing, using the senses of smell and taste; predicting

READING INTEGRATION: rhyming, recalling details, main idea

VOCABULARY: Review the words from pages 1 through 9.

MATERIALS NEEDED: words cards from pages 1 through 9, LIFEPAC Tablet, Worksheet 4, pencils, crayons

TEACHING PAGE 10:

Review the vocabulary words and the concepts:

1. You use your nose to smell.
2. Your tongue and taste buds help you taste.
3. Your nose helps you taste.

Have a child read the statement at the top of the page or read it to the group yourself.

Ask the children if anyone has had a bad cold. If so, ask if they remember how their food tasted when they were sick.

Discuss the illustration.

Proceed with the poem. Read it aloud to the class. Have them listen for the rhyming words, and the main idea of the poem (food loses its taste when you have a cold).

Have a volunteer tell the story of the poem in his own words.

Let the children complete the Tablet activity independently.

ACTIVITIES:

1. You may wish to have the children use the poem as a memory piece to be recited before the class.
2. Provide Worksheet 4 as a review for the self test.
3. Try reading or reciting the poem while holding your nose. It demonstrates the effect the nose has on speech.

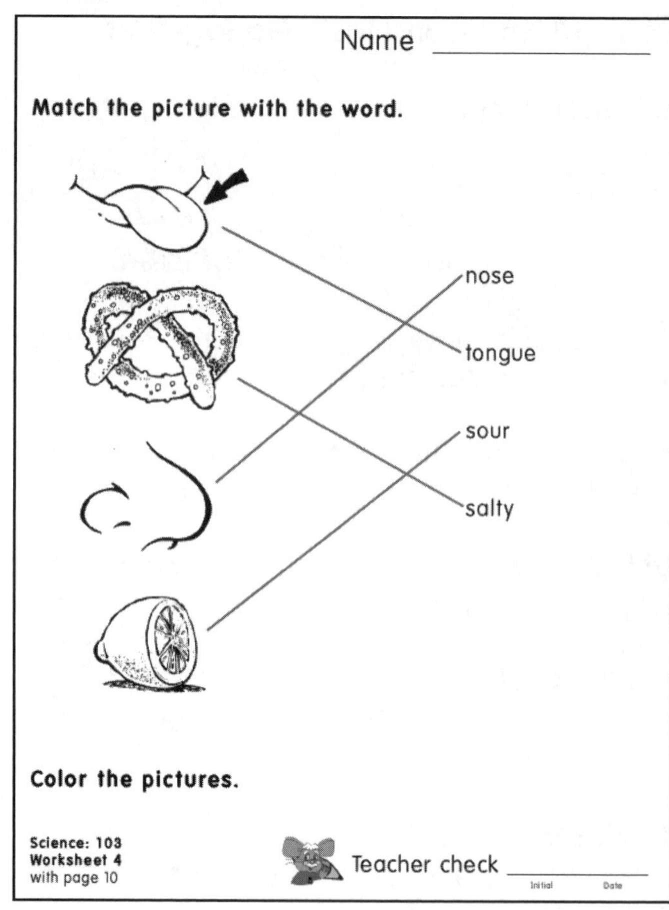
Name
Match the picture with the word.
nose
tongue
sour
salty
Color the pictures.
Science: 103
Worksheet 4
with page 10
Teacher check
Initial
Date

PAGE 11: Self Test 1

OBJECTIVES:

I can tell about the sense of smell.
I can tell about the sense of taste.

READING INTEGRATION: recall of details, word recognition, following directions

MATERIALS NEEDED: pencils

TEACHING PAGE 11:

Review the vocabulary words.

Have the children look back through the work they have completed in Section 1.

Read all the directions in the self test with the children.

The general proficiency of your group should dictate whether you choose to direct the test or to allow the children to proceed independently, once directions are given.

In either case, you should be available to answer questions and to give help with vocabulary as needed.

Check immediately and advise the child where he did well and where he needs further work.

All projects relating to the senses of taste and smell should be completed. Every child should have had a chance to spend some time in the discovery center.

For those children who have not passed the self test with a satisfactory score, some review time should be given. A helper or the child's parent may go through the LIFEPAC Section 1 with the child and supervise him as he makes all corrections necessary.

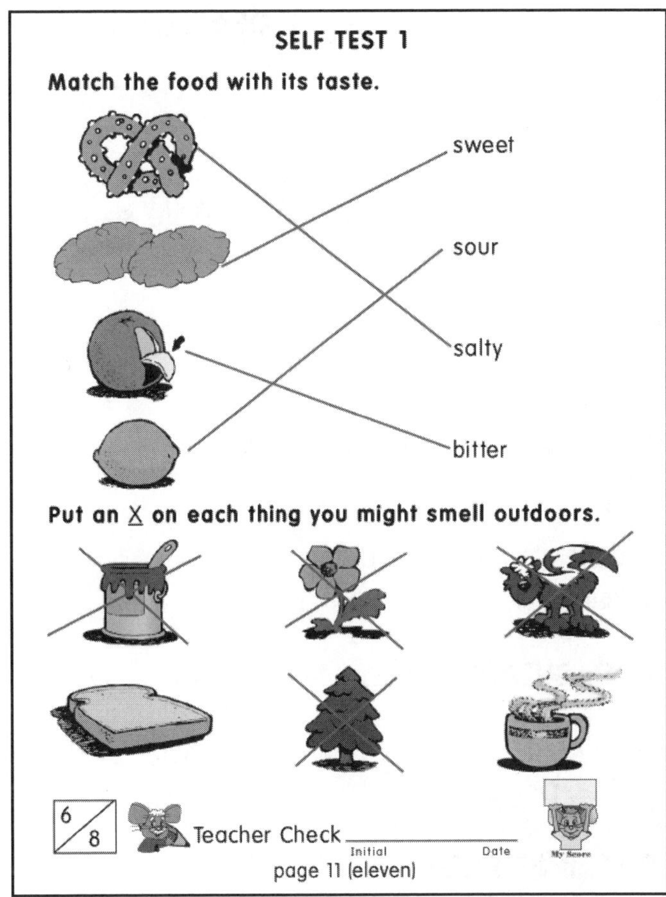

SELF TEST 1
Match the food with its taste.
sweet
sour
salty
bitter
Put an X on each thing you might smell outdoors.
6/8
Teacher Check
Initial
Date
page 11 (eleven)

PART II. TOUCH: THE SENSE OF FEELING

Page 12

CONCEPTS: The sense of touch is in the skin. Some areas of the body are more sensitive than others.

OBJECTIVE: I can tell about the sense of touch.

PROCESS: observing, using the sense of touch

READING INTEGRATION: rhyming, recalling details

VOCABULARY: (touch, feeling, skin)

MATERIALS NEEDED: word cards, LIFEPAC Tablet, pencils

TEACHING PAGE 12:

Review the vocabulary words with the word cards. Tell the children that the poem on page 13 will help them to understand that the skin on many parts of their bodies can feel things that they do not feel with just their hands.

Read the title of the section, TOUCH: THE SENSE OF FEELING. It introduces the idea of the sense of touch as a different kind of feeling from the inside feelings of happiness, sadness, and so on.

Read the poem aloud.

Reread it with the children reading along.

Ask: "What do you have on your fingers, toes, elbows, and nose that can feel things? (skin) Where else do you have skin? (answers will vary) Does the skin on other parts of your body feel things, too? (yes) What does the poem tell you that your skin can feel? What else can your skin feel besides the things mentioned in the poem?" (answers will vary)

II. TOUCH: THE SENSE OF FEELING
Use your fingers.
Use your toes.
Use your elbows,
Or your nose.
Hard and soft,
Cold and hot,
Your sense of touch
Tells quite a lot.
page 12 (twelve)

ACTIVITY:

Set up a discovery center containing labeled items of various textures. Display the names of the way these items might feel. Have the children write sentences matching the name of the item with the word that tells how it feels. Have them use their Tablets.

Page 13: I Feel with My Skin

I FEEL WITH MY SKIN

Use a feather.
Touch your friend.
Can you feel the feather?
Can your friend
feel the feather?

page 13 (thirteen)

CONCEPT: You feel with your skin.

OBJECTIVE: I can tell about the sense of touch.

PROCESS: observing, using the sense of touch

READING INTEGRATION: following directions

VOCABULARY: feather (introduce the word but do not hold children responsible for its spelling at this point)

MATERIALS NEEDED: feathers, enough for at least one for every two or three children, LIFEPAC Tablet, pencils, Worksheet 5, crayons

TEACHING PAGE 13:

Tell the children that this page will give them time to discover how well the skin on various places of their bodies feels things.

Have a volunteer read the sentences on the page. Ask a child to identify the sentences that tell them what they are to do.

Let the children choose partners and do the activity suggested. Provide time for discussion.

Ask: "Where could your skin feel the feather the best? Where did it tickle? Where was it hard to feel?"

ACTIVITIES:

1. Do Worksheet 5.

Read the directions. Instruct the children to begin at *A* and to follow the alphabet dots until the picture is complete. Ask the children what picture they have made (hand or finger). Ask if they use their finger to tickle.

Let them color the picture and draw a picture of what the finger might be tickling. Children should use their alphabet charts if needed. Make note of any child who still has difficulty with the alphabet and give special help and drill.

2. Have the children write sentences about the activity in their Tablets.

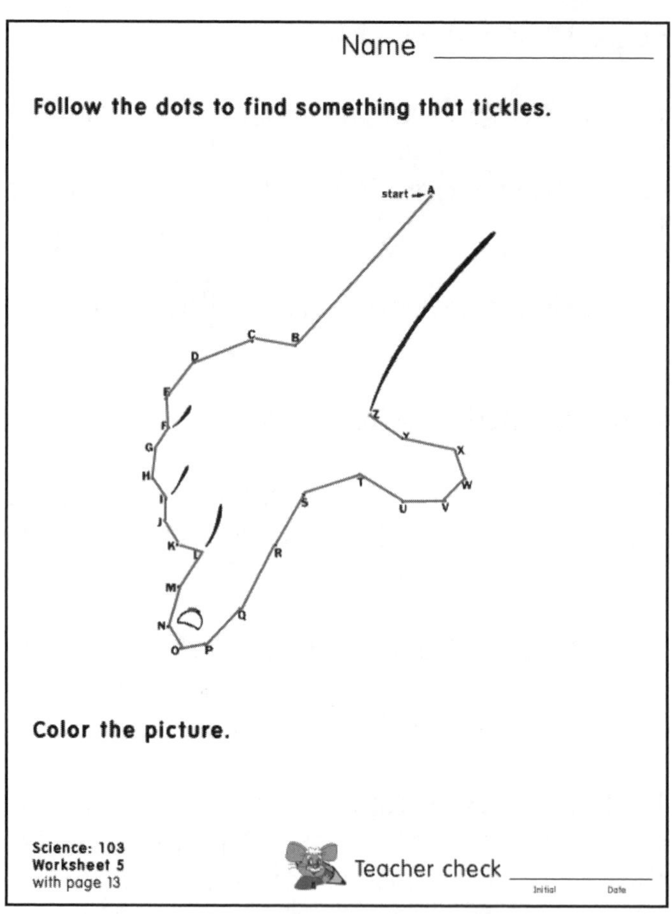

Name ____________

Follow the dots to find something that tickles.

Color the picture.

Science: 103
Worksheet 5
with page 13

Teacher check ____________
Initial Date

Pages 14, 15, and 16: Textures

CONCEPTS: Your skin can feel hard, soft, rough, and smooth. Your skin can feel hot and cold.

OBJECTIVE: I can tell about the sense of touch.

PROCESSES: observing, using the sense of touch, comparing

READING INTEGRATION: following directions, sentence structure (question)

VOCABULARY: hot, cold, soft, rough, smooth, (hard)

MATERIALS NEEDED: pencils, cotton, sandpaper, a rock, word cards, LIFEPAC Tablet, old magazines, chart paper, Worksheet 6, crayons.

TEACHING PAGES 14, 15, and 16:

Teach the vocabulary. Have the children think of examples for each of the words. *Example:* soft—a kitten or a pillow.

Choose a volunteer to read the introductory sentence. Another child may read the direction. Choose another to find the box with the words they are to write for each activity. As you proceed through the activities on the pages, have the children identify the questions and tell the punctuation mark that follows each question.

ACTIVITIES:

1. Make a chart for each of the textures (hard, soft, rough, smooth). Have the children list, illustrate, or bring pictures for each chart.
2. Do Worksheet 6.

Read the directions to the children.

Let them complete the page independently.

Let them work in the discovery center if they have not had the opportunity to do so or if they are having difficulty distinguishing the textures.

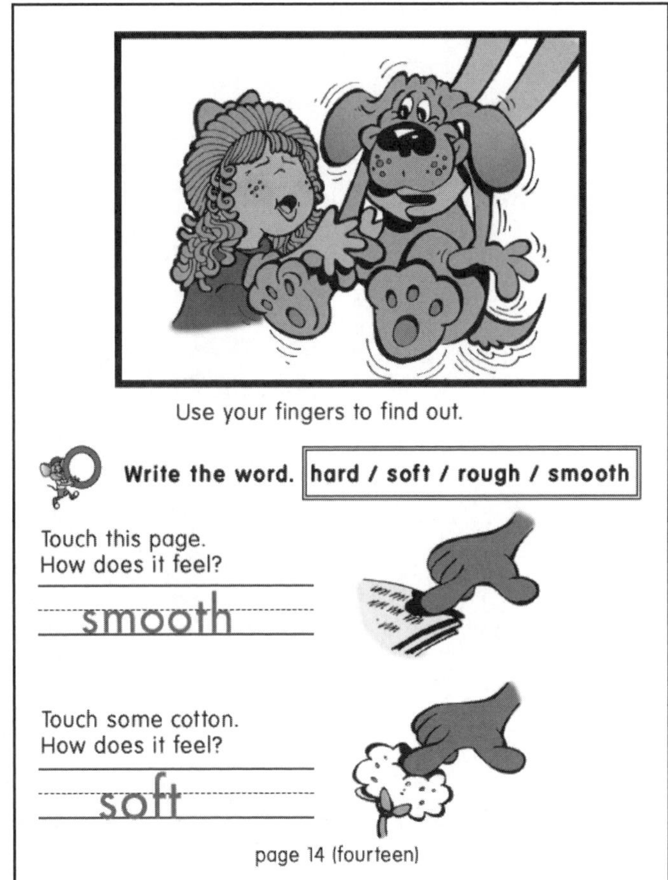

page 14 (fourteen)

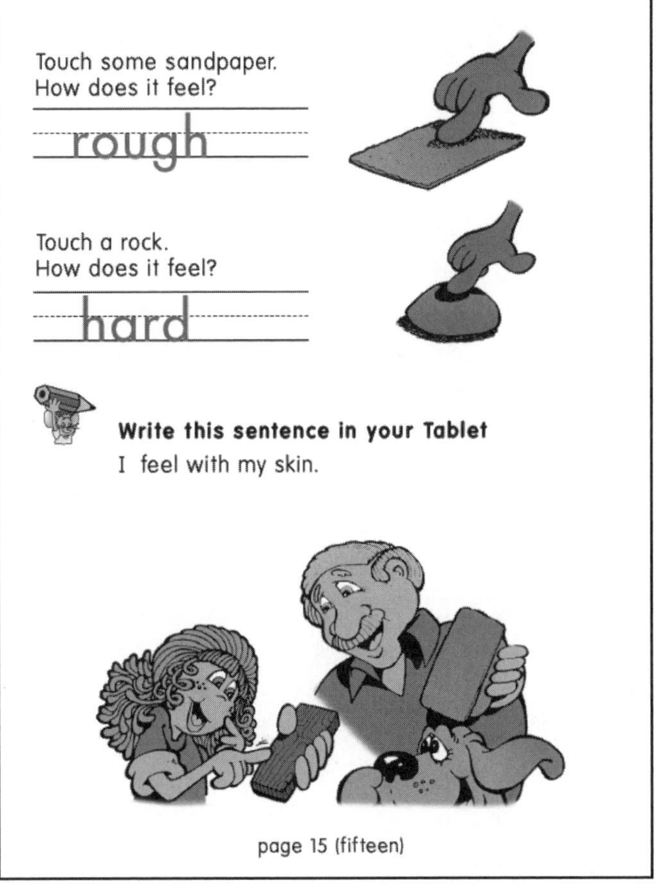

page 15 (fifteen)

You feel hot and cold.
Write hot or cold under the picture.
hot
cold
cold
cold
hot
page 16 (sixteen)

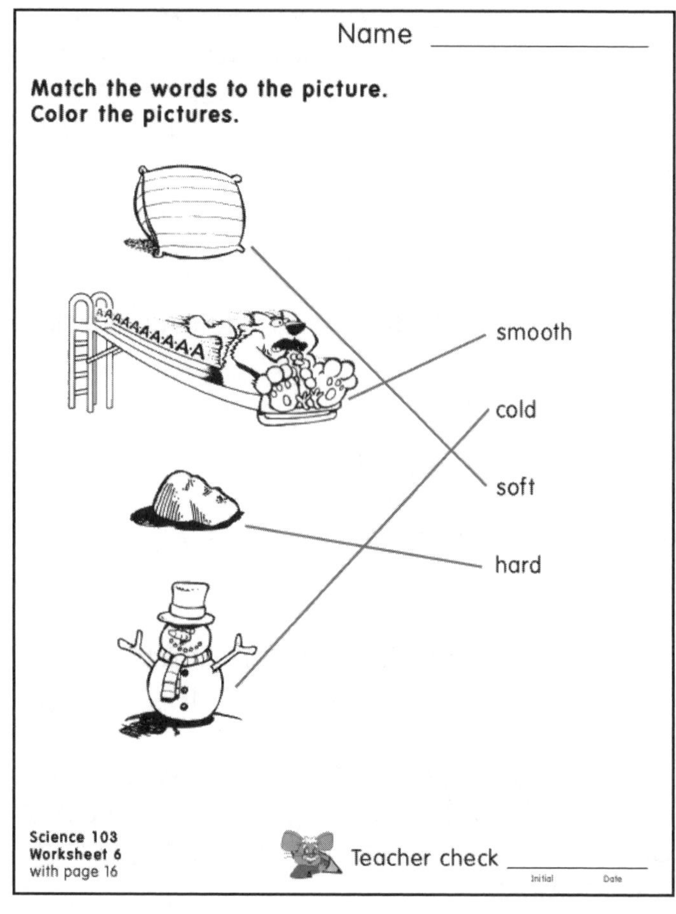
Name
Match the words to the picture.
Color the pictures.
AAAAAAAAAA
smooth
cold
soft
hard
Science 103
Worksheet 6
with page 16
Teacher check
Initial
Date

Page 17: Wet and Dry

You feel wet and dry.
Try this activity.
Put your hand in a dish of water.
How does it feel?
Write the word.
wet
Wave your hand.
How does it feel now?
Write the words.
cool
and
dry
page 17 (seventeen)

CONCEPTS:

Your skin can feel wet and dry.
As your skin dries, it gets cool.

OBJECTIVE: I can tell about the sense of touch.

PROCESSES: observing, using the sense of touch; comparing

READING INTEGRATION: following directions, sentence structure (question)

VOCABULARY: wet, dry

MATERIALS NEEDED: a pan of water (more than one if you wish to divide the class into small groups to do this activity)

TEACHING PAGE 17:

Present the vocabulary. Have the children think of examples for each word. Remind the children to watch for the questions on the page.

Read through the sentences, questions, and directions for the page. You may want to have them read by volunteers. Allow the children to experience the feelings of wet and dry. Pay particular attention to the fact that as they wave their hands to dry them, their hands will feel cool or cold. This cooling process is the result of evaporation.

Have the children complete the written portion of the page. Check together.

ACTIVITIES:

1. Continue the discovery center activities. Be sure that every child has a chance to participate by the end of Section II.
2. Encourage use of the reading-table materials. You could have the children illustrate and write a sentence about each book they read. Have available several books about the senses.

Page 18 : Activity Page

MATERIALS NEEDED: crayons, LIFEPAC Tablet, pencils, Worksheet 7

TEACHING PAGE 18:

Discuss different ways of getting wet on purpose or by accident.

Read the directions or have them read by a child. Let the class complete both activities independently. When *all* are finished, allow time for the discussion of the picture and the sentences the children have written.

ACTIVITY:

Provide Worksheet 7.

Read the directions.

Have the children read the words and identify the rebus pictures.

Let the children complete the page independently.

Check together and discuss.

Color the picture.

Write a sentence about the picture in your Tablet.

page 18 (eighteen)

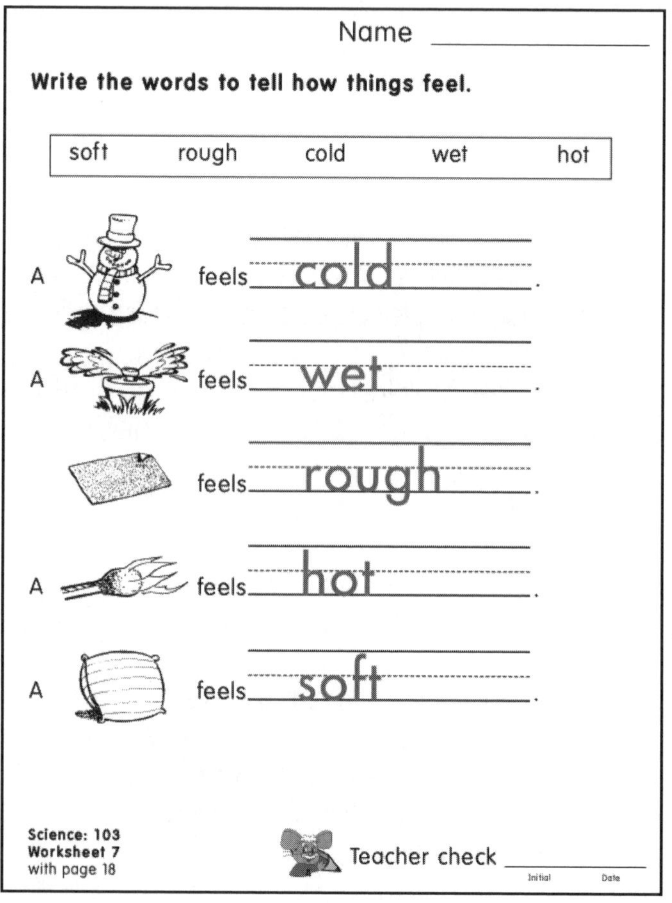

Name ____________

Write the words to tell how things feel.

soft	rough	cold	wet	hot

A [snowman] feels cold.

A [sprinkler] feels wet.

[sandpaper] feels rough.

A [match] feels hot.

A [pillow] feels soft.

Science: 103
Worksheet 7
with page 18

Teacher check ________ Initial Date

Page 19: Listening

CONCEPT: Your skin can feel many things.

OBJECTIVE: I can tell about the sense of touch.

PROCESSES: observing, using the sense of touch, predicting

READING INTEGRATION: listening, recalling details, predicting outcome following directions

VOCABULARY: sticky, slippery, thick, peanut butter, jelly, sandwich

MATERIALS NEEDED: crayons, word card Worksheet 8

TEACHING PAGE 19:

Prepare the children for listening. Explain that you are going to read a rhyming story out loud to them. They are to listen for all the words that tell how something feels. When the story is over, the children should have an idea about what will happen next.

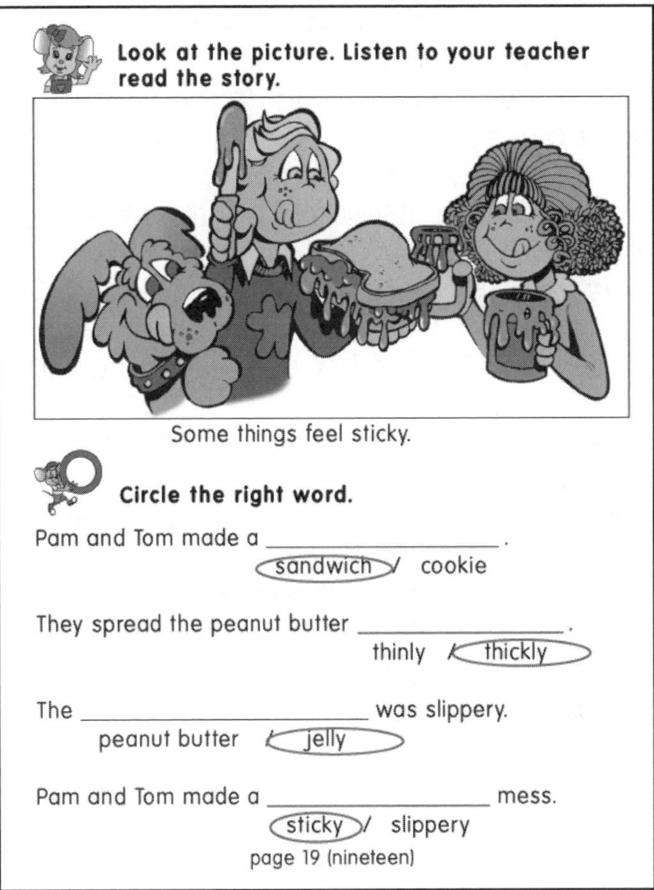

Look at the picture. Listen to your teacher read the story.

Some things feel sticky.

Circle the right word.

Pam and Tom made a ________________.
(sandwich) / cookie

They spread the peanut butter ________________.
thinly / (thickly)

The ________________ was slippery.
peanut butter / (jelly)

Pam and Tom made a ________________ mess.
(sticky) / slippery

page 19 (nineteen)

A Sticky, Sticky Story

Pam was very hungry.
Tom was hungry, too.
So they made themselves a sandwich
Big enough for two.

They spread the peanut butter
So very, very thick,
Then smeared on lots of jelly;
They put it on real quick.

Now when they bit the sandwich,
The slippery jelly slid
Right out between the edges
Of the peanut buttery bread.

Jelly's only slippery when
You want it not to slip,
But when it lands on something
It's a sticky messy drip.

Peanut butter's different.
It spreads out nice and smooth,
And stays right where you want it.
It will hardly ever move.

When peanut butter's in your mouth,
It's sticky stuff to chew.
It hangs right on to tongue and teeth.
Pam thinks it's peanut glue.

Now Tom and Pam are finished
With the sandwich made for two.
Their faces are all sticky;
And I think their ears are, too.
They've run away to wash them.
Pam's cleaning up her dress.
But just look at the kitchen.
Who'll clean up the mess?

Phyllis A. MacDonald

Read the poem aloud. Repeat it if you think it would be wise.

Ask the children to name the words that tell how something feels (hungry, thick, slippery, sticky, messy, smooth).

Ask some questions about the making of the sandwich: "What was put on thick? What was slippery in the sandwich? Who was hungry? What did Pam think felt like glue? Who might have to clean up the kitchen?"

After you have read the poem and discussed it, have the children take turns reading the sentences giving directions on the page. You may want to do the page together orally or let the children complete the exercise independently once the directions are given. Check the answers together and discuss them.

ACTIVITY:

Do Worksheet 8.

Read the directions to the children.

Tell them they are to draw a picture of the person they think will clean up the kitchen.

When they have finished, let each one explain his picture and tell why he thinks the person in the picture is the one to clean up the kitchen.

If a child's picture shows that he has totally missed the point of the story, work with him or have an aide work with him on several listening activities.

Name _______________

Draw and color a picture of someone cleaning the sticky, messy kitchen.

Science: 103
Worksheet 8
with page 19

Teacher check ____________
Initial Date

Page 20: Touch Can Help Me

CONCEPTS:

The sense of touch functions as a warning system.

The body will react to pain before it is actually felt.

This reaction is called a reflex action.

OBJECTIVE: I can tell about the sense of touch.

PROCESS: observing, using the sense of touch

READING INTEGRATION: speaking in a group. following directions

VOCABULARY: safe, hot

MATERIALS NEEDED: word cards, LIFEPAC Tablet, pencils

TEACHING PAGE 20:

Tell the class that the sense of touch can be helpful. It can protect them from hurt.

Example: If a baby had no sense of touch, she might put her hand on her mother's hot iron and leave it there until it was very badly burned. The sense of touch tells her to pull her hand away quickly. She still might have a burn, but it will be a little one.

Read the introductory sentence. Have the children study the pictures. Provide an opportunity for discussion of ways the sense of touch can help keep you safe.

Let the children complete the page.

ACTIVITIES:

1. Invite a doctor or nurse to visit the class to talk about the subject of feelings, such as pain. They can tell how such feelings can help them to know what might be wrong with a patient.
2. Make a chart for *hot.*

TOUCH CAN HELP ME

Look for the ways that touch can help.

Talk about the pictures.
Talk about other ways touch helps to keep you safe.

Write this sentence in your Tablet.
Touch helps to keep me safe.

page 20 (twenty)

Page 21: Activity Page

MATERIALS NEEDED: pencils, crayons, Worksheet 9

TEACHING PAGE 21:

Review the vocabulary words. Play a flash-card game with the words.

Have a volunteer read the direction sentence. Let the children complete the activity. Check it as a group.

The pictures can be shared in a class discussion.

ACTIVITIES:

1. Do Worksheet 9.

Read the directions to the children.

Make sure they know the words in the box. Have them name the rebus pictures.

Check the page. Have the children who had difficulty work with the charts and in the discovery center.

2. Be sure that all of the children have had a chance to participate in the discovery center project for this section.

Draw a line under each word that tells how things feel.
rough sticky red
soft bitter slippery
sour hard cold
dry big sweet
hot square wet
Choose a word about touch. Draw a picture about your word.
page 21 (twenty-one)

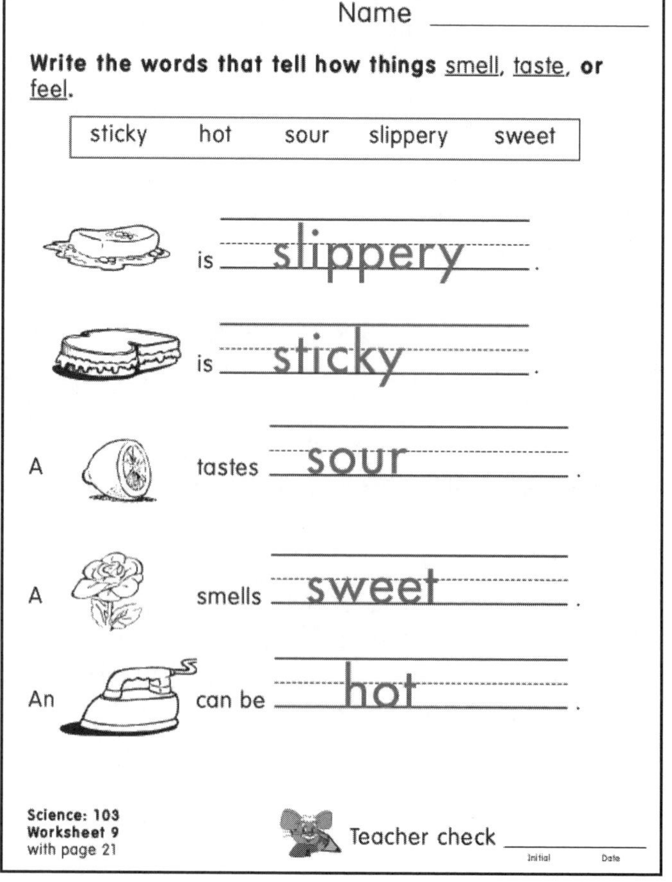

Name
Write the words that tell how things smell, taste, or feel.
sticky hot sour slippery sweet
is slippery.
is sticky.
A tastes sour.
A smells sweet.
An can be hot.
Science: 103
Worksheet 9
with page 21
Teacher check
Initial Date

Pages 22 and 23: Pain and Pressure

CONCEPT: Pain and pressure are feeling senses.

OBJECTIVE: I can tell about the sense of touch.

PROCESSES: observing, using sense of touch; comparing

READING INTEGRATION: speaking in a group, sentence structure (question), following directions

VOCABULARY: pain, (pressure)

MATERIALS NEEDED: pencils, LIFEPAC Tablet, Worksheet 10, crayons

TEACHING PAGES 22 and 23:

Introduce the vocabulary words. Have the children suggest examples of pain. They may demonstrate pressure (a pushing upon something).

Read the introductory sentence or have a student read it.

Note that the pictures on these pages are each titled with a question. Have a child read the question for the first picture. Give the children a chance to discuss what the girl might be feeling. Have them choose the vocabulary word that will describe what the girl is feeling.

Follow the same procedure with the second picture. Note that because the sweater is too tight, it is pushing on the boy's body, squeezing it. This is pressure.

Discuss the sentence in the box. Give each child an opportunity to contribute. Have the children write the appropriate words and the sentence in their Tablets.

ACTIVITIES:

1. Do Worksheet 10.

Read the directions. Instruct the children to begin at *A* and follow the dots to *Z*. Then tell them to begin at *a* and follow the dots

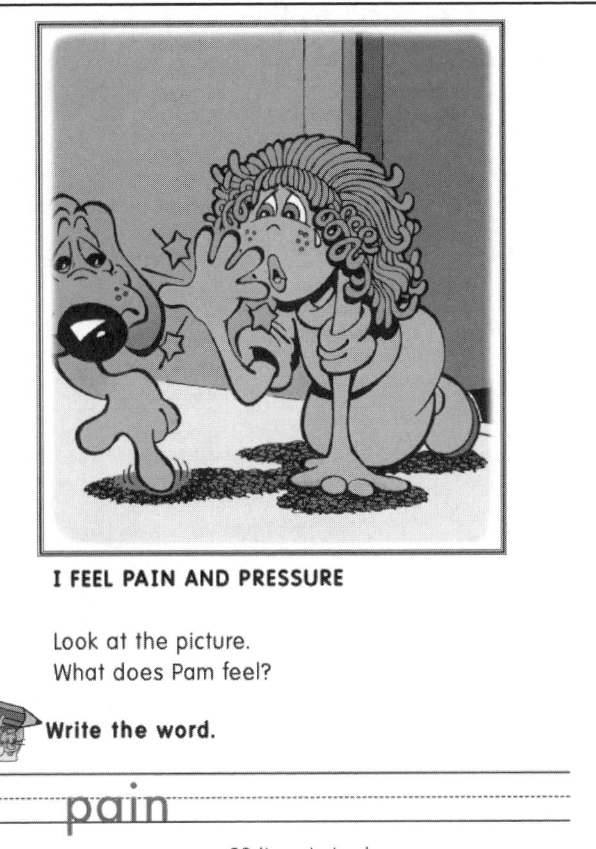

I FEEL PAIN AND PRESSURE

Look at the picture.
What does Pam feel?

Write the word.

pain

page 22 (twenty-two)

What does Tom feel?

Write the word.

pressure

Talk about other things that make you feel pain or pressure.

Write this sentence in your Tablet.
Pain and pressure are feeling senses.

Teacher Check ____________ Initial Date

page 23 (twenty-three)

to z. Tell them to use their alphabet charts if they need to do so.

Help children who still have difficulty with the alphabet.

2. Make a pain and pressure chart.

3. Check to see that the children are continuing to use the books on the reading table.

Name
Follow the dots to see who hurt his foot on a tack.
start
start
Color the picture.
Science: 103
Worksheet 10
with page 23
Teacher check
Initial
Date

Pages 24 and 25: Self Test 2

CONCEPTS: evaluation

OBJECTIVE:

I can tell about the sense of smell.
I can tell about the sense of taste.
I can tell about the sense of touch.

MATERIALS NEEDED: pencils

TEACHING PAGES 24 and 25:

Review the vocabulary and concepts for sections I and II.

Read all of the directions with the children. Be sure they are understood.

The general proficiency of your group will dictate whether you choose to direct the self test or to allow the children to proceed independently once directions are given.

In either case, you should be available to answer questions and to help with vocabulary as needed.

Check immediately and review with the student.

Some children will need extra help. If the child has not scored satisfactorily on the self test, have the LIFEPAC taken home for review with a parent. An oral retest, using the self test as a guide, should then be given before beginning Part III.

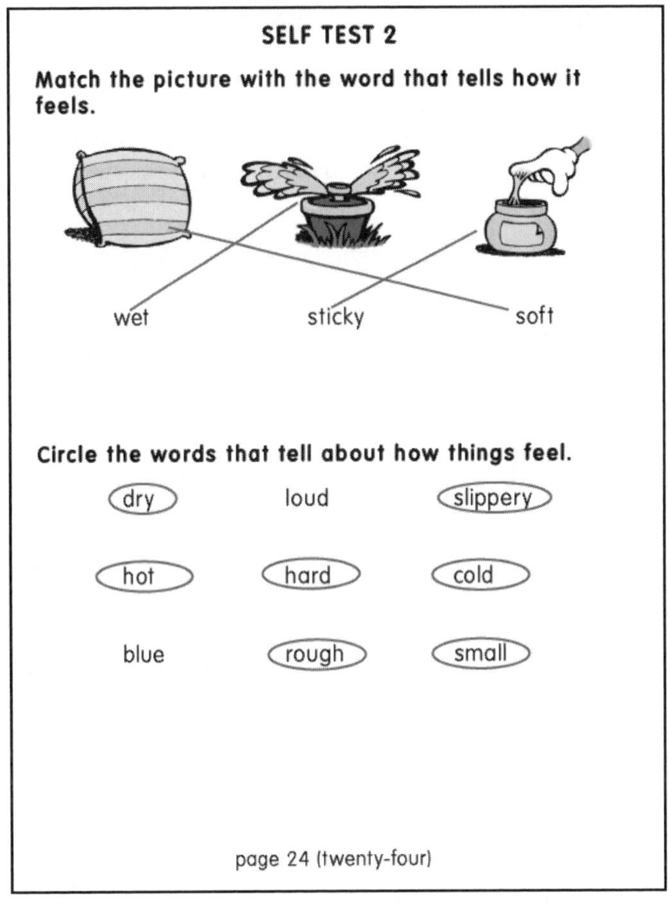

SELF TEST 2

Match the picture with the word that tells how it feels.

wet sticky soft

Circle the words that tell about how things feel.

dry	loud	**slippery**
hot	**hard**	**cold**
blue	**rough**	**small**

page 24 (twenty-four)

Circle the right word.

Touch, taste, and smell are ______________ .
feelings / **senses**

Your nose helps you ______________ .
taste / touch

You feel things with your ______________ .
skin / eyes

The sense of ______________ tells you if something is sweet. touch / **taste**

Touch helps keep you ______________ .
safe / skin

Pain and pressure are ______________ senses.
seeing / **feeling**

12/15 Teacher Check ______________ Initial Date

page 25 (twenty-five)

PART III. THE SENSES: A REVIEW
Page 26

CONCEPTS: You use all of the senses God gave you to observe the world around you.

OBJECTIVE: I can tell how my senses can work together.

PROCESSES: observing, using all of the senses

READING INTEGRATION: recalling details

VOCABULARY: Use the vocabulary words from Science LIFEPAC's 101 and 102 and from the first section of 103. Select the words that name the senses and those that most accurately tell what the senses and those that most accurately tell what the senses do. *Examples:* sight, see, look, color shapes, sizes

MATERIALS NEEDED: word; pictures representing the senses, such as a nose, an ear, the tongue, eyes and a hand to represent touch; paper; yarn; old magazines

TEACHING PAGE 26:

Tell the children that the last part of Science LIFEPAC 103 will help them remember all that they have learned about the five senses.

Make a display of all the appropriate vocabulary words visible to the children from their seats. It can be used as reference throughout the review section.

Read the introduction to the section. Have the children identify the names of the senses and the parts of the body that perform them.

Pay particular attention to the first sentence, *God gave you your senses* and to the last sentence, *You use all of your senses to observe the world around you.* These sentences constitute two main ideas of the section.

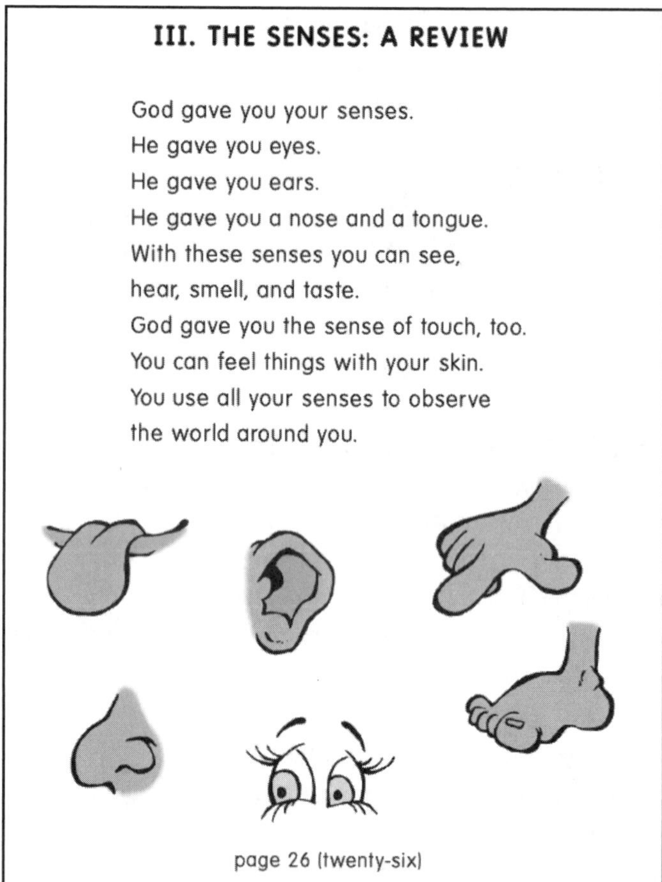
III. THE SENSES: A REVIEW

God gave you your senses.
He gave you eyes.
He gave you ears.
He gave you a nose and a tongue.
With these senses you can see,
hear, smell, and taste.
God gave you the sense of touch, too.
You can feel things with your skin.
You use all your senses to observe
the world around you.

page 26 (twenty-six)

ACTIVITY:

Have each child make a "Senses" scrapbook. You provide paper and yarn to tie it together. They find and paste or draw pictures representing each of the five senses. This project can be the cumulative one for the extended unit on the senses.

Page 27: I Learn with My Senses

CONCEPTS:

I learn with my senses.

Certain parts of the body perform each sense.

OBJECTIVE: I can tell how my senses can work together.

PROCESSES: observing, classifying

READING INTEGRATION: following directions, recalling details

VOCABULARY: (sight, hearing, smell, taste, touch)

MATERIALS NEEDED: pencils crayons, Worksheet 11

TEACHING PAGE 27:

Remind the children that they will have to remember things from earlier LIFEPACs. Tell them that they may look at the display of word cards about the senses to help them remember.

Have a volunteer read the directions. Ask other children to read the captions under the spaces for pictures. When all understand what they are to do, they may complete the page independently. Check it together.

ACTIVITY: Do Worksheet 11.

Read the directions to the children. Review the words. Let the children complete the page independently. Check together.

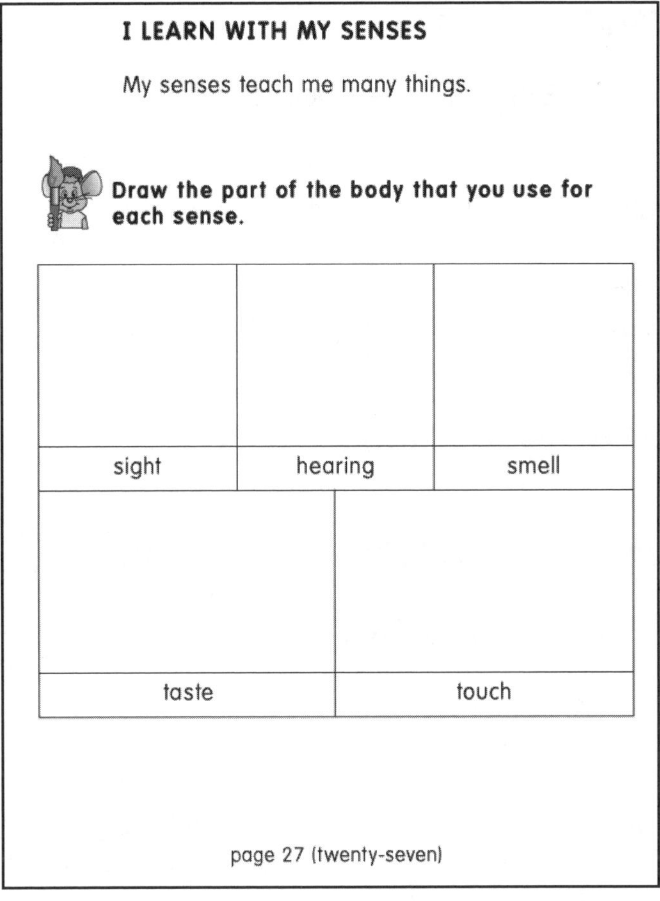

I LEARN WITH MY SENSES

My senses teach me many things.

Draw the part of the body that you use for each sense.

sight	hearing	smell

taste	touch

page 27 (twenty-seven)

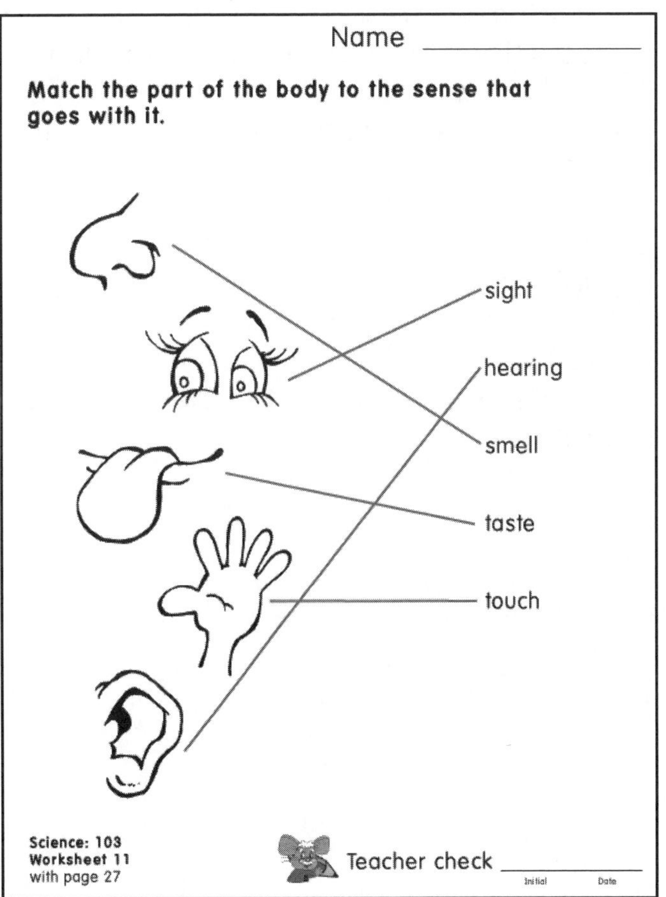

Name ______________

Match the part of the body to the sense that goes with it.

Science: 103
Worksheet 11
with page 27

Teacher check ______________
Initial Date

Page 28: Senses

CONCEPTS: Review of senses used to observe, senses work together

OBJECTIVE: I can tell how my senses can work together.

PROCESS: observing, using the senses of sight, hearing, smell, taste, and touch

READING INTEGRATION: following directions, speaking in a group, recalling details

MATERIALS NEEDED: pencils, crayons

TEACHING PAGE 28:

Have a child read the directions. Be sure the children understand what they are to do.

Let them complete the activities. Go over their answers and pictures together. Then provide time for discussion of other senses that might be used to learn about the pictures. *Example:* You can see and hear a kitten. You can also learn about how it feels by the sense of touch. Under certain circumstances, you might even smell it. The bell and the balloon can be touched. *Ask:* "How would the bell feel?" (hard, smooth) Use a similar procedure for all of the pictures including the ones the children draw.

Circle the things you can see and hear.
Draw a picture of something you can smell and taste.
Tell what other senses you can use to learn about these things.
page 28 (twenty-eight)

ACTIVITY:

Continue work on the "Senses" scrapbook.

Page 29: Senses

CONCEPT: using all the senses together

OBJECTIVE: I can tell how my senses can work together.

PROCESS: observing

READING INTEGRATION: speaking in a group, recalling details

MATERIALS NEEDED: popcorn, popper, salt, butter

TEACHING PAGE 29:

Tell the children that this page will be one to look at carefully and then to talk about. Tell them to look carefully at the picture and think of the senses they might use to enjoy the circus.

When the class has had time to study the circus picture carefully, have a volunteer read the sentences on the page. Provide a discussion time. Give each child an opportunity to tell about a part of the picture. The emphasis should be on the senses used to enjoy a circus.

Example: You can see and hear the circus band and you can feel the rhythm of the music. You can see and hear the elephants. You can smell popcorn.

ACTIVITIES:

1. Do Worksheet 12.

Read the directions. Remind the children that their picture must show something that involves all five senses.

Allow time for each child to explain his picture and to tell all five senses that are used.

2. Making popcorn in the classroom will give the children an experience of something they can observe with all five senses.

Have the children compare the appearance, feel, and smell of the popcorn before and after it is popped; listen to the sound of the popcorn; see the change in the popcorn and taste the popcorn.

Here are some things you can observe with your senses.

Tell what you can see, hear, smell, taste, and touch.

page 29 (twenty-nine)

Name ________________

Draw a picture of something you can see, hear, touch, taste, **and** smell.

Science: 103
Worksheet 12
with page 29

Teacher check ____________
Initial Date

Page 30: My Senses Send Messages to My Brain

CONCEPT: The brain is the part of the body that interprets messages of the senses.

OBJECTIVE: I can tell how my senses can work together.

PROCESS: observing

READING INTEGRATION: main idea

VOCABULARY: brain, message, nerves

MATERIALS NEEDED: word cards, LIFEPAC Tablet, pencil, Worksheet 13

TEACHING PAGE 30:

Tell the children that the senses cannot work by themselves. They need the brain to help them know what the senses are learning. Introduce the vocabulary. Compare nerves to telephone or electric wires.

Read the sentences on the page to the children. Have them examine the picture carefully and tell about it. Ask the children to point out the labeled parts. Give an opportunity for questions.

Have the children read the sentence at the bottom of the page and write the sentence in their Tablets.

ACTIVITY:

Do Worksheet 13.

Read the directions. Read the vocabulary words in the box with the children. Help the slower children with this page. Let those who are able do the page on their own.

Check together. Have the children find the sentences or one close to them on page 30. (first sentence — title and LIFEPAC Tablet sentence activity; second sentence — first sentence of text; third and fourth sentences — last two sentences of text).

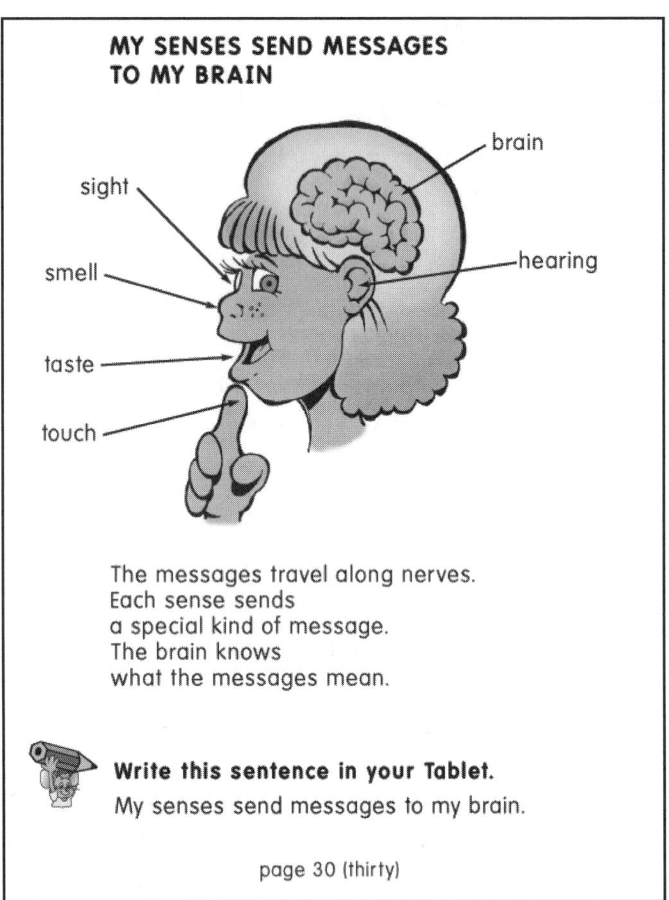
MY SENSES SEND MESSAGES TO MY BRAIN

The messages travel along nerves.
Each sense sends
a special kind of message.
The brain knows
what the messages mean.

Write this sentence in your Tablet.
My senses send messages to my brain.

page 30 (thirty)

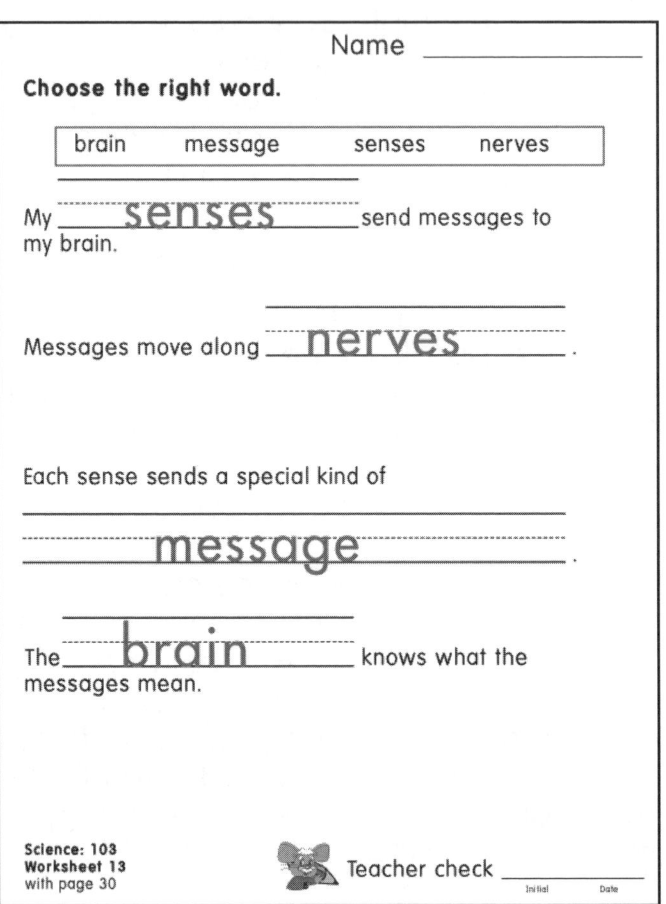
Name ____________

Choose the right word.

brain	message	senses	nerves

My **senses** send messages to my brain.

Messages move along **nerves**.

Each sense sends a special kind of **message**.

The **brain** knows what the messages mean.

Science: 103
Worksheet 13
with page 30

Teacher check ____________
Initial Date

Page 31: Activity Page

MATERIALS NEEDED: pencils

TEACHING PAGE 31:

Read the directions to the children. Explain that they will be writing more than one sense for most of the pictures.

Put an example, such as the one given here, on the board before they begin.

Example:

Ask: "What is the picture? (ice cream cone) What senses can tell you about an ice cream cone?" (sight, taste, touch, sometimes smell)

As the children name the senses, write the name of the sense under the picture of the ice cream cone on the board.

When you have finished the example, let the children finish the page. Help them with the sense words if they forget.

Check together. If children have difficulty, redo the page together and put several more examples on the board.

ACTIVITIES:

1. Complete the "Senses" scrapbook.
2. Provide time for the children to review the LIFEPAC in preparation for the last self test.

Page 32: God Has a Good Plan

CONCEPTS:
God gave you your senses.
He had a good plan.

OBJECTIVE: I can tell how my senses can work together.

PROCESS: observing

READING INTEGRATION: recalling detail

MATERIALS NEEDED: LIFEPAC Tablet, pencils

TEACHING PAGE 32:

Remind the children that they were created by God and that God gave them their senses.

Have the sentences read by volunteers. Discuss each sentence in turn. Help the children to appreciate God's good plan. Remind them that they should thank God for the good things He has given them.

Have them write the sentence and the thank-you prayer in their Tablets.

GOD HAS A GOOD PLAN

God gave you your senses.
Your senses help you to learn.
They help you to be safe.
God made a good plan.

Write the sentence in your Tablet.

God has a good plan.

Teacher Check ________________
Initial Date

Talk about God's plan.
With your class write a sentence thanking God for His plan.
Copy it in your Tablet.

page 32 (thirty-two)

Page 33: Self Test 3

CONCEPT: evaluation of work

OBJECTIVES:

I can tell about the sense of smell.
I can tell about the sense of taste.
I can tell about the sense of touch.
I can tell how my senses can work together.

MATERIALS NEEDED: pencils

TEACHING PAGE 33:

Review the vocabulary and concepts for the entire LIFEPAC. Place special emphasis on Section III.

Read through the directions for the self test with the group. Answer any questions they might have.

The general proficiency of your group should dictate whether you choose to direct the self test or to allow the children to proceed independently once directions are given.

In either case you should be available to answer questions and help with vocabulary as needed.

For those children who need extra help, have them work with a classroom helper or a parent to prepare for the LIFEPAC Test.

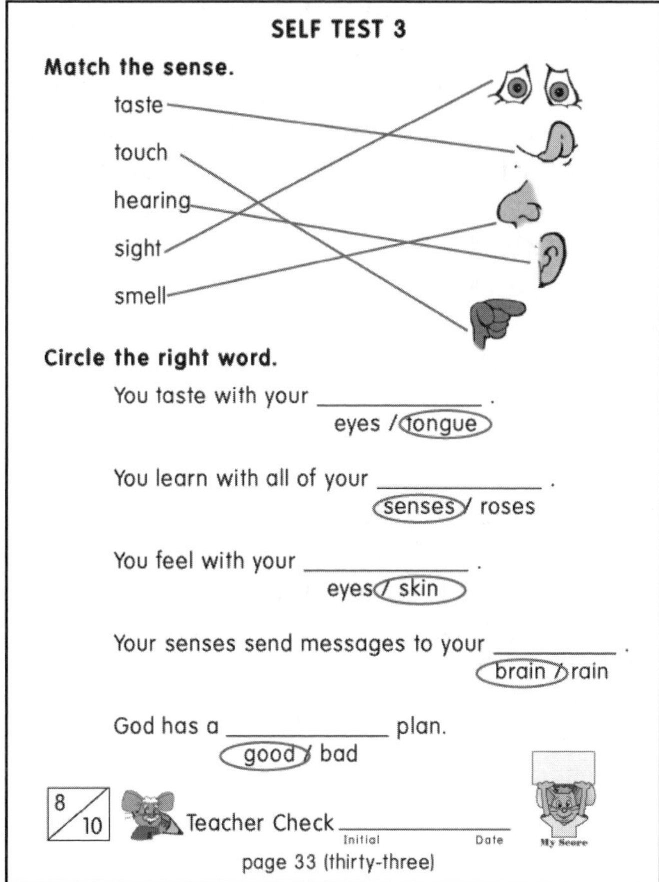

LIFEPAC TEST AND ALTERNATE LIFEPAC TEST

Administer the test to the class as a group. Ask to have directions read or read them to the class. In either case be sure that the children clearly understand. Put examples on the board it they seem necessary. Give ample time for each activity to be completed before going on to the next one.

Correct immediately and discuss with the child.

Review any concepts that have been missed.

Give those children who do not achieve the 80 per cent score, additional copies of the worksheets and a list of vocabulary words to study. A parent or a classroom helper should help in the review.

When the child is ready, give the Alternate LIFEPAC Test. Use the same procedure as for the LIFEPAC Test.

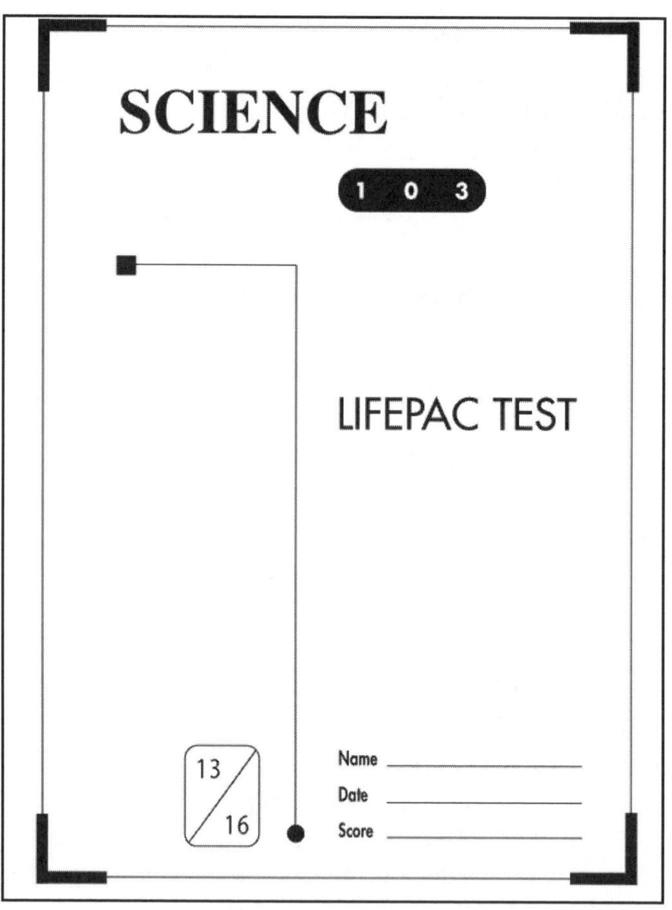

SCIENCE

1 0 3

LIFEPAC TEST

13/16

Name ____________

Date ____________

Score ____________

SCIENCE 103: LIFEPAC TEST

Circle the right word.

You can ____________ with all of your senses.
see / learn

Your nose and tongue help you ____________.
taste / smell

You taste sour things with your ____________.
nose / tongue

You ____________ with your skin.
see / feel

Draw a line under each word that names your senses.

color	smell	touch
hearing	taste	sight
sound	size	

page 1 (one)

Circle the senses you might use to learn about this lemon.

(sight) hearing (taste) (smell) (touch)

Circle the senses you might use to learn about this bell.

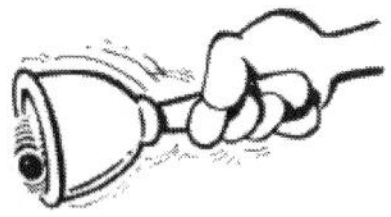

(sight) (hearing) taste smell (touch)

page 2 (two)

NOTES

page 3 (three)

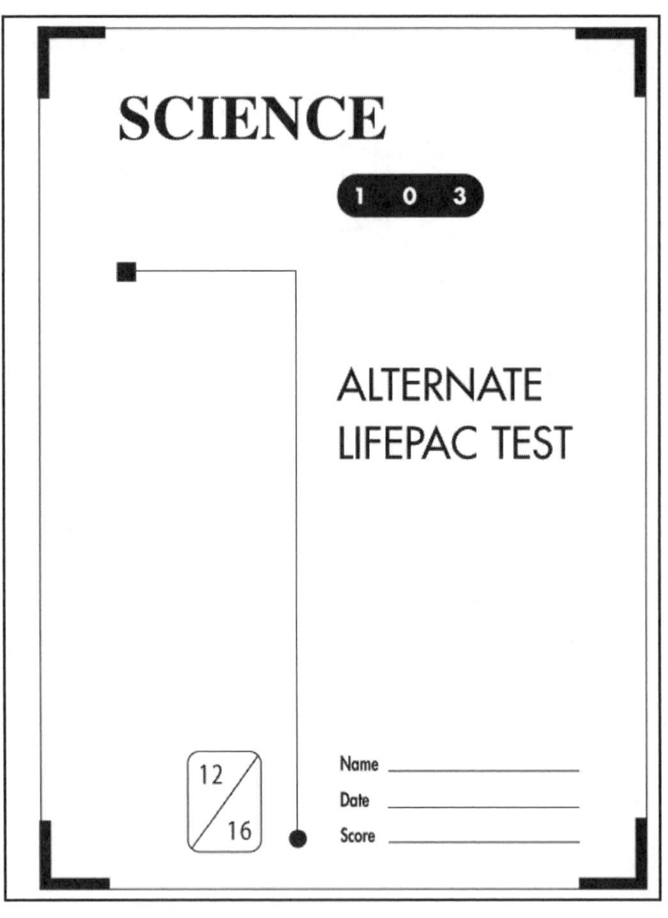

SCIENCE

1 0 3

ALTERNATE
LIFEPAC TEST

12/16

Name ______

Date ______

Score ______

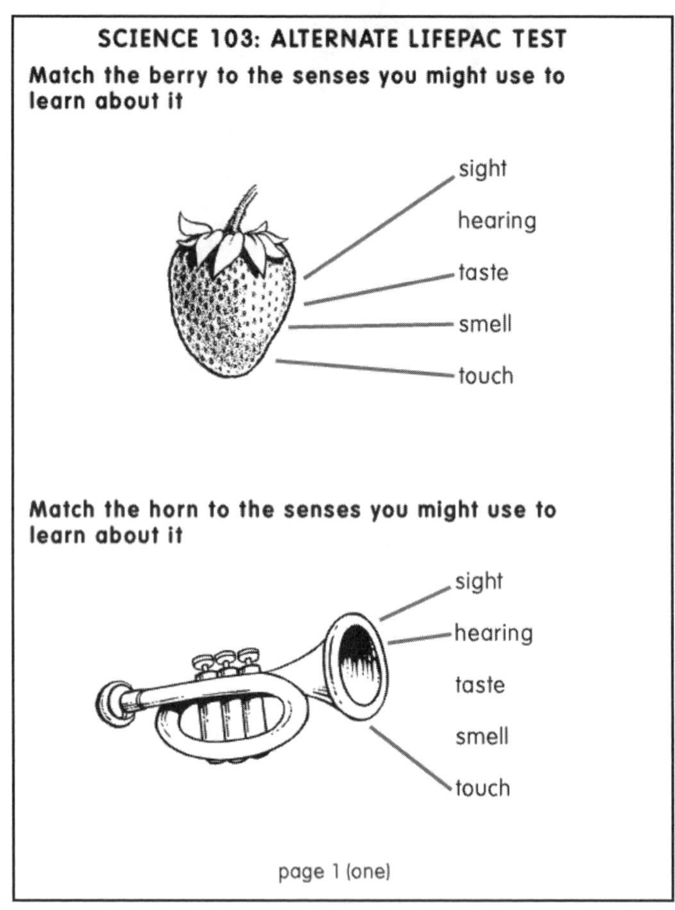

SCIENCE 103: ALTERNATE LIFEPAC TEST

Match the berry to the senses you might use to learn about it

Match the horn to the senses you might use to learn about it

page 1 (one)

Draw a line under the words that fit.

Your______________help you taste.

nose and tongue / eyes and ears

You can feel things with your______________.

nose / skin

You can observe with all of your______________.

toes / senses

You cannot______________when you have a bad cold.

smell / see

page 2 (two)

NOTES

page 3 (three)

Page 1: ANIMALS

CONCEPT: Animals need food, water, and sleep to live and grow.

OBJECTIVE: To introduce all the objectives.

BIBLE REFERENCE: Genesis 1:20 through 25, chapters 6 through 9

PROCESSES: observing, comparing

READING INTEGRATION: listening, rhyming, rhythm, recalling details, main idea

MATERIALS NEEDED: pictures of animals

TEACHING PAGE 1:

Distribute books. Allow the children a little time to look through them. Ask for a volunteer to tell what the new LIFEPAC is about.

Look together at the contents page. Read to the class or have volunteers read the list of contents. Tell the children that they will learn about these things as they study Science LIFEPAC 104.

Have the children turn to page 1 and be ready to listen.

Read the poem aloud to the class.

Read it again after asking the children to recall the important ideas of the poem.

Ask: "From where did animals come?" (God put them on the earth and saved them from the Flood.) Refer to Genesis 1:20 through 25, the Creation, and Genesis, Chapters 6 through 9, "the story of Noah." Are all animals alike?" (No. Provide time for the children to tell how animals are different.) "What do all animals need?" (food, water, sleep)" What else needs these things" (people)

ACTIVITY:

Set up a book table with books about animals.

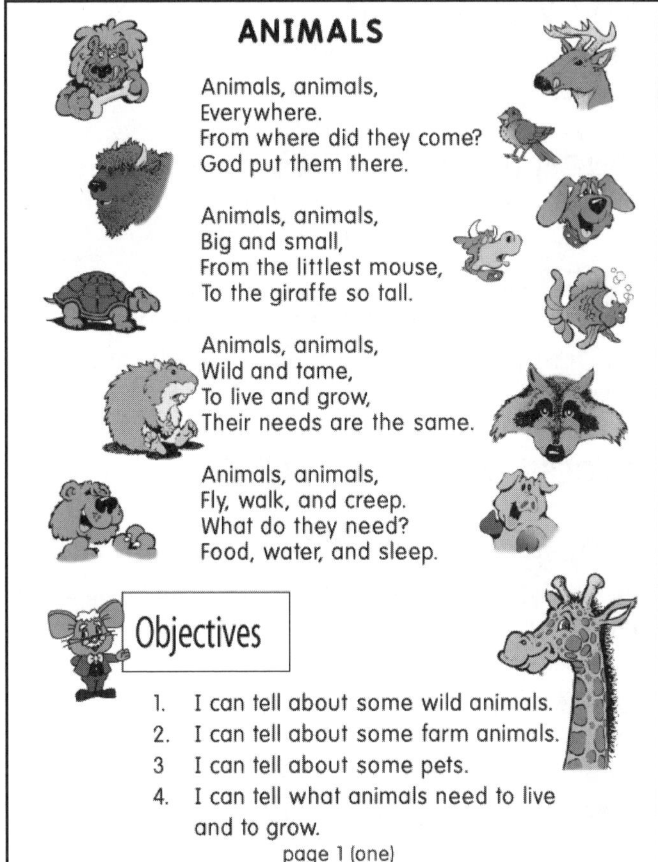

ANIMALS

Animals, animals,
Everywhere.
From where did they come?
God put them there.

Animals, animals,
Big and small,
From the littlest mouse,
To the giraffe so tall.

Animals, animals,
Wild and tame,
To live and grow,
Their needs are the same.

Animals, animals,
Fly, walk, and creep.
What do they need?
Food, water, and sleep.

Objectives

1. I can tell about some wild animals.
2. I can tell about some farm animals.
3 I can tell about some pets.
4. I can tell what animals need to live and to grow.

page 1 (one)

PART I. WILD ANIMALS

Page 2

I. WILD ANIMALS

Some animals
take care of themselves.
They find water to drink.
They find food to eat.
They find places to sleep.

page 2 (two)

CONCEPT: wild animals take care of themselves

OBJECTIVES:

I can tell about some wild animals.

I can tell what animals need to live and to grow.

PROCESS: observing

READING INTEGRATION: main idea, speaking in a group, vocabulary development

VOCABULARY: eat, drink, food, water, sleep, place, themselves

MATERIALS NEEDED: word cards, crayons

TEACHING PAGE 2:

Remind the children that the contents page showed them that they would study three main kinds of animals, wild animals, farm animals, and pets. The first part of the LIFEPAC is about wild animals.

Present the vocabulary in context.

Read the sentences to the class or have it read aloud by volunteers. Ask to have the vocabulary words identified.

Ask the children to take a few minutes to study the picture. They should look for animals eating and drinking and for places that wild animals might sleep.

Discussion questions: "Where would the animals get a drink? What is the________ eating? Where might animals sleep?"

ACTIVITIES:

1. Circle the vocabulary words.
2. Plan a visit to a local zoo, wild animal park, or animal preserve if available.

Following such a visit, do these things:

a. Have the children write thank you letters with pictures.

b. Write a class "experience story" on chart paper.

Page 3: Puzzle Page

CONCEPT: wild animals take care of themselves

OBJECTIVE: I can tell about some wild animals.

PROCESS: observing

READING INTEGRATION: following directions

MATERIALS NEEDED: crayons, LIFEPAC Tablet, pencils, Worksheet 1

TEACHING PAGE 3:

This page is a follow up of page 2. No further preparation is necessary other than making sure that the children each have red, blue, and yellow crayons.

Have the students find the arrows indicating directions for them to follow. Ask for volunteers to read each direction.

When you are sure that all understand what to do, let the children complete the page independently. Check it together.

ACTIVITY:

Do Worksheet 1.

This worksheet reinforces the three things that all animals need (food, water, sleep).

Have a child read the first direction. Read the second direction. Let the children complete the page independently.

Check together. Have the children name their animals, the kinds of food each animal eats, and where each animal lives.

Color the puzzle.

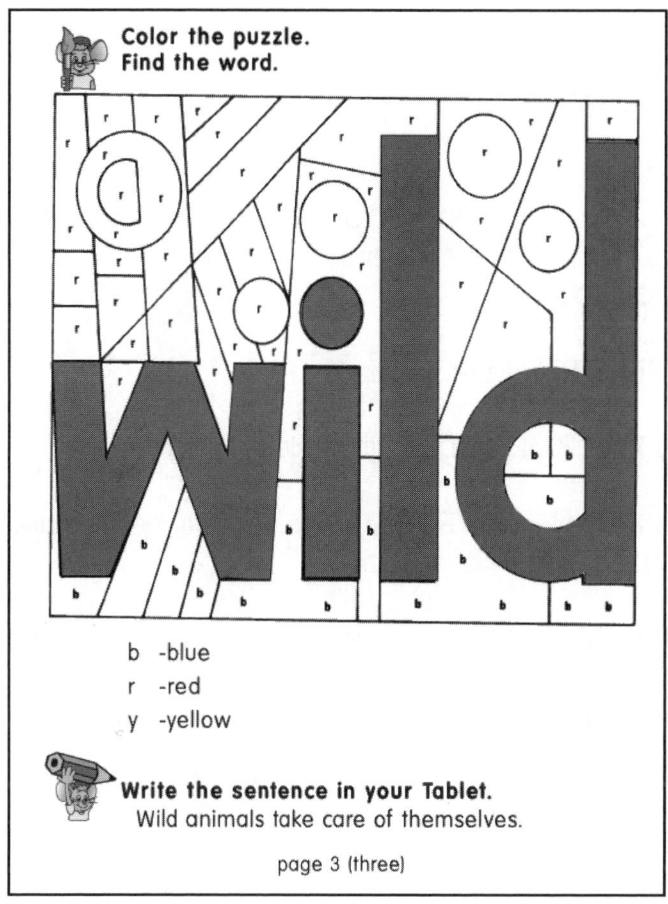
Color the puzzle.
Find the word.
wild
b -blue
r -red
y -yellow
Write the sentence in your Tablet.
Wild animals take care of themselves.
page 3 (three)

Name
Draw an animal.
Write three words to tell what the animal needs.
food
sleep
water
Science 104
Worksheet 1
with page 3
Teacher check
Initial
Date

Page 4: Animals That Eat Meat

ANIMALS THAT EAT MEAT

Some animals are hunters.
They eat other animals.
The lion is a hunter.

The lion is a big, strong cat.
He has a mane.
The lion can roar.

A baby lion is a cub.
Lions sleep in a den.
Lions drink at a watering hole.

page 4 (four)

CONCEPT: Some animals eat meat.

OBJECTIVES:

I can tell about some wild animals.

I can tell what animals need to live and to grow.

BIBLE REFERENCE: Isaiah 11:6

PROCESSES: observing, classifying

READING INTEGRATION: recalling details, speaking in a group

VOCABULARY: hunter, lion, mane, roar, cub, den, hole

MATERIALS NEEDED: Picture of some members of the cat family: leopards, pumas, cheetahs, and so on; picture of watering hole in Africa; word cards; Worksheet 2.

TEACHING PAGE 4:

Tell the children that the wild animals they will study are divided (classified) into three groups: (1) animals that eat meat, (2) animals that eat plants, and (3) animals that eat both plants and meat.

Read the sentences to the children or have them read by volunteers. Have the children look at the picture of the male lion. Note the mane. Then look at the picture of the mother and cub. The mother lion does not have a mane.

Tell the children that lions kill and eat antelope and other deerlike (giraffe, gazelle) animals that live in Africa. They only kill for food and usually kill the oldest or weakest animals.

Discussion questions:

"What do we call animals that go out and look for other animals to eat?" (hunters)

"What kind of animal is a lion?" (cat, hunter)

"Which lion has a mane?" (the father, male)

"What do you call a baby lion?" (cub)

"Where do lions sleep?" (den)

"Where does the lion get water?" (watering hole)

"What would probably happen if a lion saw a lamb?" (the lion would eat it)

ACTIVITIES:

1. Extend the concept by discussing other meat-eating wild animals. Include the wolves and predatory birds such as the hawk.

2. Do Worksheet 2.

Read the directions. Tell the children to begin first with the capital A and to follow the dots to Z. Then tell them to begin with small a and follow the second set of dots to z. Tell them to consult their alphabet charts if they are uncertain about the letters.

When they have finished, check before they color the picture. Note any child who still has difficulty recognizing the alphabet in sequence and give extra help.

Read the final direction. Have the children read the two sentences when they have finished writing the words .

3. Isaiah tells us that there will come a day when all animals will live in peace. Isaiah 11:6: "The wolf also shall dwell with the lamb, and the leopard shall lie down with the kid; and the calf and the young lion and the fatling together; and a young child shall lead them." Discuss the quote with the children.

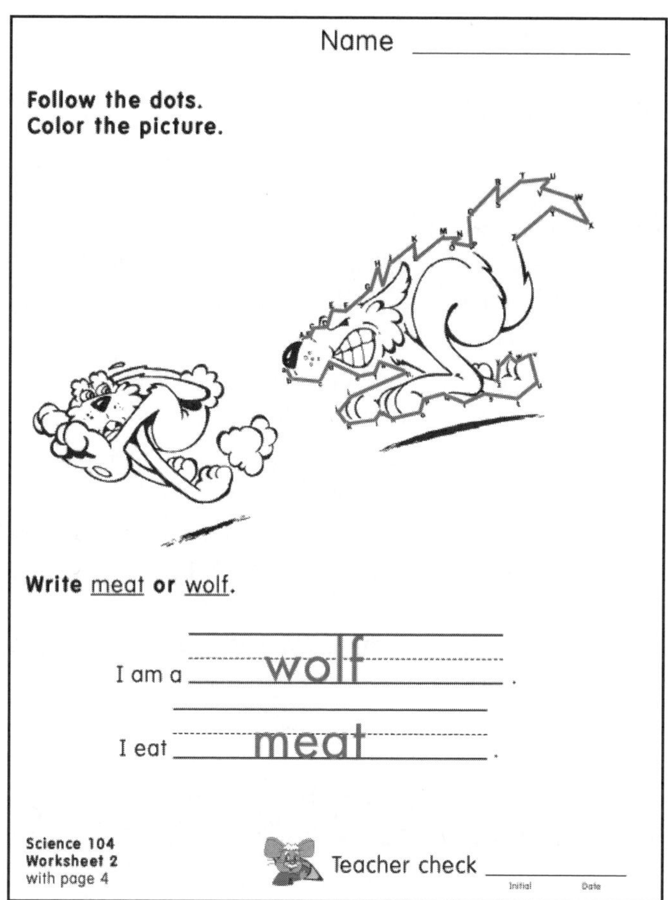

Name ______________

Follow the dots.
Color the picture.

Write meat or wolf.

I am a wolf.

I eat meat.

Science 104
Worksheet 2
with page 4

Teacher check ______________
Initial Date

Page 5: Activity Page

MATERIALS NEEDED: crayons, cat pictures, pencils, Worksheet 3

TEACHING PAGES:

Review the pictures of the members of the cat family. Have the children identify as many as they can.

Remind them that the babies of the large cats are called cubs.

Ask what the babies of the smaller cats might be called (kittens).

Say: "This page will help you to remember what you have learned about lions."

Have a student volunteer find and read the directions.

Read the sentences with the children if necessary.

Have the children complete the page independently. Check it together.

ACTIVITY:

Do Worksheet 3.

Read the directions. Talk about each illustration. Ask about the differences and similarities between a cat and her kittens and a lioness and her cub. Let the children complete the page on their own.

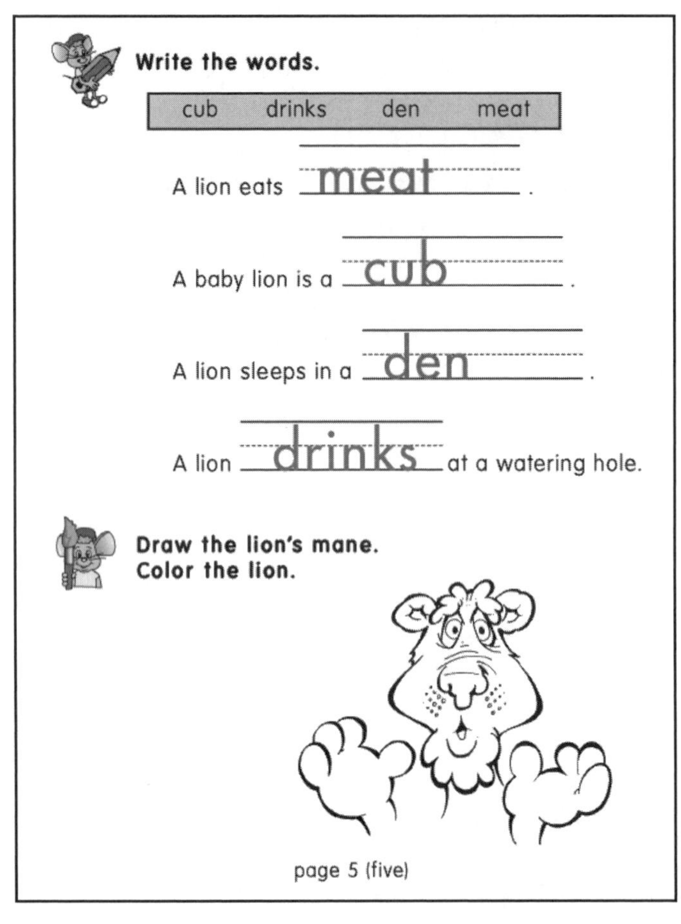

Write the words.
cub drinks den meat
A lion eats meat .
A baby lion is a cub .
A lion sleeps in a den .
A lion drinks at a watering hole.
Draw the lion's mane.
Color the lion.
page 5 (five)

Name
Color the mother bear and her cub.
Color the mother cat and her kittens.
Science 104
Worksheet 3
with page 5
Teacher check
Initial
Date

Page 6: Eagles

CONCEPT: Some birds are meat eaters.

OBJECTIVES:

I can tell about some wild animals.

I can tell what animals need to live and to grow.

PROCESSES: classifying, observing

READING INTEGRATION: recalling details

VOCABULARY: eagle, eaglet, nest, dives, flies, catch

MATERIALS NEEDED: words; pictures of birds of prey: eagles, hawks, falcons, owls; fishing birds: gulls, loons, pelicans, kingfishers; insect eaters: woodpeckers; Worksheet 4; pencils; crayons

An eagle eats meat.
The eagle flies high in the air.
He hunts for fish or small animals.
The eagle dives down,
down,
down,
to catch his food.
Eagles live in nests.
The nest is in a high place.
Baby eagles are eaglets.
Eagles drink
from lakes or streams.
page 6 (six)

TEACHING PAGE 6:

Display the pictures of birds of prey. Ask the children what kinds of animals or fish the various birds would eat. *Examples:* owls and falcons eat small rodents, such as mice or chipmunks; eagles and larger hawks eat small rodents and some larger animals (rabbits), snakes, or other birds (chickens). Many farmers like to have owls around. They keep the mice from the feed.

Gulls and loons dive into the water after fish.

Read the page to the children or have volunteers read it aloud. Provide an opportunity for discussion about the eagle and its babies. (Refer to an encyclopedia or a book about eagles for additional information.)

Note that the eagle's nest is built in a very high tree or on a high rocky ledge.

ACTIVITIES:

1. To extend knowledge of meat eaters, provide materials about amphibians and reptiles that eat meat (crocodile, alligator, bullfrog).

2. Do Worksheet 4.

Read the three sentences. Talk about bullfrogs with the children. Ask them if they have ever seen a bullfrog or if they have ever seen one catching flies.

Have a child read the direction.

Name ____________

This is a bullfrog.
Bullfrogs eat insects.
Insects are meat.
Color the bullfrog.

Science 104
Worksheet 4
with page 6

Teacher check ____________
Initial Date

Page 7: Activity Page

MATERIALS NEEDED: pencils, crayons, LIFEPAC Tablet

TEACHING PAGE 7:

Review the meat-eating animals, pictures and vocabulary.

Have a child find and read the sentences on the page that tell them what to do.

Be sure all the children understand the directions.

Have the children complete the page independently. Check it together.

ACTIVITY:

As an enrichment activity suggest that those children who wish may draw an animal name from a box. They should find out what the animal eats, where it sleeps, and what its baby is called. They are also to find or draw a picture of the animal.

Note: Be sure to have available information on each animal that is in the box.

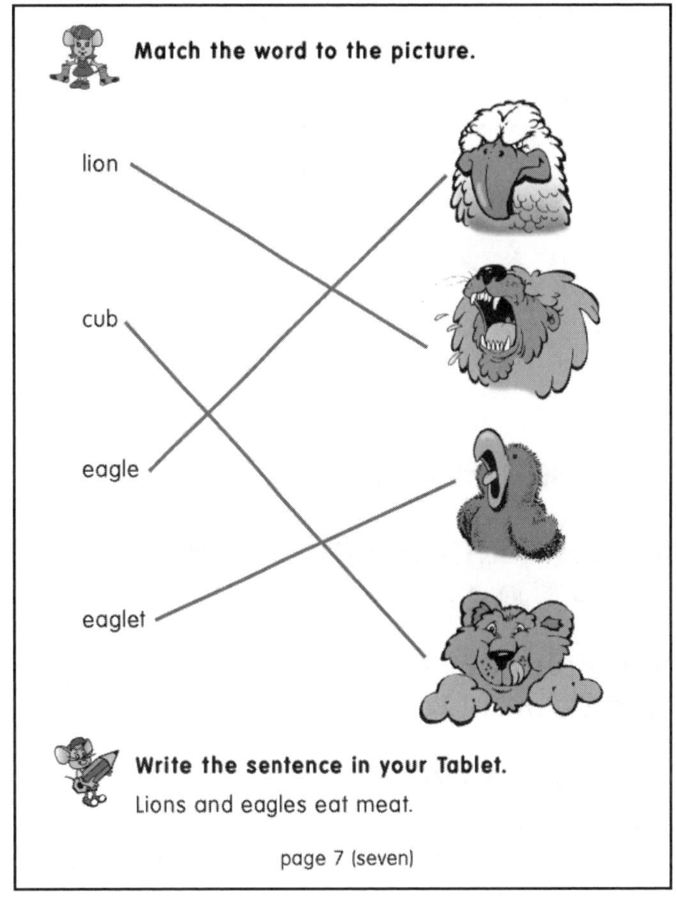

Match the word to the picture.
lion
cub
eagle
eaglet
Write the sentence in your Tablet.
Lions and eagles eat meat.
page 7 (seven)

Page 8: Animals That Eat Plants

CONCEPTS:

Some animals eat plants.

Plant-eating animals need sleep and water.

OBJECTIVES:

I can tell about some wild animals.

I can tell what animals need to live and to grow.

PROCESSES: observing, classifying

READING INTEGRATION: recalling details, speaking in a group

VOCABULARY: giraffe, leaves, calf, deer, grass, fawn, buffalo, hippopotamus

MATERIALS NEEDED: word cards; pictures of plant-eating animals other than those mentioned on the page: antelope, moose, rabbit; Worksheet 5; pencils; crayons

ANIMALS THAT EAT PLANTS

Some animals eat plants.
They eat leaves from trees.
They eat grass.
They eat seeds.

A buffalo eats grass.
A baby buffalo is a calf.

A giraffe eats leaves.
A baby giraffe is a calf.

A deer eats leaves and grass.
A baby deer is a fawn.

page 8 (eight)

TEACHING PAGE 8:

Display the pictures of some plant-eating animals. Discuss what kinds of plants they might eat.

Note that animals eat different parts of plants. Some eat leaves. Some eat roots. Some eat seeds or fruits.

Present the vocabulary.

Read the page to the group or have each section read by a volunteer.

Discussion questions: "What does the deer eat? What does the giraffe eat? What does the buffalo eat? Name the baby giraffe. Name the baby buffalo. Name the baby deer."

ACTIVITY:

Do Worksheet 5.

Read the sentence to the children. Show them a picture of a hippopotamus. Ask them how many have seen a hippopotamus in the zoo.

Read the direction. Tell them to begin with the capital letters first and to finish with the small letters. This page is more difficult. Children may need to use their charts.

Read the coloring directions after the children have finished the picture.

Name ______________

The **hippopotamus** eats grass and water plants.
Follow the dots to see the hippopotamus.

Science 104
Worksheet 5
with page 8

Teacher check ______________
Initial Date

Page 9: Sparrows

CONCEPT: Some birds are plant eaters.

OBJECTIVES:

I can tell about some wild animals.

I can tell what animals need to live and grow.

PROCESSES: observing, classifying, comparing

READING INTEGRATION: recalling details, following directions

VOCABULARY: sparrow, seed, nestling

MATERIALS NEEDED: pencils, pictures of some birds that eat plants (*examples:* starlings, wrens, finches), pictures of meat-eating birds, Worksheet 6, crayons

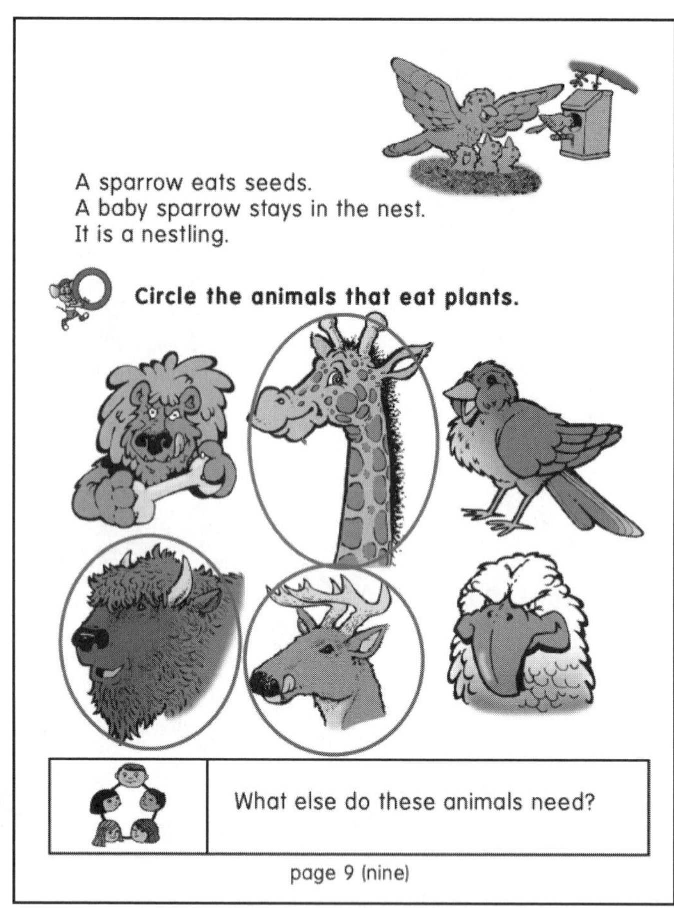

A sparrow eats seeds.
A baby sparrow stays in the nest.
It is a nestling.
Circle the animals that eat plants.
What else do these animals need?
page 9 (nine)

TEACHING PAGE 9:

Display and discuss the pictures of plant-eating birds and meat-eating birds. Compare the similarities and differences. (*Note:* shape of beaks, kind of feet, etc.)

Present the vocabulary. Read the paragraph about the sparrow. Have the children tell what else a sparrow needs.

Ask a volunteer to find and read the direction sentence.

Have the children complete the page independently. Check it together.

Note: Adult sparrows and finches eat seeds, but they feed insects to their nestlings.

Discuss the question at the bottom of the page.

Emphasize that the animals need water and sleep besides food.

ACTIVITIES:

1. Do Worksheet 6.

Read the direction. Let the children complete the page independently. Caution them to find the path first with their fingers before using their crayons to trace the path.

2. As a craft project have the children make a bird feeder. Cardboard milk cartons (2-quart) make excellent feeders. Two holes should be punched in the top for wire or string. A few holes may be punched in the bottom to allow rain to seep through. Cut windows in sides for easy viewing. Fill with commercial bird seed or bread crumbs.

Name
Help the bird find the bird seed.
FINISH
START
Science 104
Worksheet 6
with page 9
Teacher check
Initial
Date

Page 10: Animals That Eat Plants and Meat

CONCEPT: Some animals eat both plants and meat.

OBJECTIVES:

I can tell about some wild animals.

I can tell what animals need to live and to grow.

PROCESSES: classifying, observing, comparing

READING INTEGRATION: main idea, recalling details, speaking in a group

VOCABULARY: bear, berries, honey, winter, (den, cub, fish)

MATERIALS NEEDED: pictures of several kinds of bears, books about bears, Worksheet 7, pencils

TEACHING PAGE 10:

Display and discuss bear pictures. Compare the different kinds of bears: color, size, and so on.

Present the vocabulary.

Read the page to the class or have it read by volunteers.

Discussion questions:

"What are baby bears called?"

"Where do bears sleep?"

"Where do bears find water?"

"What do bears do about the bees when they find some honey?"

"Do bears eat in the winter?" (No, they get very fat before they hibernate, they live off their own fat.)

Discuss the question with the children. Refer to books on bears if necessary.

ACTIVITY:

Do Worksheet 7.

Discuss the picture with the children. Ask them if they have ever seen a polar bear in the zoo. Ask them what it looked like, what size it was, what color it was, and so on.

Read the directions. Help the children with the sentences.

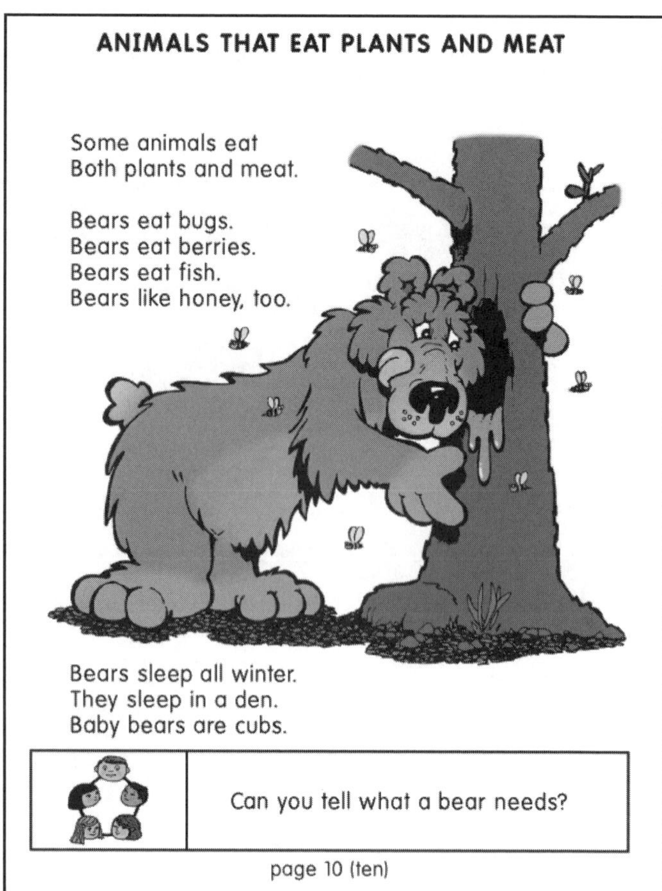
ANIMALS THAT EAT PLANTS AND MEAT

Some animals eat
Both plants and meat.

Bears eat bugs.
Bears eat berries.
Bears eat fish.
Bears like honey, too.

Bears sleep all winter.
They sleep in a den.
Baby bears are cubs.

Can you tell what a bear needs?

page 10 (ten)

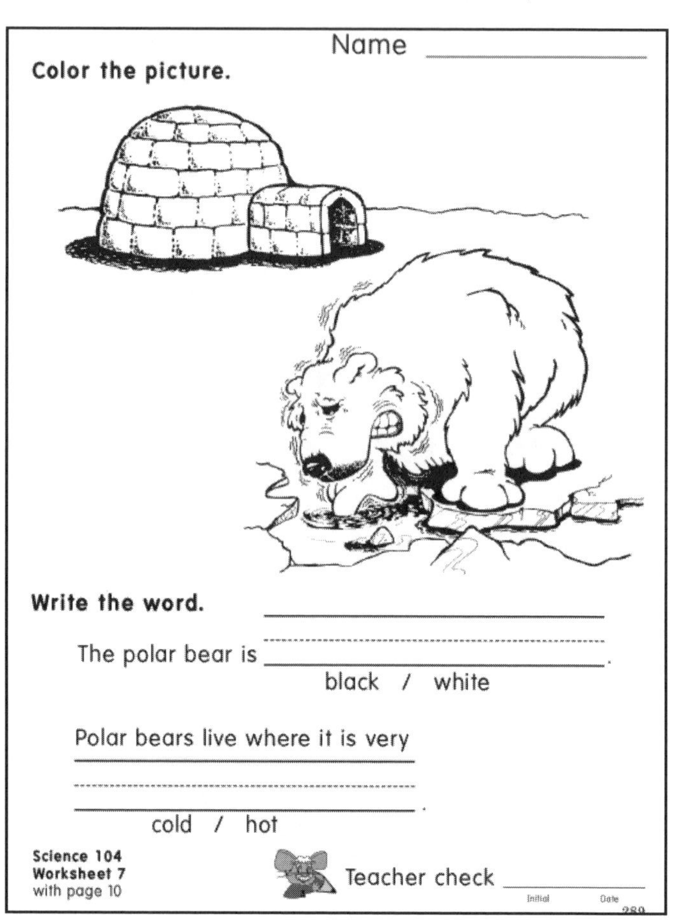
Name ______

Color the picture.

Write the word.

The polar bear is ______.
black / white

Polar bears live where it is very ______.
cold / hot

Science 104
Worksheet 7
with page 10

Teacher check ______
Initial Date

Page 11: Activity Page

MATERIALS NEEDED: pencils, crayons.

TEACHING PAGE 11:

Review main ideas about bears from page 10.

Have a student find and read the directions.

Have the children complete the page independently. Check it together.

ACTIVITIES:

1. Have the children write these sentences in their LIFEPAC Tablets. Bears eat plants and meat. Bears need water. Bears need sleep.
2. Ask the children to read a book about bears and to tell the class or the teacher about it when they have finished.

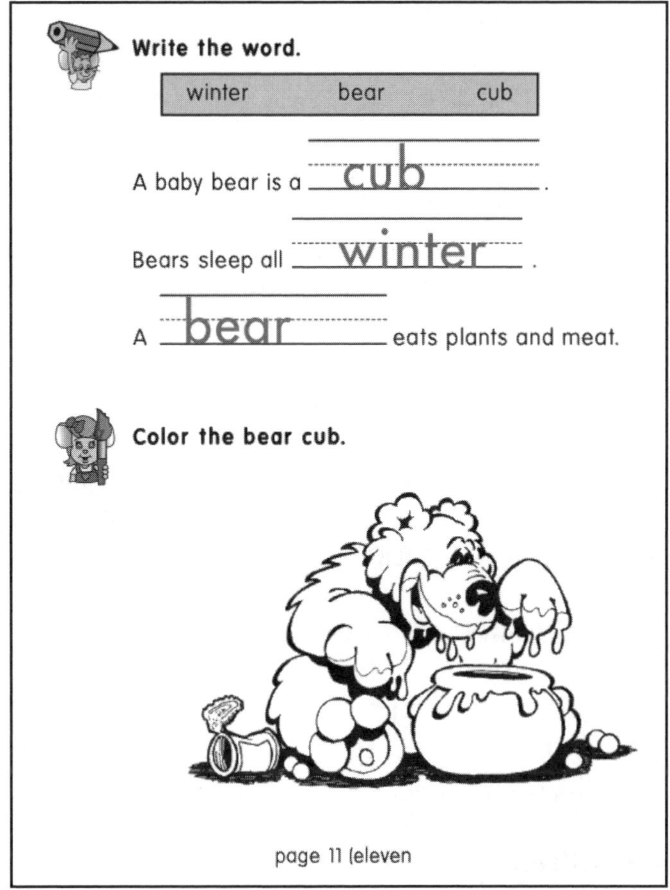

Write the word.
winter bear cub
A baby bear is a cub.
Bears sleep all winter.
A bear eats plants and meat.
Color the bear cub.
page 11 (eleven

Page 12 : Raccoons

CONCEPT: Some animals eat plants and meat.

OBJECTIVES:

I can tell about some wild animals.

I can tell what animals need to live and grow.

PROCESSES: observing, classifying

READING INTEGRATION: main idea, recalling details, following directions, speaking in a group.

VOCABULARY: raccoon, almost, anything

MATERIALS NEEDED: alphabet charts, word cards, picture of raccoon, Worksheet 8, pencils, crayons

TEACHING PAGE 12:

Tell the class that the raccoon is an animal that eats all kinds of things: fish, berries, a farmer's corn, or even garbage.

Present the vocabulary.

Read the sentences about the raccoon to the class or have them read by volunteers.

Have a child find and read the direction sentences.

Let the children complete the activity before you have the discussion.

Discuss the question. Emphasize that raccoons also need sleep and water.

ACTIVITY: Do Worksheet 8.

Read the sentence. Talk about crows. Tell the children that crows like corn and seeds but will eat almost anything. Children may have seen more crows than the other animals they have studied.

Read the directions. Ask the children how many know what a scarecrow is. If they do not know, show them pictures or draw a model on the board.

Let them finish the picture and color it.

The raccoon eats meat.
The raccoon eats plants.
The raccoon eats almost anything.

Follow the dots.
Color the picture.

What else do raccoons need?

page 12 (twelve)

Name ______________

This crow wants to eat the farmer's corn.
Draw a scarecrow to keep him away.
Color the picture.

Science 104
Worksheet 8
with page 12

Teacher check ______________
Initial Date

Page 13: Grouping Animals

CONCEPT: Animals need food, water, and sleep.

OBJECTIVES:

I can tell about some wild animals.

I can tell what animals need to live and grow.

PROCESSES: classifying, comparing

READING INTEGRATION: recalling details, classifying, speaking in a group

MATERIALS NEEDED: pictures and word cards from Part 1, Worksheet 9, pencils

TEACHING PAGE 13:

Play matching game with words and pictures for a review.

Using the chalkboard and these headings, *Animals That Eat Meat, Animals That Eat Plants, and Animals That Eat Plants and Meat,* have the children tell in which column each animal belongs.

Extend by having them add the names of more animals they know about.

ACTIVITIES:

1. Do Worksheet 9.

Read the directions. Let the children do the page independently.

Check together and have the children give the similarities and differences.

Row 1: All eat both plants and animals. The cow is the answer because it does not eat both plants and animals (only plants).

Row 2: The eagle and owl eat meat. The sparrow is the answer because sparrows are primarily seed eaters.

Row 3: The deer and giraffe are plant eaters. The lion is the answer because it is a meat eater.

2. Have wild animal "reports" from page 7 presented to the class and displayed if possible.

Look at the wild animals.
Can you put them in groups?
Can you tell what they need?
Animals that eat meat.
Animals that eat plants.
Animals that eat plants and meat.
Teacher Check
Initial
Date
page 13 (thirteen)

Name
Circle the one that does not belong.
Circle the one that does not belong.
Circle the one that does not belong.
Science 104
Worksheet 9
with page 13
Teacher check
Initial
Date

Pages 14 and 15: Self Test 1

CONCEPTS: evaluation of work

OBJECTIVES:

I can tell about some wild animals.

I can tell what animals need to live and to grow.

READING INTEGRATION: recalling details, following directions

MATERIALS NEEDED: pencils, Worksheet 10

TEACHING PAGES 14 and 15:

Review the vocabulary words.

Practice classifying animals into groups of meat-eating and plant-eating animals and those that eat both.

Read all directions with the children. Be sure they are understood.

The general proficiency of your group should dictate whether you choose to direct the self test or to allow the children to proceed independently once directions are given.

In either case you should be available to answer questions and to help with the vocabulary as needed.

For those children who do not achieve an acceptable score on the self test you should provide extra help.

Let the children take the LIFEPAC home for parent help or provide classtime with a helper to aid in review.

Provide Worksheet 10 as a retest for those who did poorly or as a review for the remaining students.

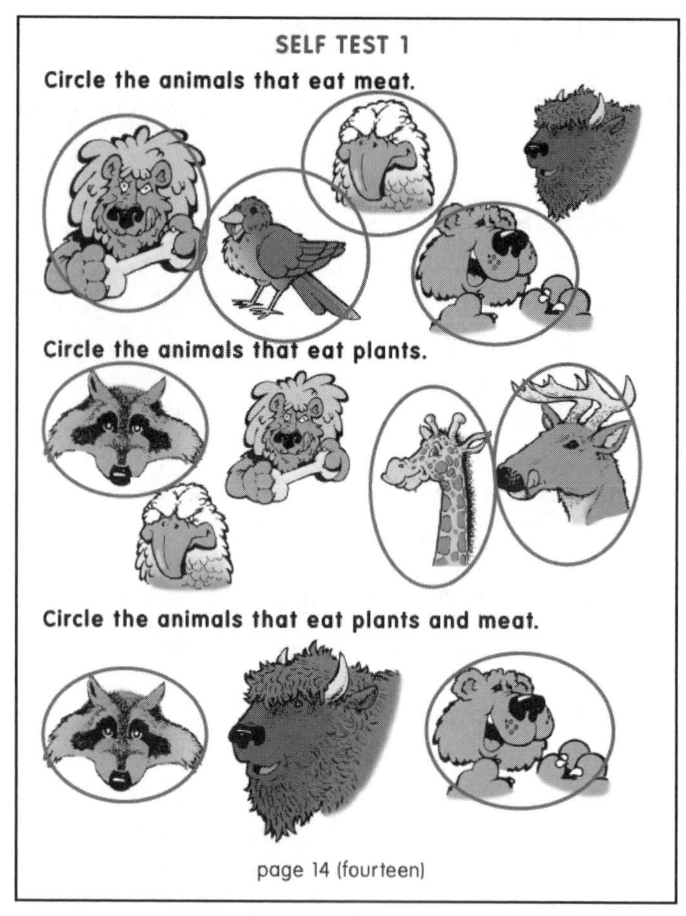

SELF TEST 1
Circle the animals that eat meat.
Circle the animals that eat plants.
Circle the animals that eat plants and meat.
page 14 (fourteen)

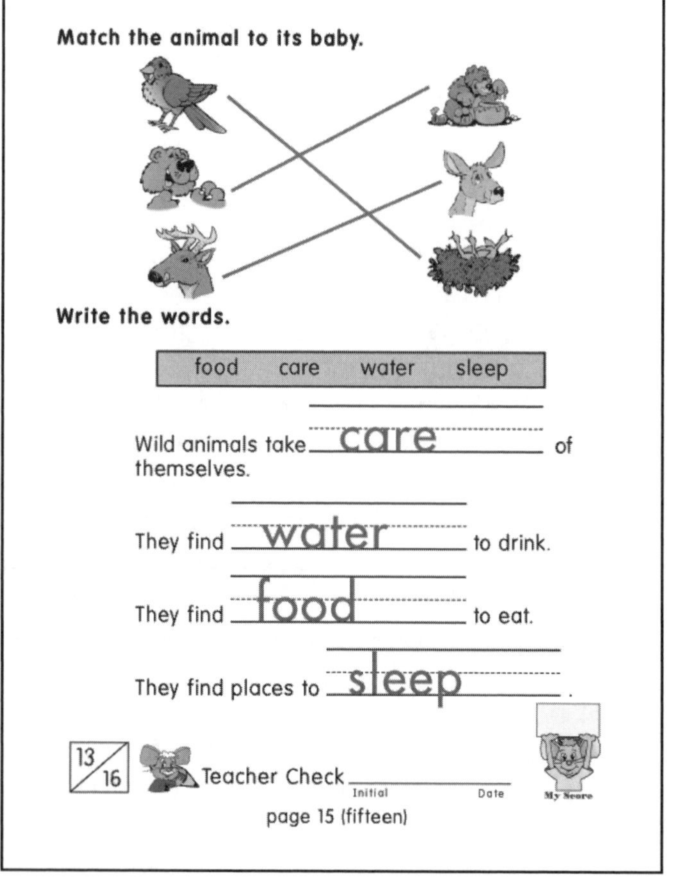

Name ______________

Animals That Eat Plants	Animals That Eat Meat	Animals That Eat Both

Cut out the animals.
Glue them into the right column.

Science 104
Worksheet 10
with page 15

Teacher check ______________
Initial Date

PART II. FARM ANIMALS THAT GIVE US FOOD

Pages 16 and 17

CONCEPTS: The farmer takes care of his animals. Farm animals need food, water, and sleep. Some farm animals provide food.

OBJECTIVES:

I can tell about some farm animals.

I can tell what animals need to live and to grow.

PROCESSES: observing, classifying

READING INTEGRATION: main idea, speaking in a group, recalling details

VOCABULARY: milk, eggs, cheese, meat, farm, farmer, eat, drink, food, water, sleep

MATERIALS NEEDED: pictures of farm animals, pencils, Worksheet 11, crayons, alphabet chart

TEACHING PAGES 16 and 17:

Have the children check the contents of the page to find out what Section II will be about.

Ask them to name some animals they might see on a farm. Display and have the children identify pictures of farm animals.

Tell the children that the farm animals they will learn about will be divided into two groups: those that provide food for people to eat and those that do work on a farm.

Discuss the illustration that begins on page 16 and is continued on page 17. Have the children identify as many animals as possible.

Read the sentences to the class or have them read aloud by volunteers.

Ask the children to take a few minutes to study the picture again. They should look for animals eating, drinking, and for the places they might sleep. *Discussion questions:*

"Where do the animals get a drink?"

"What is the ________ eating?"

II. FARM ANIMALS

Some animals live on a farm.
The farmer takes care of them.
He gives them water to drink.
He gives them food to eat.
He gives them places to sleep.

ANIMALS THAT GIVE US FOOD

Milk and eggs,
Cheese and meats,
All come from animals
A farmer keeps.

page 16 (sixteen)

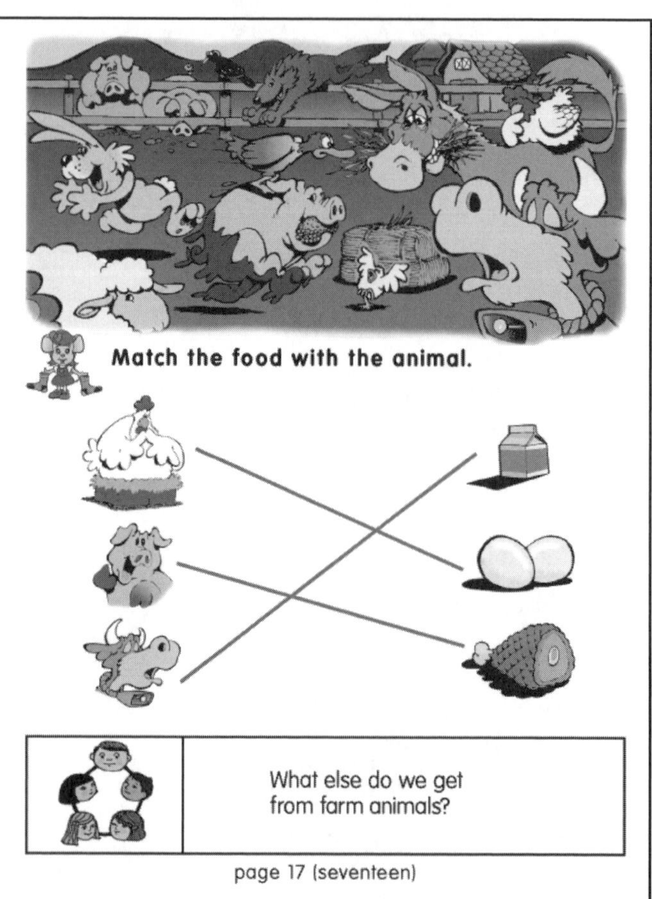

Match the food with the animal.

What else do we get from farm animals?

page 17 (seventeen)

"Where might the animals sleep?"

Read the title, *Animals That Give Us Food.* Ask the children if they can find meat-producing animals in the picture.

Read the poem aloud or have it read aloud by a volunteer. Ask for the vocabulary words to be identified and circled.

Have a child find and read the direction sentence. Be sure the children understand what to do. Have the activity completed independently. Check it together.

Give the children an opportunity to volunteer ideas of what other products (food, material for clothes, etc.) are provided by these and other farm animals.

ACTIVITIES:

1. Do Worksheet 11.

Read the sentences with the children. Read the directions. Let the children complete this page on their own using their alphabet charts if necessary. Ask the children what they have drawn.

Ask the children how many have seen a goose or how many have had roast goose for dinner.

Ask how many sleep on a goose down pillow.

Have the children color the picture.

2. Plan a visit to a farm. Following the visit, do these things:

a. Have the children write thank-you notes with pictures.

b. Write an experience story on chart paper, describing animals seen on the farm.

3. Set up a book table with stories about farm animals to be used for independent reading and projects.

Name ____________

I live on a farm.
I honk.
I make a good Christmas dinner.
My feathers make a very soft pillow.

Follow the dots to see who I am.

Science 104
Worksheet 11
with page 17

Teacher check ____________
Initial Date

Page 18: Animals That Work

CONCEPTS: Some farm animals work. They make the farmer's work easier.

OBJECTIVE: I can tell about some farm animals.

PROCESSES: observing, classifying

BIBLE REFERENCES: Psalm 144:14; Matthew 21:5; I Corinthians 9:9

READING INTEGRATION: rhyming, recalling details, speaking in a group, vocabulary development

VOCABULARY: plow, herd, mouse, guard, catch

MATERIALS NEEDED: pictures of animals that make the farmer's work easier, construction paper, magazines, crayons, glue

ANIMALS THAT WORK
To pull a plow,
Or herd a cow–
To catch a mouse,
Or guard the house–
Animals work on a farm.
Can you tell what
these animals are doing?
page 18 (eighteen)

TEACHING PAGE 18:

Remind the children that animals have been helping people for a long time. The Bible tells how Jesus rode an ass into Jerusalem (Matthew 21:5) and how oxen used to help the farmers (Psalm 144:14; 1 Corinthians 9:9).

Display pictures of farm animals that help the farmer work.

Present the vocabulary and explain the meanings.

Read the poem aloud or have it read by volunteers.

Ask for the vocabulary words to be identified and circled.

Have the children study the picture and read the discussion question.

Ask: "What animal can pull a plow? (horse) "What else do farmers use to pull a plow?" (tractor) "What animal can herd cows and sheep?" (dog) "What else can a dog do?" (guard, seeing eye, etc.) "What does a cat do to help?" (catches mice)

ACTIVITIES:

1. Classify names and pictures of farm animals. Use chart or banner paper. Use these headings:

Animals for Food/Animals for Work

2. Have each child choose a farm animal. Using materials from the reading table, old magazines, construction paper, glue and crayons, the child should make a book about the animal. The child should write a sentence or paragraph about the animal to be included in the book.

Page 19: Activity Page

MATERIALS NEEDED: crayons, pencils

TEACHING PAGE 19:

This page is a follow-up for page 18. No further preparation is needed.

Ask for a volunteer to find and read the two direction sentences. Be sure the children can name the animals pictured.

Ask what animal a cat might catch.

Give a mini art lesson "How to draw a mouse."

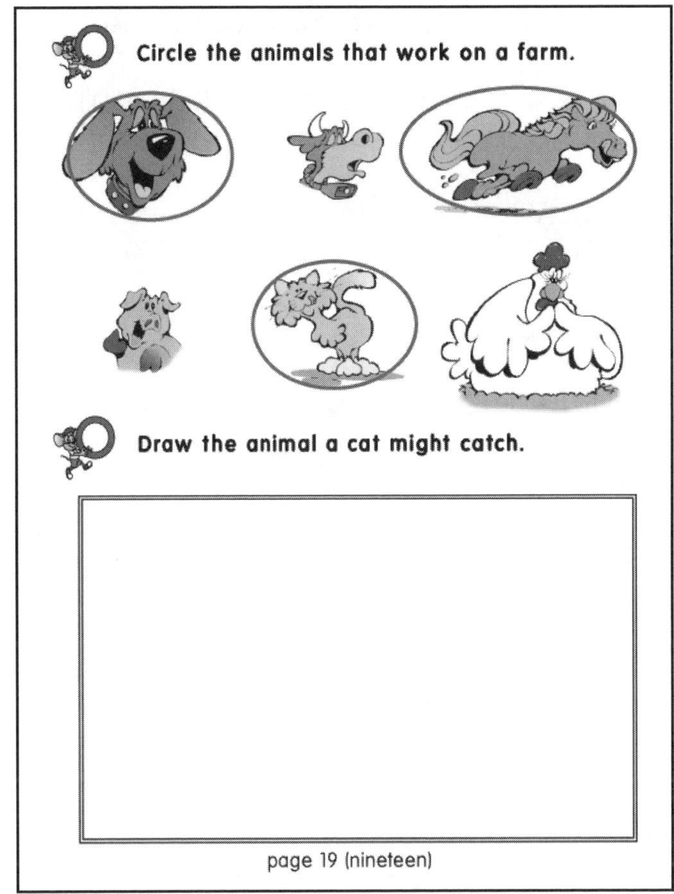

Page 20: Care That Farm Animals Need

CONCEPT: A farmer must provide his animals with food, water, and a place to sleep.

OBJECTIVE: I can tell about some farm animals.

PROCESSES: observing, comparing

READING INTEGRATION: main idea, recalling details, rhyming, vocabulary development, synonyms

VOCABULARY: calf/cow, kitten/cat, chicken/chick, creature, harm

MATERIALS NEEDED: pictures of baby and adult farm animals, Worksheet 12, pencils, crayons

TEACHING PAGE 20:

Present the vocabulary and pictures of baby and adult animals.

Play a matching game with words and pictures for adult and baby.

Note that the synonyms for creature is animal and for harm is hurt.

Discuss the kinds of food each animal might eat.

Ask how the farm animals are alike or different from wild animals.

Read the poem aloud to the class. Have the children read along as you repeat it.

Ask the children to find and circle the vocabulary words.

Provide time for examination and discussion of illustration.

ACTIVITY:

Do Worksheet 12.

Read the directions or have a child read them. Let the children complete the page independently. Check together and discuss.

CARE THAT FARM ANIMALS NEED
To help a calf grow to a cow
Or a kitten to a cat
To raise a chicken from a chick
And make the pigs grow fat–
The farmer must take special care
Of each creature on the farm.
He gives each animal what it needs
And keeps it safe from harm.
page 20 (twenty)

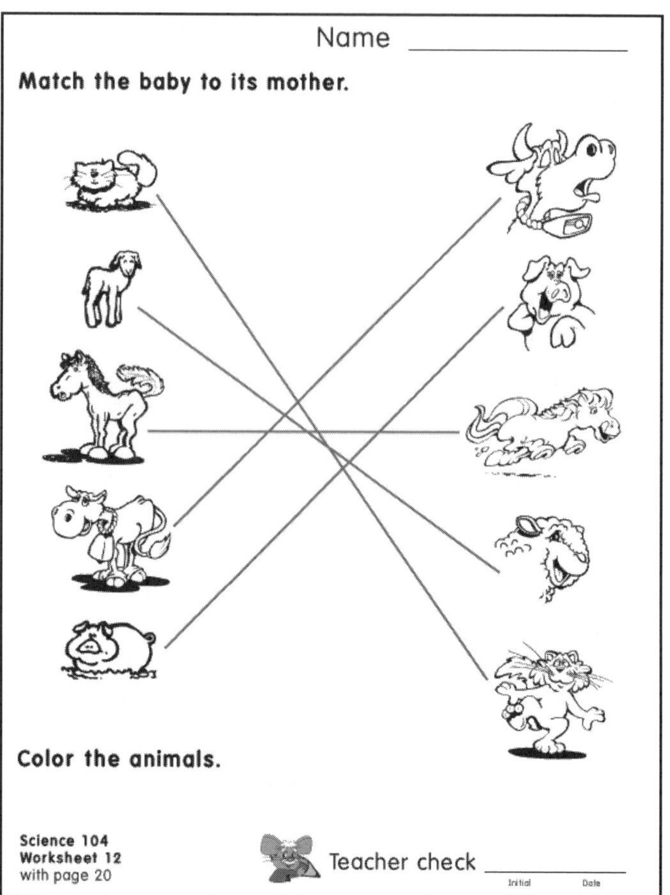
Name
Match the baby to its mother.
Color the animals.
Science 104
Worksheet 12
with page 20
Teacher check
Initial
Date

Page 21: Farm Animals

CONCEPT: The farmer takes care of his animals.

OBJECTIVE: I can tell about some farm animals.

PROCESS: observing

READING INTEGRATION: recalling details, listening, speaking in a group

MATERIALS NEEDED: story "A Bad Day on the Farm," flannel-board figures for the story (see patterns), Worksheet 13, pencils

TEACHING PAGE 21:

Have a volunteer read the direction sentences. Provide help with the vocabulary as needed.

Let the children complete the activity independently. Check it together.

Using the patterns provided at the end of the handbook, make story characters of flannel or construction paper with rolled tape on backs.

Read the story "A Bad Day on the Farm" to the class.

"A Bad Day on the Farm"

It was a hot summer day.

The sun was shining. The grass was green in the pasture. The water was sparkling and gurgling in the creek at the bottom of the hill.

It should have been a happy day at the farm. But it wasn't! It was a very sad day for the animals.

Farmer Jim had gone away and no one came to take care of them.

"Moo-oo," cried the cows as they looked over the fence of the dusty barnyard at the lovely green grass.

"Oink-oink," squealed the pigs as they snuffled around their empty trough.

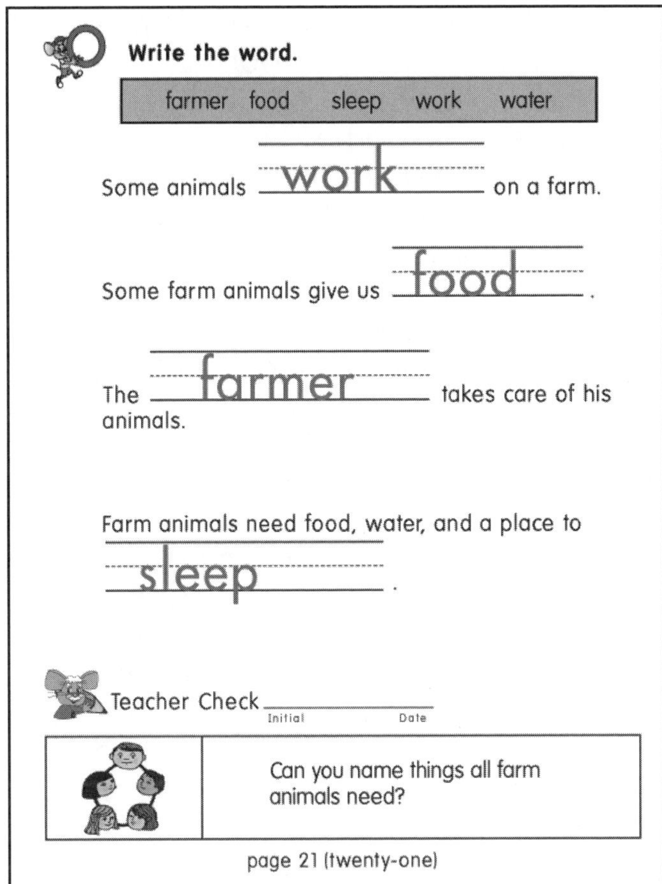
Write the word.

farmer food sleep work water

Some animals work on a farm.

Some farm animals give us food.

The farmer takes care of his animals.

Farm animals need food, water, and a place to sleep.

Teacher Check ______ Initial Date

Can you name things all farm animals need?

page 21 (twenty-one)

"Cluck, cluck, cluck," complained the chickens as they pecked about the gravel of the henyard looking for bits of dried corn.

Only the barn cat did not complain. She had plenty of fat mice to catch.

"Moo-oo." "Oink-oink."

"Cluck, cluck, cluck."

"Moo-oo-oo"

The noise those poor animals made got louder and louder. They were hungry and they were thirsty.

"Moo-oo." "Oink-oink." "Cluck, cluck, CLUCK."

Suddenly the noise stopped.

The animals heard something.

"Whew—wh-whew—wh-whew—whewwhew."

Someone was coming.

The whistle came closer and closer.

"Whew—wh-whew—wh-whew—whewwhew."

The cows, the pigs, and the chickens saw a boy come whistling up the road.

Over his shoulder was a fishing pole and in his hand was a can of worms.

"Whew—wh-whew—wh-whew—whewwhew," he came.

"Moo-oo-oo-oo MOO."

"Oink-oi-oi-oi-OINK."

"Cluck-uck-uck-uck-CLUCK," cried all the animals together.

The boy stopped.

He looked at the animals.

The boy could see that they had no food and no water.

"Well," he said to himself, "Fishing can wait."

"Whew—wh-whew—wh-whew—whewwhew." he whistled as he opened the barnyard gate to let the cows into the pasture where the grass was green and the creek water gurgled and splashed.

"Whew—wh-whew—wh-whew—whewwhew," he whistled as he filled the pig trough with slops he found next to the farmhouse kitchen door.

"Whew—wh-whew—wh-whew—whewwhew," he whistled as he tossed dried corn to the chickens from the bucket he found in the barn.

"Whew—wh-whew—wh-whew—whew-whew," he whistled as he petted the cat who was licking her whiskers by the barn door.

"Whew—wh-whew—wh-whew—whewwhew," he whistled as he picked up his fishing pole and his worms and went up the road to his favorite fishing spot.

The bad day on the farm was not so bad after all.

The cows ate lovely green grass.
The pigs snuffled happily in the trough full of slops.

The chickens pecked at corn instead of gravel.

The cat purred in the warm sunshine.

And that night Farmer Jim came home.

Follow the story with any or all of these activities.

1. Have the children draw pictures about the story.

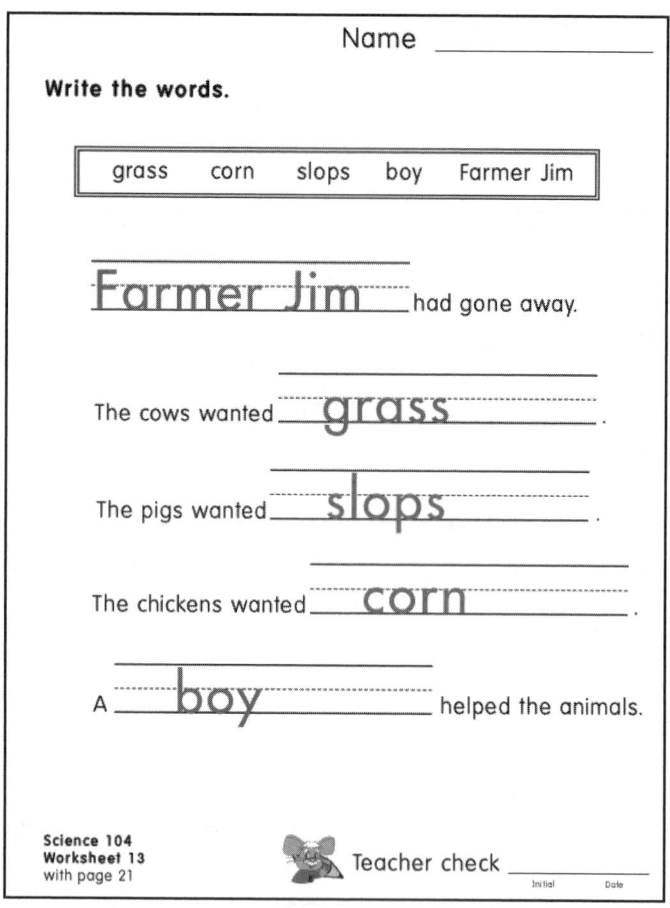
Name ____________

Write the words.

grass	corn	slops	boy	Farmer Jim

Farmer Jim had gone away.

The cows wanted grass.

The pigs wanted slops.

The chickens wanted corn.

A boy helped the animals.

Science 104
Worksheet 13
with page 21

Teacher check ____________
Initial Date

2. Discuss the kinds of food the animals in the story eat:

cow: grass or other grain food.
pigs: corn mash or slops (garbage)
cat: meat, meat products.

3. Discuss what farm animals need: food, water, and places to sleep.

ACTIVITY:

Do Worksheet 13.

Have a child read the directions. Review the words in the box.

Let the children complete the page on their own. Help them with the words if they need it.

Check together and recall the story as the answers are checked.

Page 22 and 23:

CONCEPT: evaluation of work

OBJECTIVES:

I can tell about some wild animals.

I can tell about some farm animals.

I can tell about what animals need to live and to grow.

MATERIALS NEEDED: pencils, crayons, Worksheet 14, scissors, paste or glue

TEACHING PAGES 22 and 23:

Review vocabulary and concepts for Sections I and II.

Practice classifying the animals studied. Use these headings:

1. Meat-eating animals
2. Plant-eating animals
3. Wild animals
4. Farm animals
5. Animals that give us food
6. Animals that work and
7. Birds

Emphasize that all wild animals and farm animals need food, water, and sleep.

The general proficiency of your group will dictate whether you choose to direct the self test or to allow the children to proceed independently once directions are given.

In either case you should be available to answer questions and to help with vocabulary as needed.

Have those children who need review go over the first two sections with their parents or with a classroom helper.

Give Worksheet 14 as a second check or use it as a review.

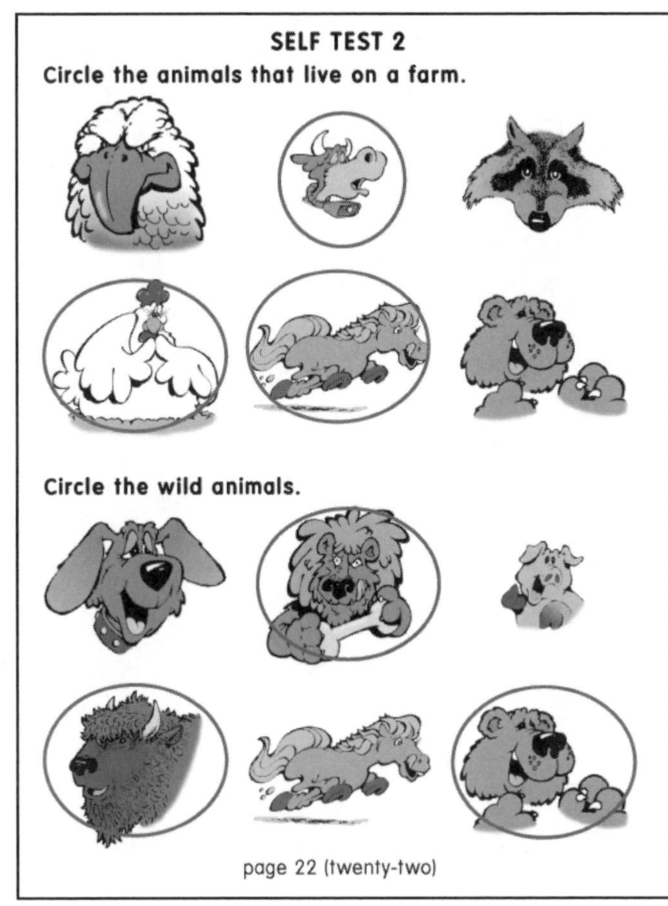

SELF TEST 2
Circle the animals that live on a farm.
Circle the wild animals.
page 22 (twenty-two)

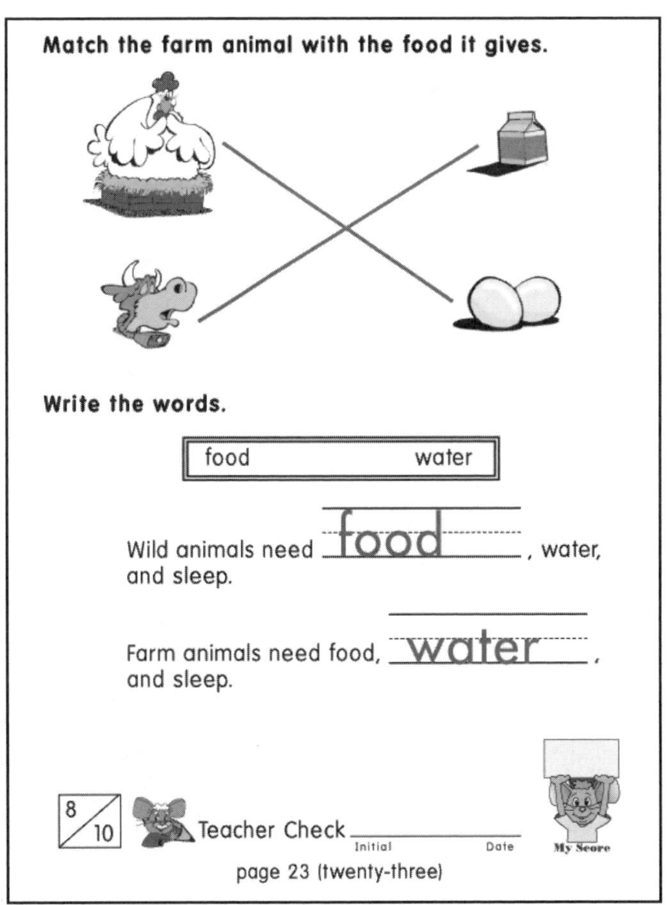

Match the farm animal with the food it gives.
Write the words.
food water
Wild animals need food, water, and sleep.
Farm animals need food, water, and sleep.
8/10
Teacher Check
Initial
Date
My Score
page 23 (twenty-three)

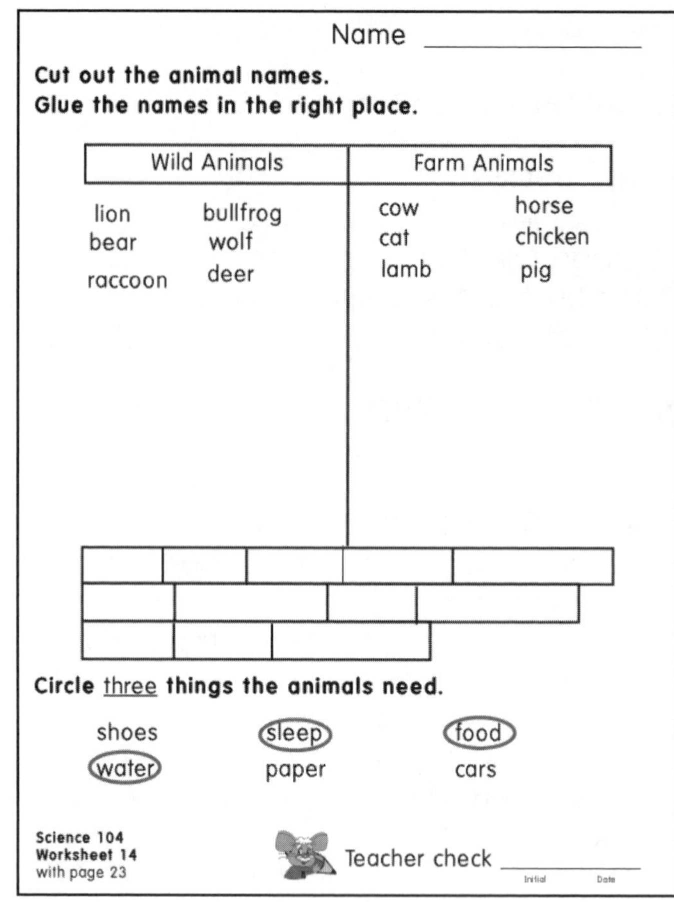
Name

Cut out the animal names.
Glue the names in the right place.

Wild Animals		Farm Animals	
lion	bullfrog	cow	horse
bear	wolf	cat	chicken
raccoon	deer	lamb	pig

Circle three things the animals need.

shoes, sleep, food, water, paper, cars

Science 104
Worksheet 14
with page 23

Teacher check

PART III. PET ANIMALS

Page 24

CONCEPTS: You take care of your pets. Pets need food, water, and sleep.

OBJECTIVES:

I can tell about some pets.

I can tell what animals need to live and to grow.

PROCESS: observing

READING INTEGRATION: rhyming, main idea, vocabulary development

VOCABULARY: yard, cage, bowl, parakeet, goldfish, dog, mouse, watch, (choose, cat)

MATERIALS NEEDED: word cards, pictures of pets

TEACHING PAGE 24:

Have the children look carefully at the pictures on the page. Ask a volunteer to tell what the section will be about.

Present the vocabulary by use of the word cards. Match the words to pictures of pets. As you present such words as cage, ask the children to match it with the animal who might live there.

Read the poem to the class. Reread it with the children following along. Ask for the vocabulary words to be identified.

Discussion questions: "What do pets need?" "Who takes care of pets?"

ACTIVITY:

Prepare the book table with books about pets. Have each child choose a pet to find out about. They may be able to prepare a book about the pet they choose. They should include these things: What the pet eats. Where the pet sleeps. Special care the pet needs.

III. PET ANIMALS

In your room or in the yard,
In a cage or bowl,
You might have an animal
To pet and love and hold.

A dog, a cat, a parakeet,
A goldfish, or a mouse–
An animal can be a friend
To have around the house.

Some animals can play with you
Or learn a fancy trick.
Other pets are fun to watch.
Which one would you pick?

No matter which pet
you might choose,
There's one thing to remember.
It's you who must take care of it
And give it love, so tender.

page 24 (twenty-four)

Page 25: Activity Page

MATERIALS NEEDED: crayons, word cards (from page 24), pictures of pets

TEACHING PAGE 25:

Prepare the children to make a wise choice of pet. Remind them that some pets need large spaces to run and play. Other pets can stay in bowls, tanks, or cages and are better suited to apartment or small-home living.

Ask: "How would a great big dog like living in a tiny apartment or in a house with a little yard?" "Which of the pets do you think would be most comfortable living at your house?"

Ask for a volunteer to find and read the two direction sentences.

When the children understand what to do, let them complete the page independently.

When all are finished, provide time to share the pictures. As the children show the pet they have chosen, ask them to explain why they chose it.

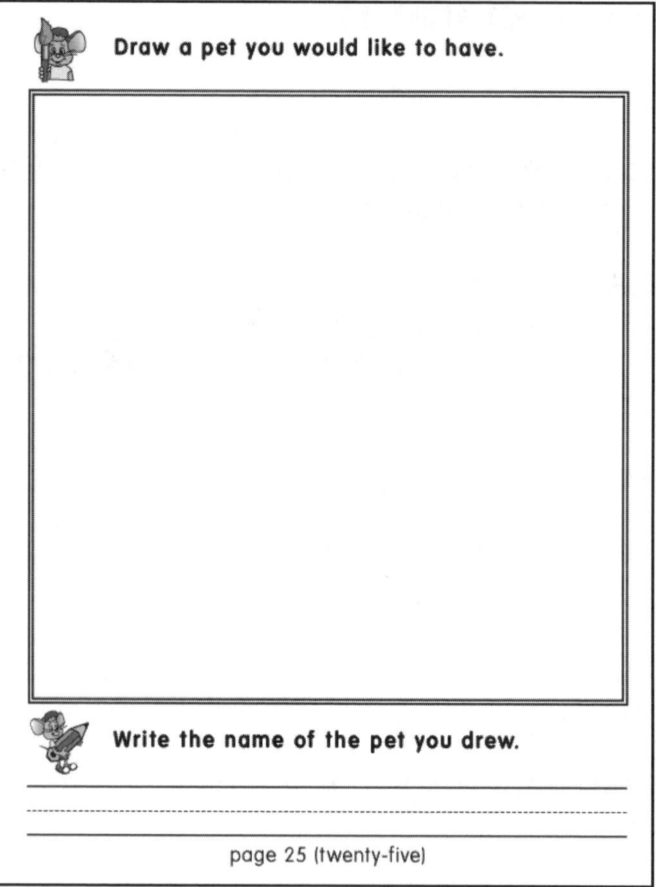
Draw a pet you would like to have.

Write the name of the pet you drew.

page 25 (twenty-five)

Page 26: Pets That You Can Play With

CONCEPT: Some pets will play with you.

OBJECTIVE: I can tell about some pets.

PROCESSES: observing, predicting, classifying, comparing

READING INTEGRATION: main idea, speaking in a group

MATERIALS NEEDED: pictures of different kinds of dogs and cats, Worksheet 15, pencils, crayons, LIFEPAC Tablet

TEACHING PAGE 22:

Display the dog and cat pictures. Discuss and compare the animals by color, size, and so on. Have the children tell how a dog or a cat can play.

Read or have a volunteer read the sentences on the page. Ask other children to describe the pictures.

Ask to have them read and answered by volunteers.

ACTIVITIES:

1. Do Worksheet 15.

Read the directions. Let the children do the page on their own using their alphabet charts if they need them.

2. In their Tablets have the children write this sentence:

Dogs and cats play with you.

PETS THAT YOU CAN PLAY WITH
Puppies like to play.
Kittens like to play.
When a puppy grows up,
what will it be?
When a kitten grows up,
what will it be?
page 26 (twenty-six)

Name
Follow the dots.
Color the picture.
Science 104
Worksheet 15
with page 26
Teacher check
Initial
Date

Page 27: Activity Page

MATERIALS NEEDED: pencils

TEACHING PAGE 27:

This page is a follow-up of the previous page. No further preparation is necessary.

Have a volunteer find and read the direction sentences. When children understand what they are to do, have them complete the page independently.

ACTIVITY:

Check on the progress of the individual pet books.

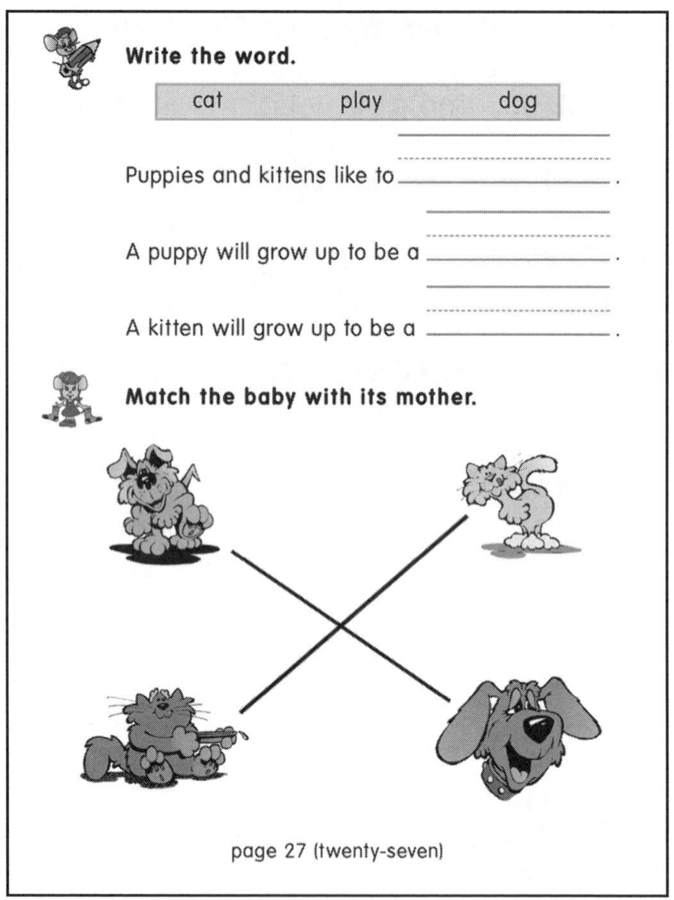

Write the word.
cat play dog
Puppies and kittens like to ____.
A puppy will grow up to be a ____.
A kitten will grow up to be a ____.
Match the baby with its mother.
page 27 (twenty-seven)

Pages 28 and 29: Pets That You Can Watch

CONCEPT: Some pets are fun to watch.

OBJECTIVE: I can tell about some pets.

PROCESSES: observing, comparing

READING INTEGRATION: recalling details, speaking in a group

VOCABULARY: fish, bird, hamster, bowl, cage, watch

MATERIALS NEEDED: pictures of different kinds of pets that might live in confined spaces: bowls, cages, and so on; word cards; Worksheets 16 and 17; crayons

TEACHING PAGES 28 and 29:

Display pictures of confined pets. Match the animals by the kind of home they might occupy. Compare types of cages.

Read or have a volunteer read the sentences on the page. Have the children identify the vocabulary words on the page.

Give the children an opportunity to discuss the pets pictured.

Give each child an opportunity to answer the discussion questions.

Have a volunteer find and read the direction. Allow the children to complete the page independently. Check it together.

If a child owns a confined pet and could bring it to school, providing this experience now would be good. You might plan a pet day at school. A good idea may be to limit it to confined pets unless you can get several parents' help to supervise children and animals.

ACTIVITIES:

1. Do Worksheet 16.

Read the direction. Tell the children to trace the path from the turtle to its bowl. Let them finish the page on their own.

PETS THAT YOU CAN WATCH
You can watch a fish.
The fish swims in a bowl.
You can watch a bird.
The bird lives in a cage.
page 28 (twenty-eight)

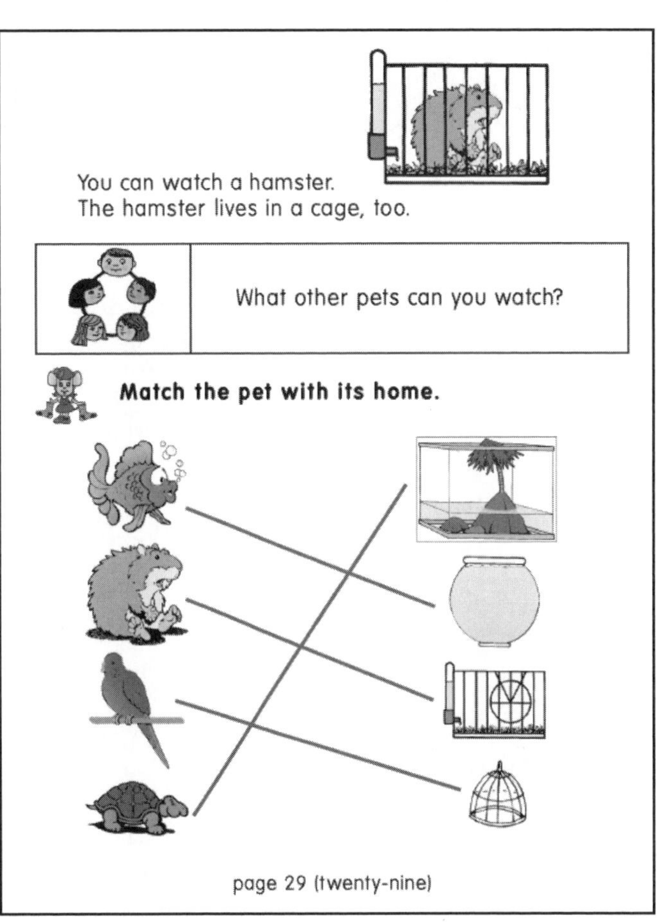
You can watch a hamster.
The hamster lives in a cage, too.
What other pets can you watch?
Match the pet with its home.
page 29 (twenty-nine)

2. Do Worksheet 17.

Read the directions. After the children have finished their drawings, let each one talk about the picture.

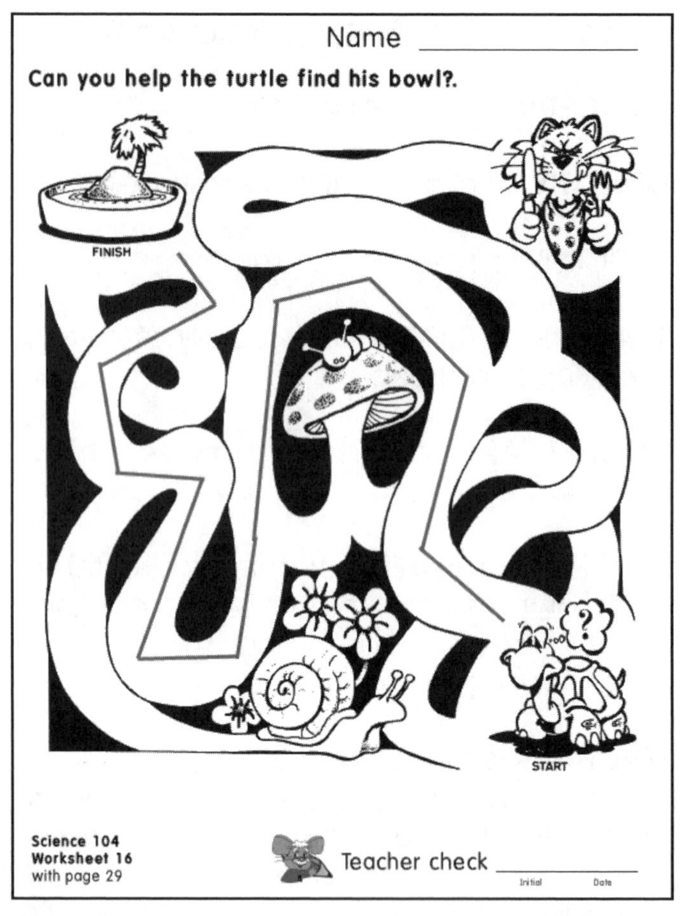

Name
Can you help the turtle find his bowl?.
FINISH
START
Science 104
Worksheet 16
with page 29
Teacher check
Initial
Date

Name ______________

Draw a pet that lives in a bowl.

Draw a pet that lives in a cage.

Science 104
Worksheet 17
with page 29

Teacher check ______________
Initial Date

Page 30: Ways That You Care For Your Pets

CONCEPTS: Pets need food, water, and sleep. You take care of your pet.

OBJECTIVE: I can tell what animals need to live and grow.

PROCESSES: observing, predicting

READING INTEGRATION: recalling details, vocabulary development (proper names)

VOCABULARY: Buddy Bird, Timmy Turtle, Dandy Dog, Candy Cat

MATERIALS NEEDED: Worksheet 18, crayons

TEACHING PAGE 30:

Give the children some practice in recognizing proper names. Remind them of the need for capital letters on all proper names: names of people, places, and pets.

Read the paragraphs to the class or have them read by volunteers. Give the children an opportunity to discuss the kinds of food each pet eats.

Note: Dogs and cats eat meat or meat products.

Most caged birds eat seeds and other plant products.

Turtles will eat both meat and plant products.

ACTIVITY:

Do Worksheet 18.

Read the direction.

Talk about the house in the picture. Ask what kind of pet lives in the house. Tell the children to draw that pet.

WAYS THAT YOU CARE FOR YOUR PETS

I'm Buddy Bird.
I need seed and water.
I sleep on my perch.

I'm Timmy Turtle.
I need food and water.
I sleep on my rock.

I'm Dandy Dog.
I need dog food and water.
I sleep on the floor.

I'm Candy Cat.
I need cat food and water.
I sleep on a pillow.

page 30 (thirty)

Name ________________

Draw the animal who lives here.
Color the picture.

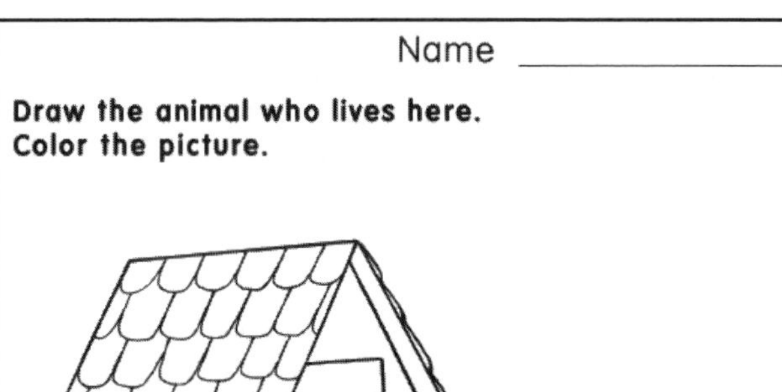

Science 104
Worksheet 18
with page 30

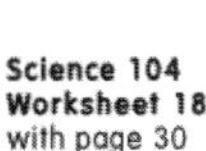

Teacher check __________
Initial Date

Page 31: Activity Page

MATERIALS NEEDED: pictures of animals studied in the LIFEPAC, pencils

TEACHING PAGE 31:

Using the pictures of the animals studied in the LIFEPAC, have the children try to recall what each one needs to live and grow. Have them tell whether each animal takes care of itself or needs to be taken care of. The most important concept of this LIFEPAC is that all animals need food, water, and sleep to live and grow. This point cannot be stressed too often.

The children should realize and be able to verbalize that pets need the care of their owners.

Have a volunteer find and read the direction sentence. Have the children complete the page independently, giving help with vocabulary as needed. Check the page together.

ACTIVITY:

Make a class chart with the animals word-name cards from the LIFEPAC. Classify the animals into groups: wild, farm, and pet.

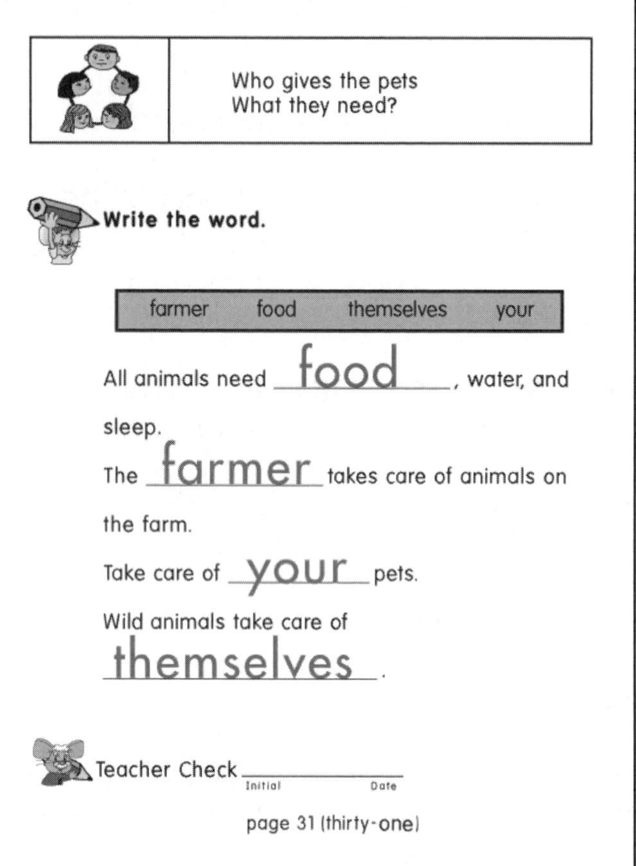
Who gives the pets
What they need?

Write the word.

farmer	food	themselves	your

All animals need food, water, and sleep.

The farmer takes care of animals on the farm.

Take care of your pets.

Wild animals take care of themselves.

Teacher Check ________
Initial Date

page 31 (thirty-one)

Pages 32 and 33: Self Test 3

CONCEPT: evaluation

OBJECTIVES:
I can tell about some wild animals.
I can tell about some farm animals.
I can tell about some pets.
I can tell what animals need to live and grow.

READING INTEGRATION: following directions, recalling details

MATERIALS NEEDED: pencils, Worksheet 19, crayons

TEACHING PAGES 32 and 33:
Review the vocabulary and concepts for the entire LIFEPAC with special emphasis on Section III.

ACTIVITY:
Do Worksheet 19.
Read the directions. Let the children complete the page independently. Check together and discuss. Use this sheet and discussion as a final review for the LIFEPAC Test.

SELF TEST 3
Circle the pets you watch.
Circle the pets that play with you.
Circle the animals that work on a farm.
Circle the wild animals that eat plants.
page 32 (thirty-two)

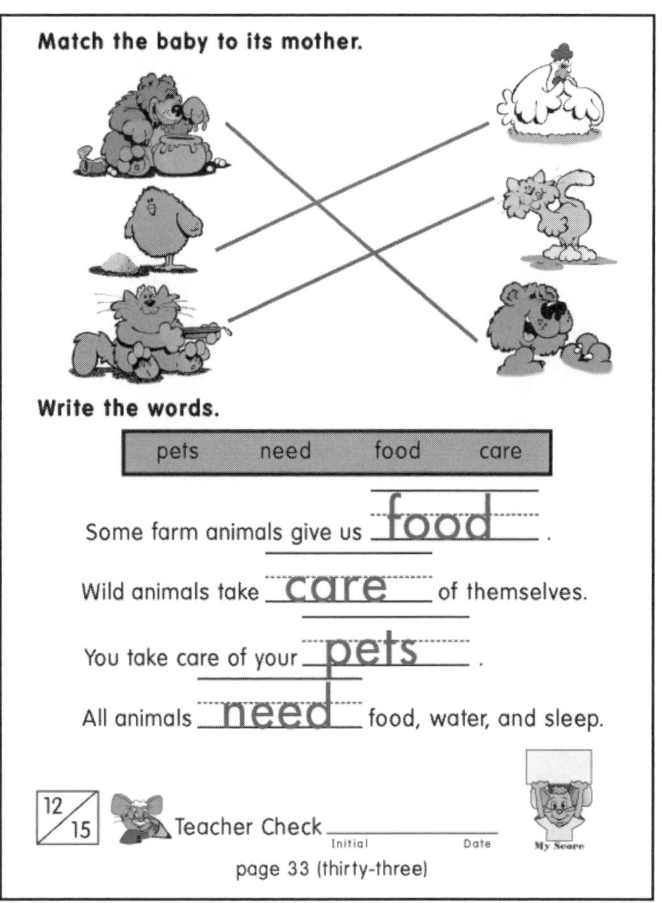

Match the baby to its mother.
Write the words.
pets need food care
Some farm animals give us food .
Wild animals take care of themselves.
You take care of your pets .
All animals need food, water, and sleep.
12/15
Teacher Check
Initial Date
My Score
page 33 (thirty-three)

Name

Write wild, farm, **or** pet.

farm

pet

wild

wild

farm

pet/wild

Science 104
Worksheet 19
with page 33

Teacher check
Initial Date

LIFEPAC TEST AND ALTERNATE LIFEPAC TEST

Administer to the class as a group. Ask to have directions read or read them to the class. In either case be sure that the children clearly understand. Put examples on the board if it seems advisable. Give sufficient time for each activity to be completed before going on to the next item.

Give additional copies of the worksheets and a list of vocabulary words to study to children who did not achieve the 80% score. A parent or classroom helper should help in the review. When the child is ready, administer the Alternate LIFEPAC Test. Use the same procedure as for the LIFEPAC Test.

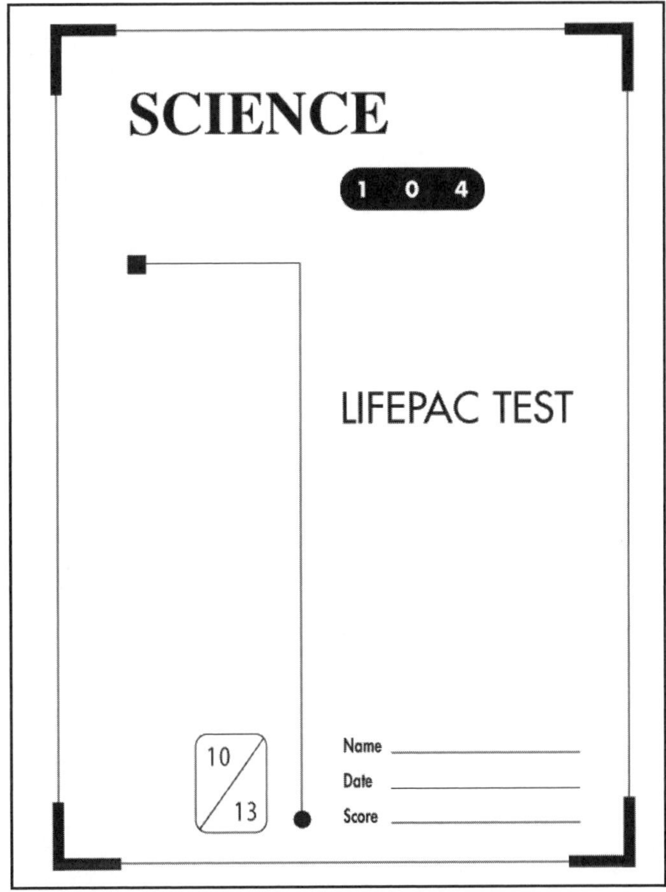

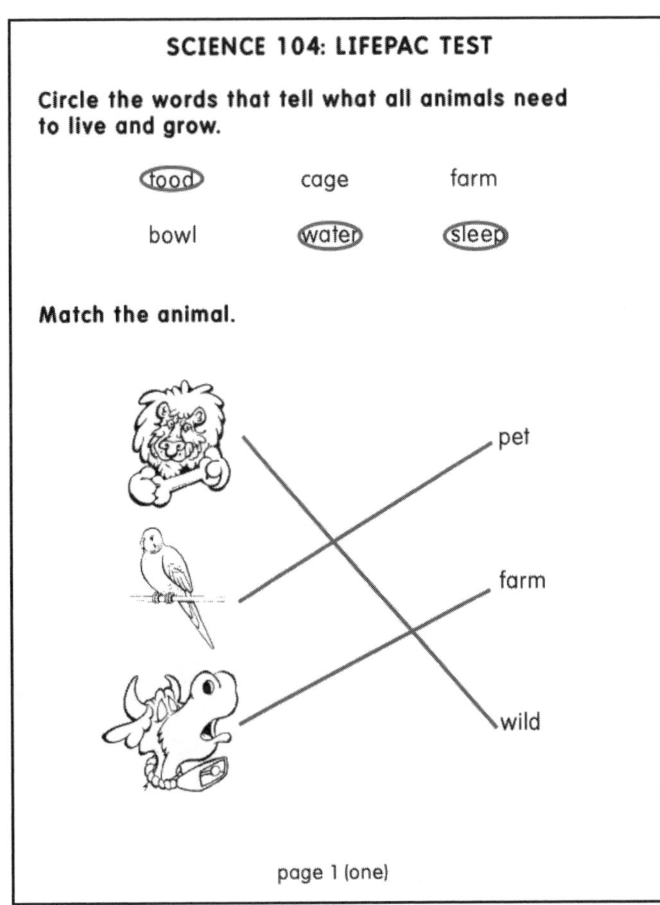
SCIENCE 104: LIFEPAC TEST

Circle the words that tell what all animals need to live and grow.

food cage farm
bowl water sleep

Match the animal.

page 1 (one)

Write the word.

themselves	farmer	cow
farm	plants	meat
care		

A horse works on a farm.

A cow gives us food.

The farmer takes care of his animals.

You take care of your pet.

Wild animals take care of themselves.

Lions and eagles eat meat.

Deer and buffalo eat plants.

page 2 (two)

NOTES

page 3 (three)

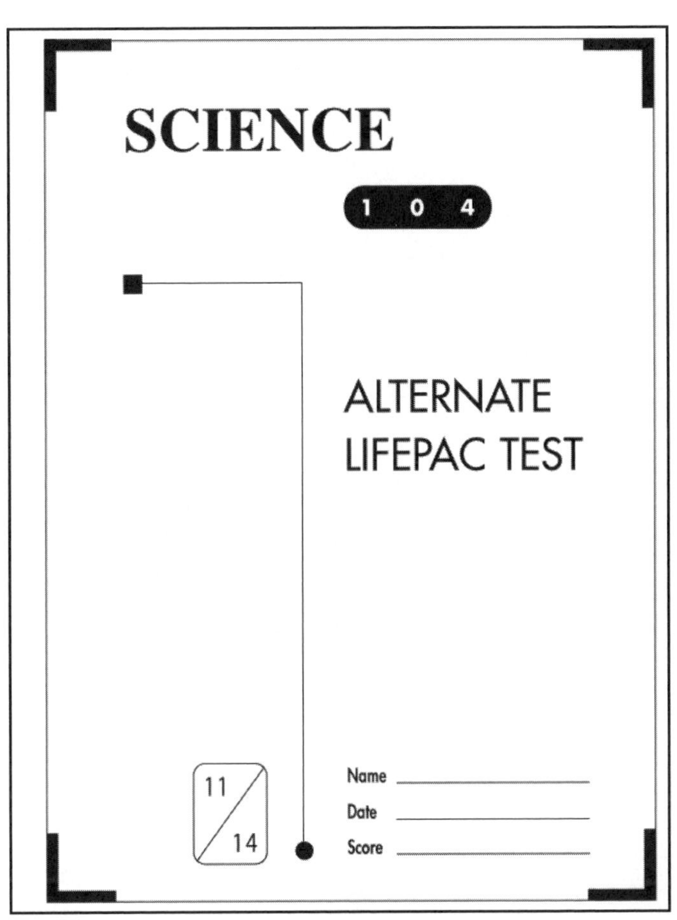
SCIENCE
1 0 4
ALTERNATE
LIFEPAC TEST
11
14
Name
Date
Score

SCIENCE 104: ALTERNATE LIFEPAC TEST
Write food, water, and sleep.
all animals need food,
water and sleep.
Match the animal to the word.
wild
farm
pet
page 1 (one)

Circle the animals that gives us food.
Circle the wild animals that eat meat.
Circle pets that live in cages.
page 2 (two)

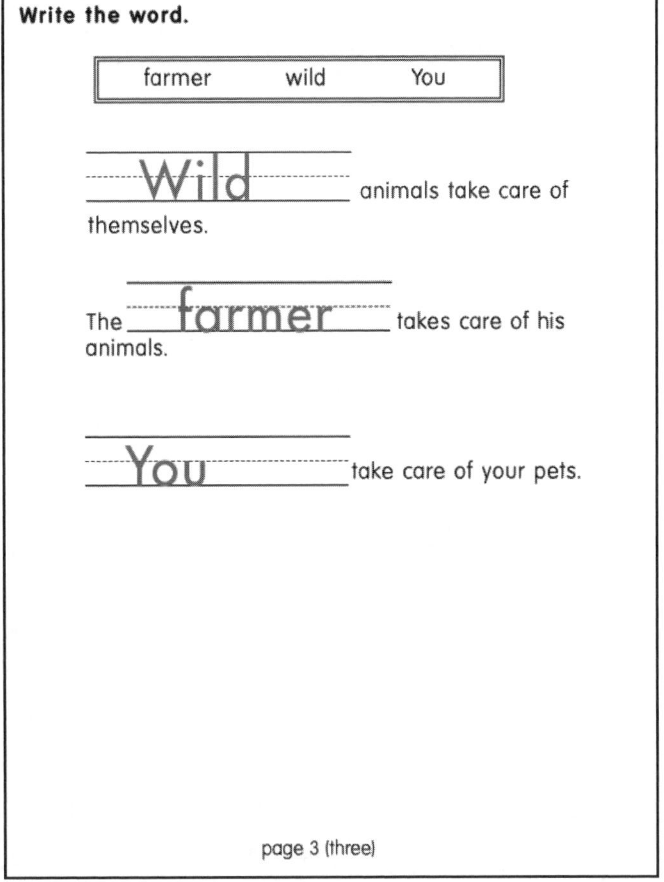
Write the word.
farmer wild You
Wild animals take care of themselves.
The farmer takes care of his animals.
You take care of your pets.
page 3 (three)

Page 1: Plants

CONCEPT: Plants grow everywhere.

OBJECTIVE: Introduction to the objectives of the LIFEPAC.

TEACHER GOALS: To prepare the students to learn and understand about plants to know where they grow and what they need.

BIBLE REFERENCE: Genesis 1:11

PROCESSES: observing, comparing

READING INTEGRATION: listening, vocabulary development, main idea

VOCABULARY: farm, garden, house, nature, plants

MATERIALS NEEDED: pictures of plants growing in nature, on a farm, in a garden, and in the house; provide pictures of the different types of plants: trees, grasses; a growing plant

TEACHING PAGE 1:

Show the plant you have growing in the classroom. Ask the children to tell about what you have. Encourage them to use their senses to describe the plant (except taste).

Ask the children to tell what the plant needs. Some may be able to identify the needs (water, light, good soil).

Display the plant pictures. Have the children try to match the word cards (farm, garden, house, and nature) to the pictures.

Read the Bible verse to the class. Ask the children to tell who created the plants they see around them. You might take a minute to thank God for plants.

Read the introductory sentences to the class. Have the children identify the vocabulary words in the sentences and circle them.

PLANTS

Plants grow everywhere.
Plants grow
in nature,
on a farm,
in a garden, and
in the house.

God helps plants grow.
A farmer helps plants grow.
You can help plants grow, too.

1. I can tell about some plants that grow in nature.
2. I can tell about some plants that grow on a farm.
3. I can tell about some plants that grow at home.
4. I can tell what plants need to live and grow.

page 1 (one)

Ask these questions: "Where do plants grow?" "Who helps plants grow?"

Read the objectives to the class. Be sure that they understand these are things they will be able to do when they have completed the LIFEPAC.

ACTIVITIES:

1. Prepare a "discovery center." Include potting materials, assorted seeds, and picture directions for planting them. As your class proceeds through the LIFEPAC, allow each child to have an opportunity to plant and care for a plant.
2. Prepare a Book Table. For the first section of the LIFEPAC, include books about plants in nature. These books may be used to provide free-time activities, resources for individual projects, and so on.

I. PART ONE

Page 2: Plants in Nature

CONCEPT: God created many kinds of plants that grow in nature.

OBJECTIVE: I can tell about some plants that grow in nature.

TEACHER GOAL: To help the children to identify some of the many kinds of plants that grow in nature.

BIBLE REFERENCE: Genesis 1:11 and 12

PROCESS: observing

READING INTEGRATION: rhyming, recalling detail

VOCABULARY: trees, cactus, seaweed, meadow, spring, (grass)

MATERIALS NEEDED: pictures representing the vocabulary words, Worksheet 1, crayons

TEACHING PAGE 2:

Present the vocabulary words. Match them with the pictures. Read the Bible verses aloud. Have the children name the plants mentioned.

Read the poem aloud to the children. Read it again. Have the children find and circle the vocabulary words in the poem.

As you reread the poem, have the children read along. *Ask these questions:*

"Who made the trees?"
"Who made the cactus?"
"Who made the meadow grass?"
"Who made the seaweed?"
"Where do each of them grow?"

ACTIVITIES:

1. Continue use of discovery center and book center.

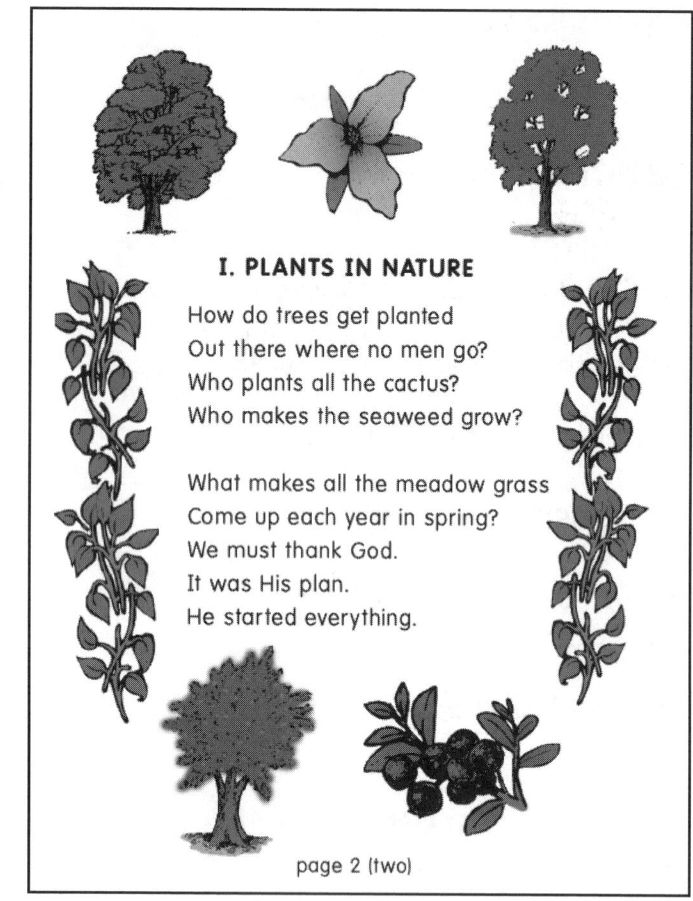

I. PLANTS IN NATURE

How do trees get planted
Out there where no men go?
Who plants all the cactus?
Who makes the seaweed grow?

What makes all the meadow grass
Come up each year in spring?
We must thank God.
It was His plan.
He started everything.

page 2 (two)

2. Do Worksheet 1.
   Read the direction.
   Discuss each of the plants. Have pictures available so that children use the correct colors.

Name ________________

Color the plants.

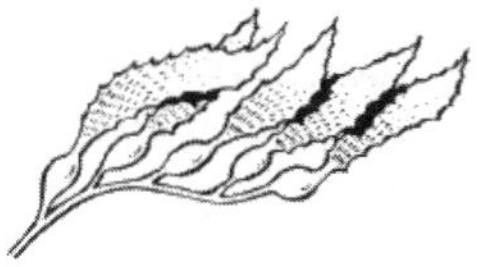

seaweed

cactus

grass

tree

Science: 105
Worksheet 1
with page 2

Teacher check ____________
Initial Date

Page 3: Activity Page

MATERIALS NEEDED: pencils

TEACHING PAGE 3:

Review the vocabulary words, matching them with the corresponding pictures.

Read the directions to the children, or have them read by a volunteer. Be sure all of the class knows what to do. Let the children complete the page independently. Check it together.

ACTIVITY:

Continue the use of the centers.

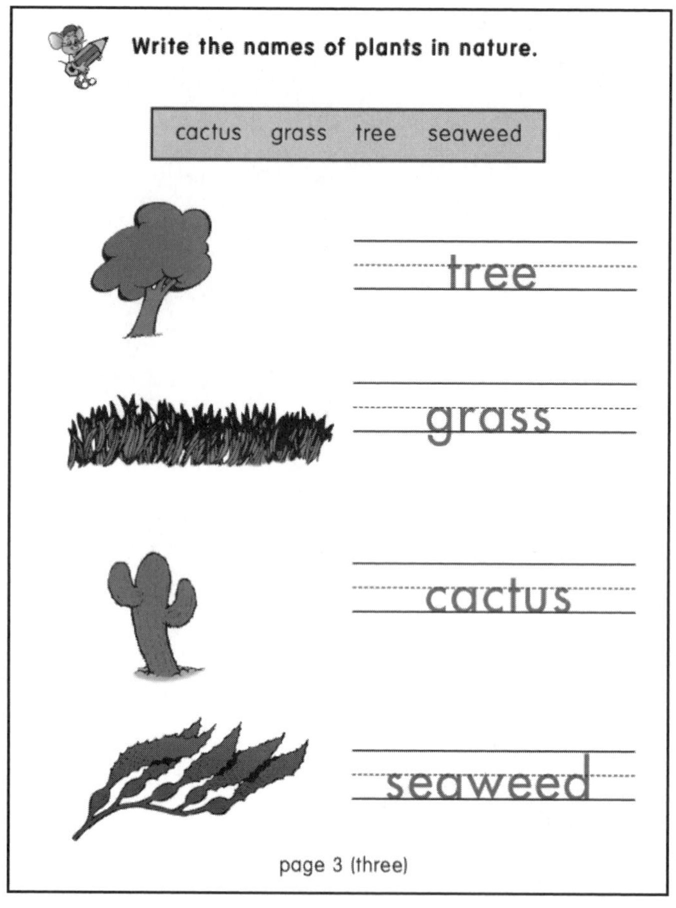

Write the names of plants in nature.
cactus grass tree seaweed
tree
grass
cactus
seaweed
page 3 (three)

Page 4: Big Plants

CONCEPTS: Trees are big plants. They grow from seeds.

OBJECTIVE: I can tell about some plants that grow in nature.

TEACHER GOAL: To develop the concept that big plants (trees) grow from small seeds.

PROCESSES: observing, comparing

READING INTEGRATION: vocabulary development, main idea

VOCABULARY: apple, maple, oak, root, trunk, leaves, (seeds)

MATERIALS NEEDED: seeds of various kinds of trees, as available; pictures of the trees whose seeds you can provide; Worksheet 2; pencils; diagram of a tree (showing roots, trunks, branches, fruit or seeds, and leaves).

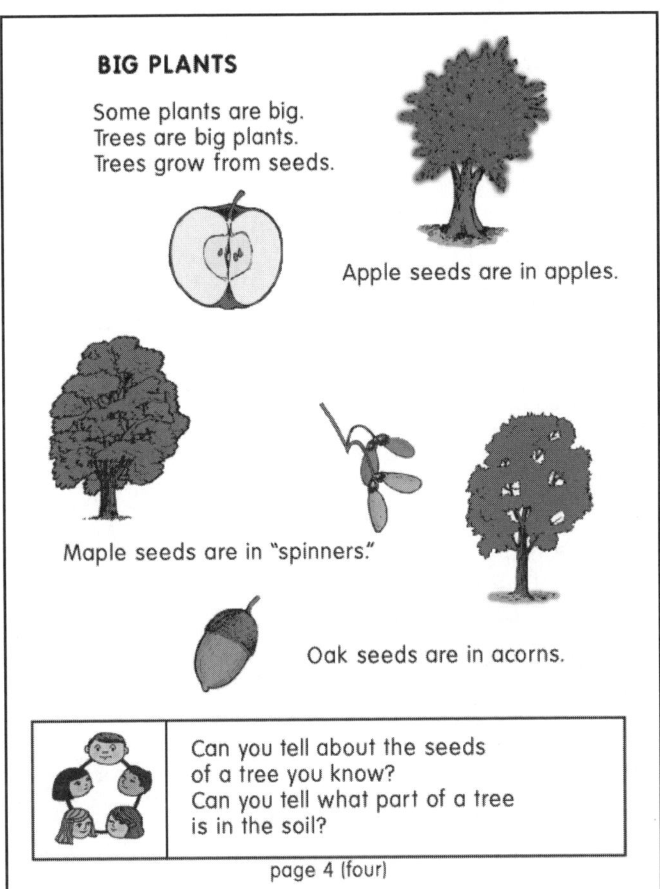

BIG PLANTS
Some plants are big.
Trees are big plants.
Trees grow from seeds.
Apple seeds are in apples.
Maple seeds are in "spinners."
Oak seeds are in acorns.
Can you tell about the seeds
of a tree you know?
Can you tell what part of a tree
is in the soil?
page 4 (four)

TEACHING PAGE 4:

Display the seeds and the pictures of trees you have. Present the vocabulary words.

Read the sentences to the class or have them read by volunteers. Discuss the pictures. Pay particular attention to the different ways trees have of distributing their seeds. Birds and animals eat apples and drop the seeds. Maple spinners are blown on the wind. Many of them fall in good soil and grow. Acorns are gathered and buried by squirrels. Many of them grow.

Discussion questions: Have a child read the first question. Give each child an opportunity to respond.

Read the second question. Help the children with this discussion. The part of a tree in the soil is the roots (show diagram). The roots have two jobs. They hold the tree up (provide support) and pull water and nutrients from the soil to make the tree grow strong.

ACTIVITY:

Provide Worksheet 2.

Read the directions. Have the children read the words in the box.

Have the children label the diagram.

Check together using your diagram.

Have the children correct any mistakes.

Have them color the picture.

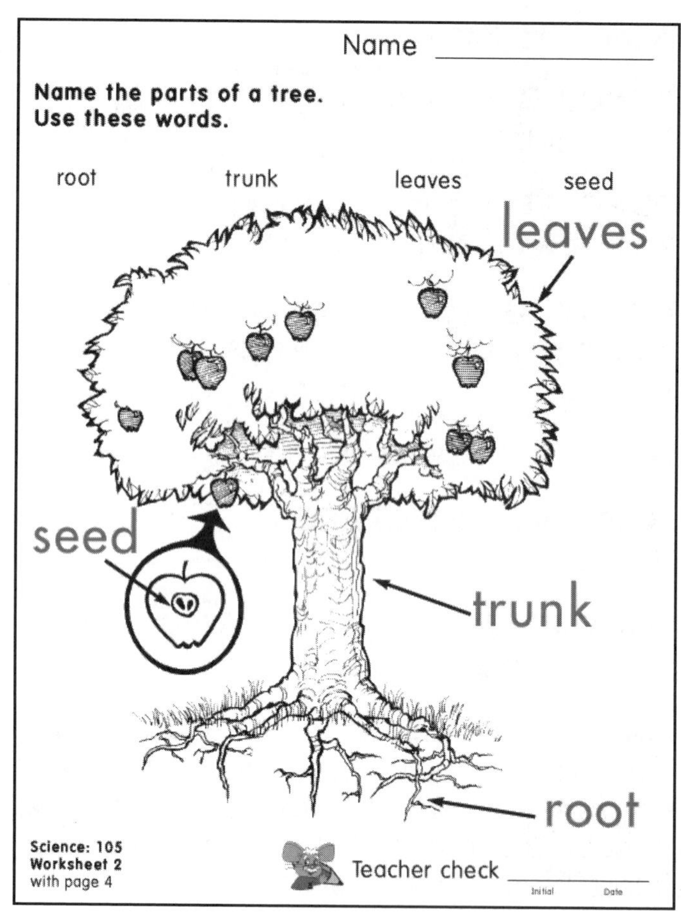

Name ________________

Name the parts of a tree.
Use these words.

root trunk leaves seed

leaves

seed

trunk

root

Science: 105
Worksheet 2
with page 4

Teacher check ________________
Initial Date

Page 5: Activity Page

MATERIALS NEEDED: pencils, LIFEPAC Tablets, alphabet chart, crayons

TEACHING PAGE 5:

Read the direction sentences to the class, or have them identified and read by a volunteer. When all the children understand what to do, let them complete the activity independently. Check it together.

Read the statement and the first question. Give the children an opportunity to suggest some animals that might live in a tree.

Read the second question. Other things that trees provide are lumber for building, shade from the sun, and spaces between the roots for burrowing animals. Accept any reasonable response.

ACTIVITIES:

In their Tablets, have the children write *Thank you, God, for trees.*

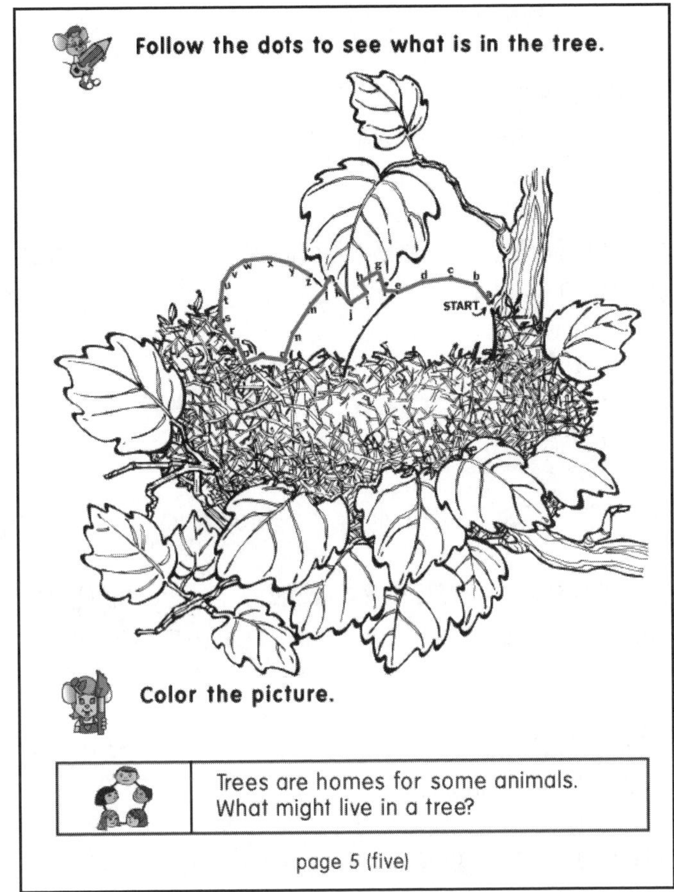

Follow the dots to see what is in the tree.
START
Color the picture.
Trees are homes for some animals.
What might live in a tree?
page 5 (five)

Page 6: Trees

CONCEPTS:

Some trees grow in special places.
The seed bearing parts of trees differ.

OBJECTIVE I can tell about some plants that grow in nature.

TEACHER GOAL: To develop the idea of God's specialization of trees to fit their environment.

PROCESSES: observing, comparing

READING INTEGRATION: vocabulary development, speaking in a group, recalling detail

VOCABULARY: bear (to produce), coconut, date (the fruit), pine, cone

MATERIALS NEEDED: pictures of special kinds of trees: palm, pine, palo verde or others that might be familiar to your area; the seeds of the trees pictured: coconut, date, pine, leaves

Some trees grow in special places.
Palm trees grow where it is warm.
Some palm trees bear coconuts.
Other palm trees bear dates.
Most pine trees grow where it is cool.
Pine trees bear pine cones.
Pine seeds hide in the cones.
What do trees need to live and grow?
Who gives the trees what they need?
page 6 (six)

TEACHING PAGE 6:

Discuss the kinds of trees you might see in the area where you live. If the season of the year permits, have the children make leaf collections to compare the different shapes and colors of the leaves (see activity section for art projects using leaves). Note that the seeds of these trees are different, too. Try to provide seeds for examination.

Read the sentences to the children. Discuss the sentences and the pictures. Have the children identify and circle the vocabulary words. Share seeds, pine cones, and so on. If you have them, show that pine cones come in different shapes and sizes. Read the first question. Give the children opportunity to answer. Guide responses if necessary. (Trees need water, sunlight, and good soil.)

Read the second question. Give the children an opportunity to answer. Guide responses, if necessary. (In nature the things that the trees need to grow are provided as part of God's Creation plan.)

ACTIVITY:

If your class has collected leaves, you might try these projects.

a) Provide newsprint or other paper about that weight. Have the children place the paper over the leaves and rub with the side of a crayon. This makes an impression of the structure of the leaf. An interesting pattern can be developed by moving the paper about and repeating the rubbing with different colors or shades of the same color.

b) Make an outline of a tree trunk and branches with black or brown banner paper. Have the children attach their collected leaves. This project is very effective with colored leaves in the autumn.

c) If you are unable to collect leaves, you may wish to have the children simulate a tree using 3 inch squares of tissue paper. Wrap the paper around the end of a pencil starting with the eraser in the center of the tissue square. Dip the tissue into white glue and apply gently to the paper branches. As the glue dries the tissue may be fluffed open to give at three-dimensional effect.

Page 7: Activity Page

VOCABULARY: sunlight, soil (water)

MATERIALS NEEDED: LIFEPAC Tablet, pencils, pictures of trees and seeds, Worksheets 3 and 4

TEACHING PAGE 7:

Review the various trees and seeds studied. Have the children match the seed to the tree (pictures).

Have a volunteer identify and read the direction sentences. Be sure all the children understand what they are to do. Have the page completed independently. Check it together.

ACTIVITY:

Provide Worksheets 3 and 4.

Have the children color and cut out the pictures of the seed, the seedling, a tiny tree and a large tree (Worksheet 3). They should glue them into the spaces on Worksheet 4, in the right order.

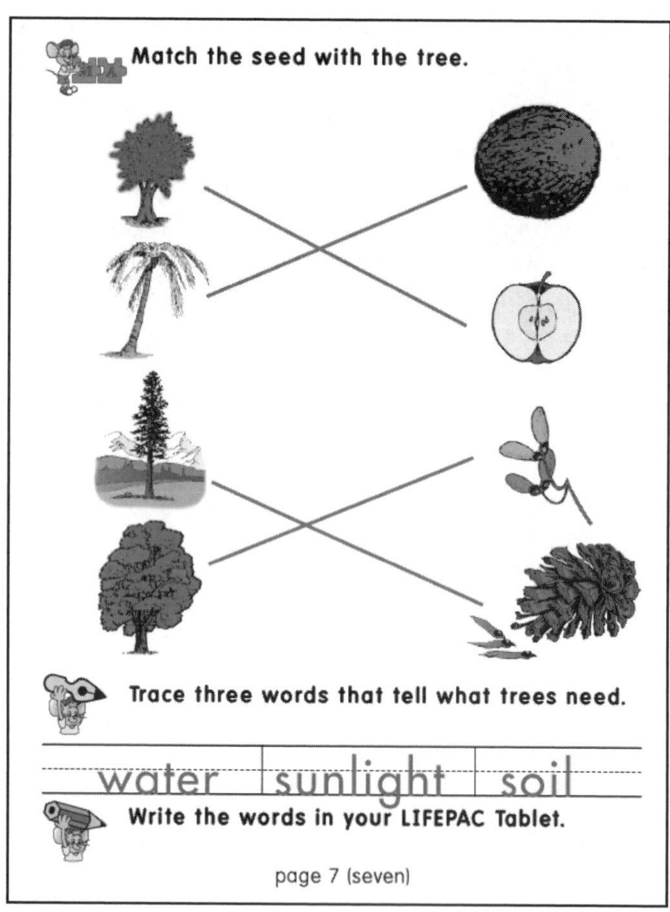

Match the seed with the tree.
Trace three words that tell what trees need.
water
sunlight
soil
Write the words in your LIFEPAC Tablet.
page 7 (seven)

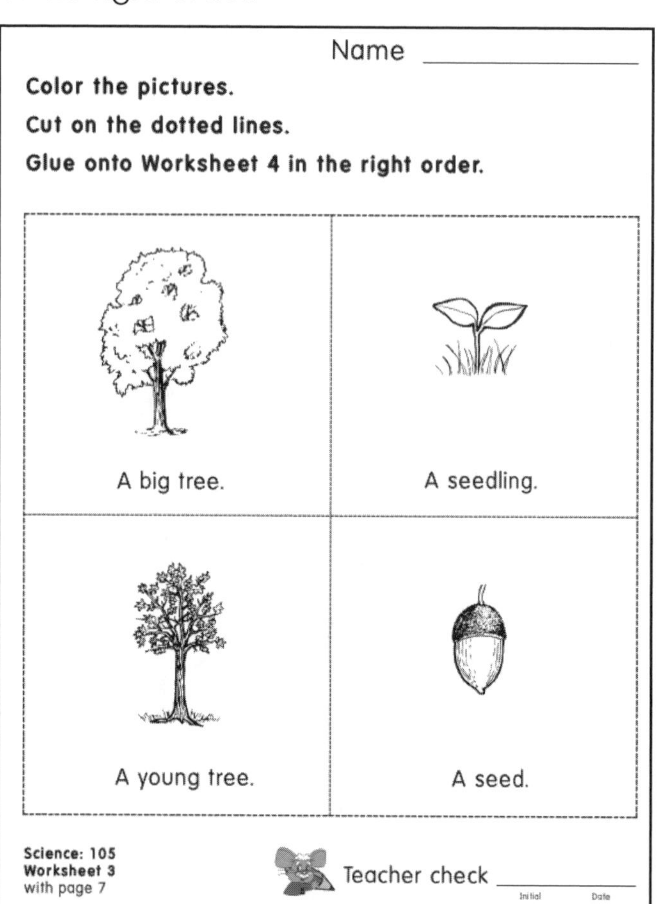

Name
Color the pictures.
Cut on the dotted lines.
Glue onto Worksheet 4 in the right order.
A big tree.
A seedling.
A young tree.
A seed.
Science: 105
Worksheet 3
with page 7
Teacher check
Initial
Date

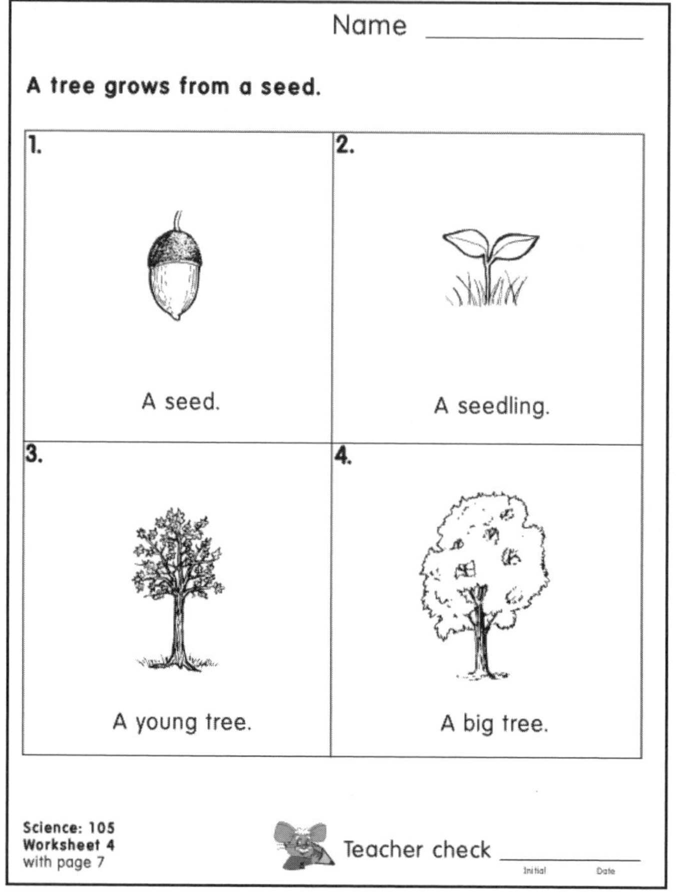

Name
A tree grows from a seed.
1.
A seed.
2.
A seedling.
3.
A young tree.
4.
A big tree.
Science: 105
Worksheet 4
with page 7
Teacher check
Initial
Date

Page 8: Small Plants

CONCEPT: Grass is a small plant.

OBJECTIVE: I can tell about some plants that grow in nature.

TEACHER GOALS: To encourage children to recognize the properties of grass as a plant that grows in nature.

PROCESSES: observing, comparing

READING INTEGRATION: main idea, recalling detail, vocabulary development, speaking in a group

VOCABULARY: plains, mountains, goats, (grass), (meadows)

MATERIALS NEEDED: pictures of grass growing in various places (plains, meadows), diagram of mature grass plant with seeds

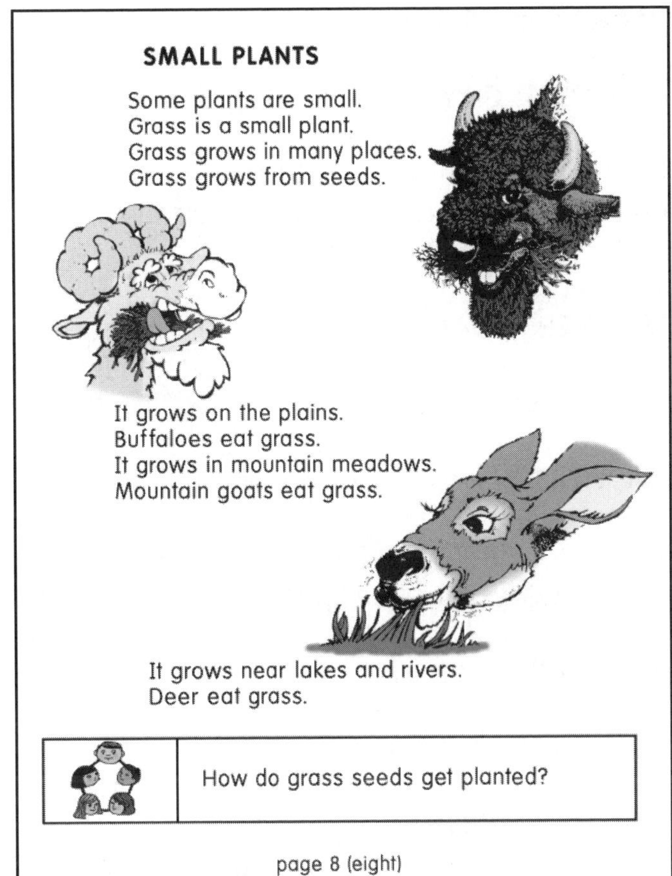
SMALL PLANTS
Some plants are small.
Grass is a small plant.
Grass grows in many places.
Grass grows from seeds.
It grows on the plains.
Buffaloes eat grass.
It grows in mountain meadows.
Mountain goats eat grass.
It grows near lakes and rivers.
Deer eat grass.
How do grass seeds get planted?
page 8 (eight)

TEACHING PAGE 8:

Show the pictures of grass. Promote discussion of the differences between grass and trees. Note that grass is much smaller. It is easily blown by the wind. Trees have woody hard trunks. Trees live a long time. Grass comes up new each year.

Show the diagram of a grass plant. Ask the children to identify the parts that are the same as the parts of a tree. Tell what parts are not part of both.

Read the sentences to the class or have them read by volunteers. Ask the children to find and circle the vocabulary words. Discuss the pictures. Compare the kinds of places shown.

Have the children tell where they have seen grass grow (besides their lawns).

Read the question. Have children contribute ideas of ways wild grasses might get planted.

Possible answers: Seeds could fall to the ground; they could stick to the fur of animals and fall off later; they could be blown by the wind.

ACTIVITY:

Obtain some grass seed from a local garden or farm supply center. Plant the seed in a shallow pan of soil. Water and watch it grow. Provide opportunity for the children to experiment with the needs of a grass plant (water, sunlight, and soil). If you cover part of the pan with opaque plastic, the grass will turn almost white. This color change is due to a lack of sunlight.

Page 9: Small Plants

CONCEPT: Grass needs sunlight, water, and soil.

OBJECTIVE: I can tell about some plants that grow in nature.

TEACHER GOAL: To encourage children to recognize the properties of grass as a plant that grows in nature.

PROCESSES: observing, comparing

READING INTEGRATION: main idea, recalling detail, following directions

VOCABULARY: leaf, leaves, stalk, (root)

MATERIALS NEEDED: Worksheet 5, pencils

TEACHING PAGE 9:

This page is a continuation of the previous one. No further preparation is necessary.

Continue with the reading and discussion of the sentences and pictures, paying particular attention to the diagram. Have the children find and circle the vocabulary words.

Have a volunteer find and read the direction sentence. When all understand the direction, have the page completed independently.

ACTIVITIES:

1. To extend the concept, have the children think of and share some ways grass is useful in nature. *Possible answers:* Some animals eat grass; the roots of grass help to keep the soil from eroding away.
2. Do Worksheet 5.

Have the children label the parts of the grass plant as on the diagram you have on display.

Have the children check their work together. Let them color the picture.

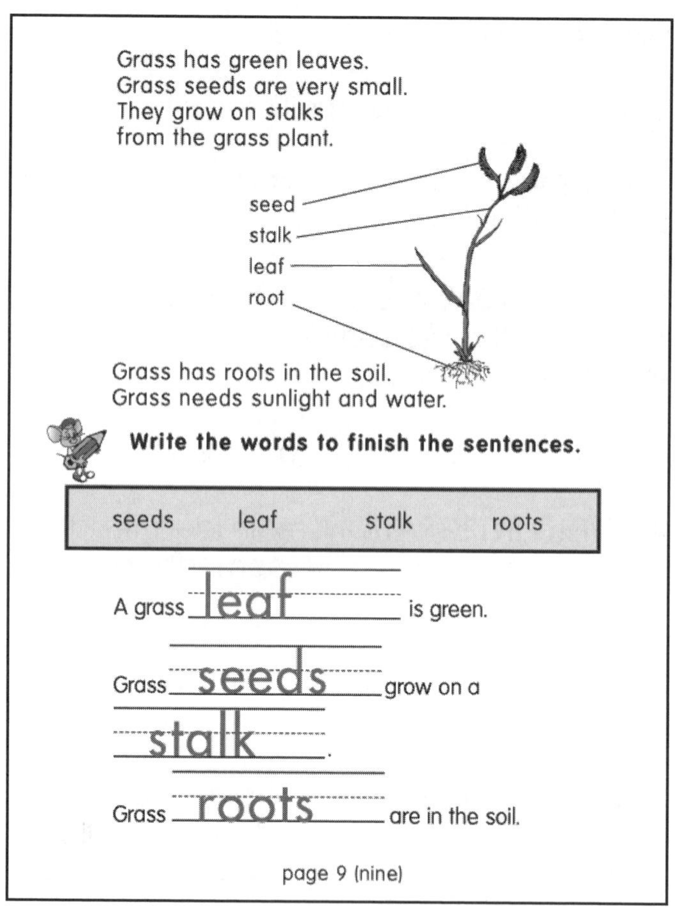
Grass has green leaves.
Grass seeds are very small.
They grow on stalks
from the grass plant.
seed
stalk
leaf
root
Grass has roots in the soil.
Grass needs sunlight and water.
Write the words to finish the sentences.
seeds leaf stalk roots
A grass leaf is green.
Grass seeds grow on a stalk.
Grass roots are in the soil.
page 9 (nine)

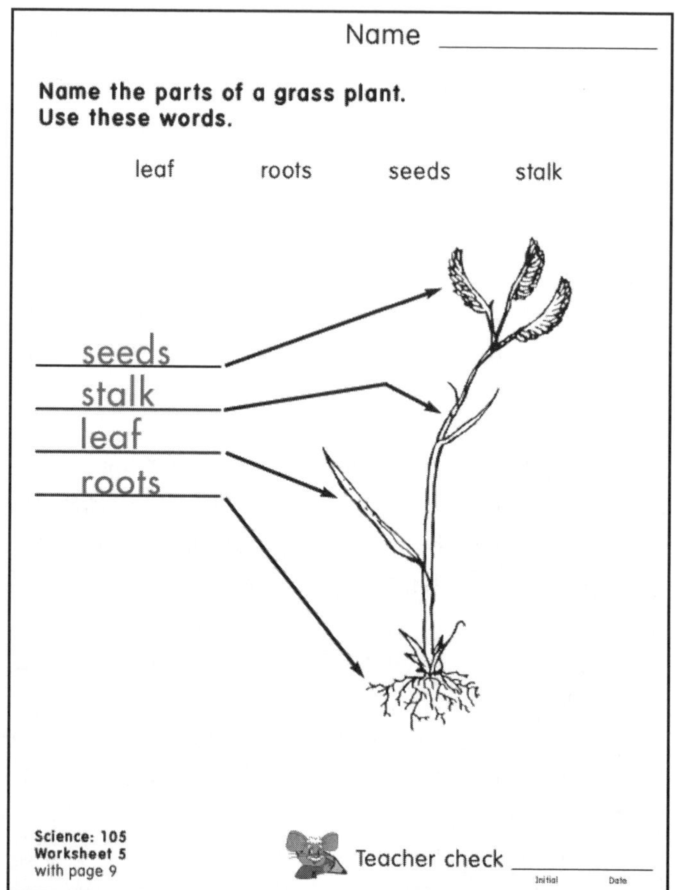
Name
Name the parts of a grass plant.
Use these words.
leaf roots seeds stalk
seeds
stalk
leaf
roots
Science: 105
Worksheet 5
with page 9
Teacher check
Initial Date

Page 10: Small Plants

CONCEPT: Many other small plants grow in nature.

OBJECTIVE: I can tell about some plants that grow in nature.

TEACHER GOALS: To teach the children to introduce several more types of small plants and to review relativity of size (as introduced in LIFEPAC 101).

PROCESSES: observing, comparing, predicting, measuring

READING INTEGRATION: vocabulary development, recalling detail

VOCABULARY: wild, flowers, berries, ferns, vines

MATERIALS NEEDED: pictures of small plants and shrubs that are found in nature

TEACHING PAGE 10:

Present the vocabulary. Match the vocabulary to the pictures of the plants.

Read each sentence to the group, or have it read by a volunteer. Discuss the pictures of the plants. Note similarities and differences. A small bush is larger than a large wild flower. A large fern is smaller than a small tree. *Discussion question:* This question reviews the idea that all plants need sunlight, water, and soil.

ACTIVITY:

If all of the children have planted their seeds, begin a measuring activity. At regular intervals, have the children graph the height of the plant. Use centimeters or inches as your standard unit of measurement.

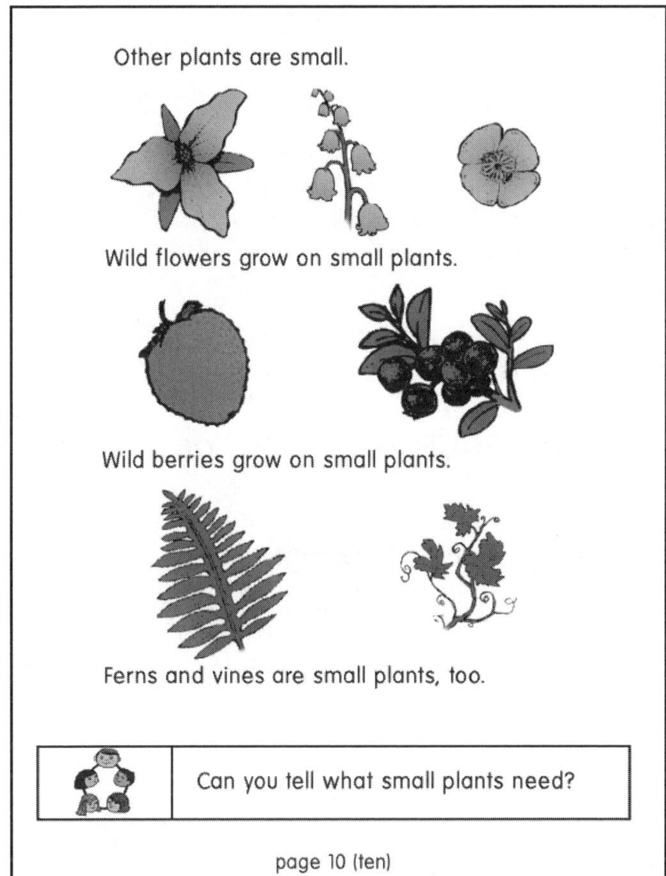
Other plants are small.
Wild flowers grow on small plants.
Wild berries grow on small plants.
Ferns and vines are small plants, too.
Can you tell what small plants need?
page 10 (ten)

Page 11: God Cares for Plants

CONCEPT: God takes care of plants that grow in nature.

OBJECTIVE: I can tell about some plants that grow in nature.

TEACHER GOAL: To develop appreciation for God's care of the plants of nature.

BIBLE REFERENCE: Psalms 147:7 and 8; Psalms 74:16

READING INTEGRATION: vocabulary development, following directions

MATERIALS NEEDED: pencils, Worksheet 6, crayons, LIFEPAC Tablet

TEACHING PAGE 11:

Review the needs of all plants (sunlight, water, and good soil). Present the Bible verses.

Read the sentences to the class, or have them read by volunteers.

Ask these questions: "Who gives the plants what they need?" "What does God provide for the plants?" "What would happen to plants if God did not send rain or sunlight?"

Have a child find and read the direction sentences. When all understand what to do, have the children complete the page and the Tablet activity independently. Give help as needed. Check the work together.

ACTIVITY:

Provide Worksheet 6.

Read the directions. Have the children read the words in the box.

Have the children write the words under the picture.

Check the work together.

Let the children color the pictures.

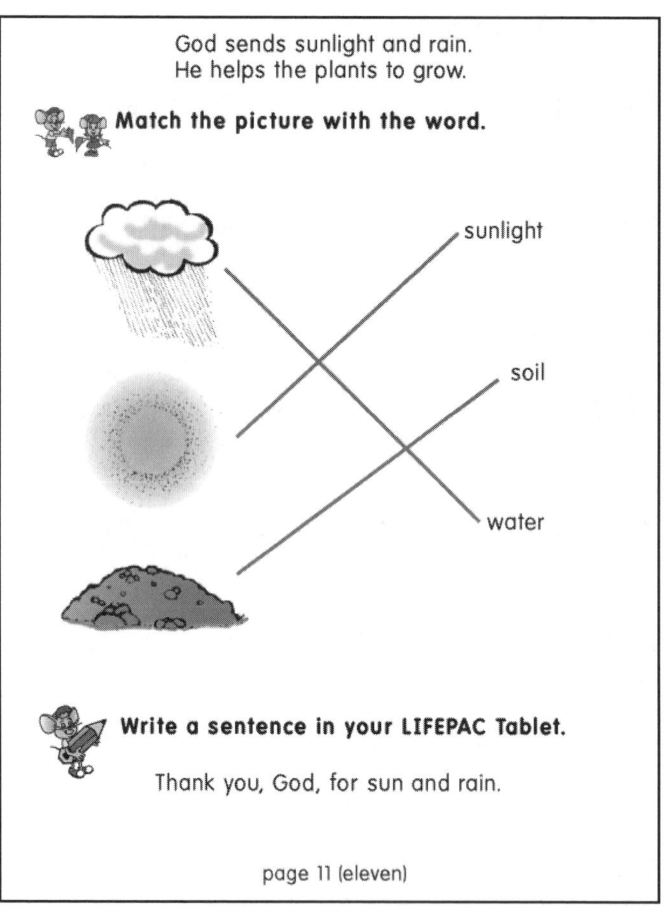

God sends sunlight and rain.
He helps the plants to grow.
Match the picture with the word.
sunlight
soil
water
Write a sentence in your LIFEPAC Tablet.
Thank you, God, for sun and rain.
page 11 (eleven)

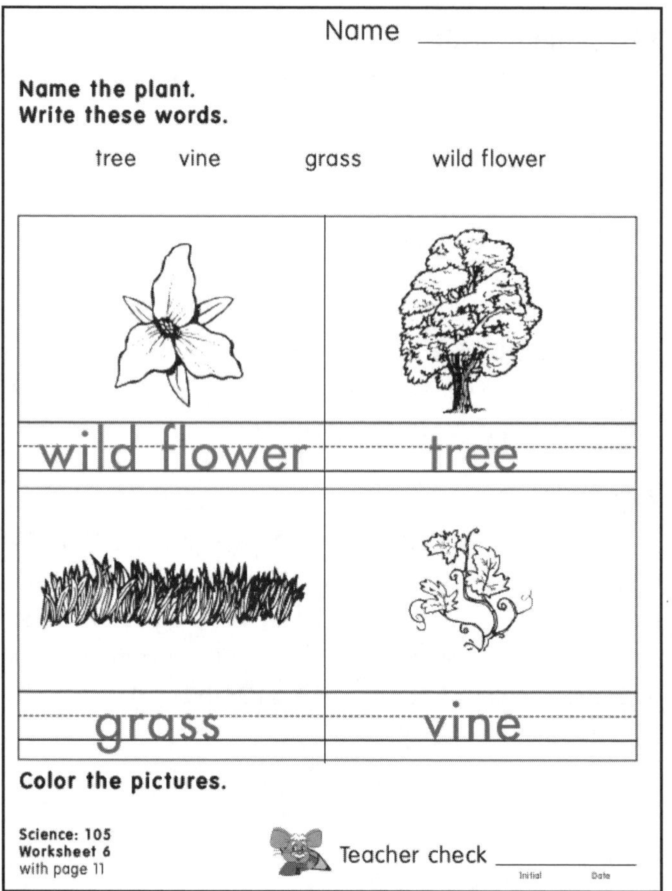

Page 12: Special Plants

CONCEPT: Some plants grow in special places.

OBJECTIVE: I can tell about some plants that grow in nature.

TEACHER GOAL: To help the children to understand that some plants are especially created by God to fit their environmental conditions.

PROCESSES: observing, comparing, predicting

READING INTEGRATION: vocabulary development, recalling detail, speaking in a group

VOCABULARY: desert, forest, damp, dark, mushroom, (cactus)

MATERIALS: pictures representing vocabulary words

TEACHING PAGE 12:

Present the vocabulary by matching the words with the corresponding pictures.

Read the sentences to the group or have them read by a volunteer.

Discuss the kinds of plants that might grow in a desert.

Note: Plants that grow in a desert must be able to get along with very little water and lots of sun. Most desert plants have spikes or thorns.

Discuss the kinds of plants that might grow in a damp rain forest.

Note: Plants of the rain forest must have lots of water. They can grow well in dark shaded places.

Discussion questions: Give the children a chance to contribute ideas. *Note:* A mushroom would dry up in the desert and a cactus would rot with too much water and too little sunlight in a rain forest.

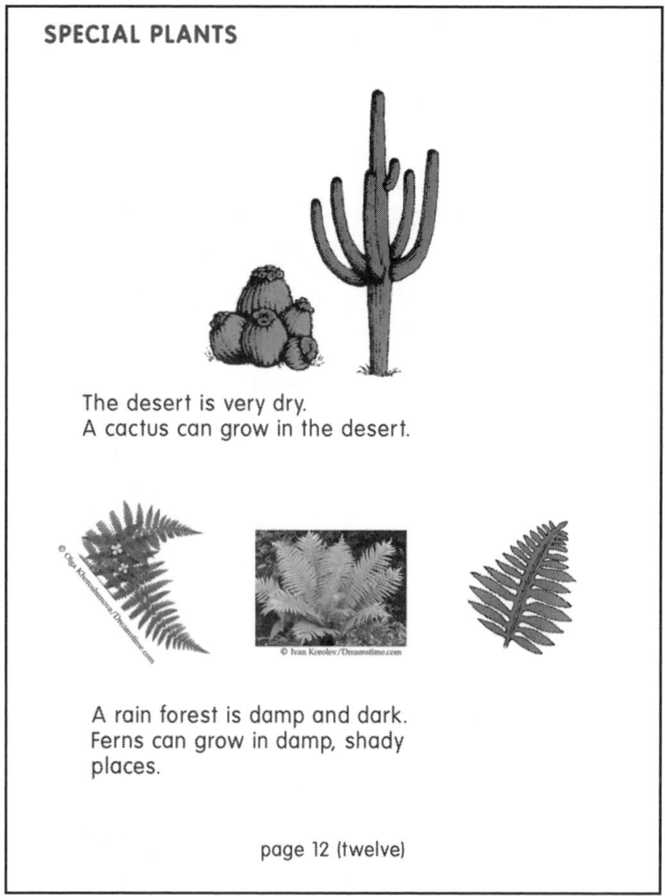

SPECIAL PLANTS

The desert is very dry.
A cactus can grow in the desert.

A rain forest is damp and dark.
Ferns can grow in damp, shady places.

page 12 (twelve)

ACTIVITIES:

1. Provide potted cactus for the children to examine and perhaps draw.
2. Give the children a chance to examine a mushroom (available at a grocery store).
3. Have them compare the two very different plants, finding likenesses and differences.

Page 13: Activity Page

MATERIALS NEEDED: crayons

TEACHING PAGE 13:

Ask a volunteer to read the directions.

Review the vocabulary words, *cactus* and *fern,* and the color word, *green.*

Have the children complete the page independently.

Page 14: Special Plants

CONCEPT: Some plants grow in special places.

OBJECTIVE: I can tell about some plants that grow in nature.

TEACHER GOAL: To reinforce the idea that many plants are created by God to fit a special environment.

PROCESSES: observing, comparing

READING INTEGRATION: vocabulary development, recalling detail, speaking in a group

VOCABULARY: lily pad, (seaweed)

MATERIALS NEEDED: pictures representing the vocabulary words

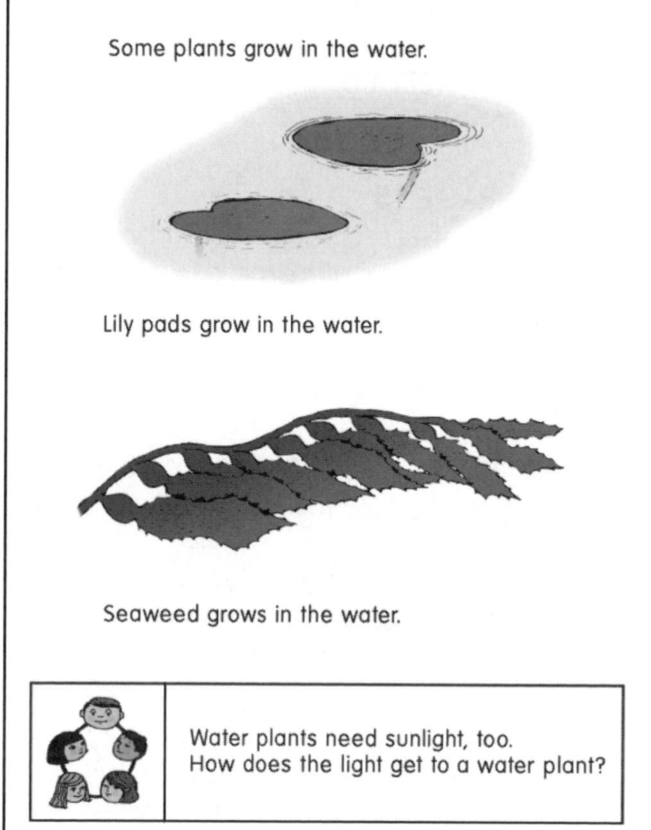

Some plants grow in the water.
Lily pads grow in the water.
Seaweed grows in the water.
Water plants need sunlight, too.
How does the light get to a water plant?
page 14 (fourteen)

TEACHING PAGE 14:

Present the vocabulary by matching the words with corresponding pictures.

Read the sentences to the group or have them read by a volunteer.

Discuss the two kinds of water plants.

Note: The leaf and blossom of a lily pad float on top of the water. The stem reaches down through the water where its roots are attached to the bottom of the pond or lake.

Seaweed grows entirely underwater.

Discussion question: Read it aloud or have it read.

Note: Sunlight filters through the water to the plant. You might hold up a clear glass of water to demonstrate how light passes through.

ACTIVITY:

You might set up an aquarium including some water plants or fish. This will demonstrate how plants (and animals) live underwater.

Page 15 : Activity Page

MATERIALS NEEDED: pencils, crayons, alphabet chart

TEACHING PAGE 15 :

Ask a volunteer to read the direction.

Have the children complete the page independently.

When the pictures are completed, discuss the ways the frog and the fish are using the lily pad.

Note: The frog sits on top waiting for insects, or perhaps just to rest and sun himself.

The fish hides in the shady places the lily pad makes in the water. The fish may find food around the lily pad stems.

Discussion question: Allow the children to speculate about the plant's roots.

Note: The roots are attached to the floor or bottom of the lake or pond. They serve as an anchor to hold the lily pad in place. New plants grow up from the roots.

Follow the dots and color the picture.
See who likes a lily pad.
START
Where are the roots of a water plant?
Teacher Check
Initial
Date
page 15 (fifteen)

ACTIVITY:

Provide green construction paper for the children to draw and cut out a lily pad. Provide a pattern if you feel it would be helpful. Let the children draw and color frogs to put on their lily pads.

Pages 16 and 17: Self Test 1

CONCEPT: Evaluate the children's progress

OBJECTIVE: I can tell about some plants that grow in nature.

READING INTEGRATION: following directions, main idea, recalling details

VOCABULARY: Review all vocabulary.

MATERIALS NEEDED: pencils, Worksheet 7, scissors, paste or glue

TEACHING PAGES 16 and 17:

Review the vocabulary words.

Practice matching the words to pictures.

Review the major concepts: Plants grow in nature; some plants are large; some plants are small; and some plants grow in special places.

The general proficiency of your group should dictate whether you choose to direct the self test or allow the children to proceed independently, once directions are given.

In either case you should be available to answer questions and to help with the vocabulary as needed.

Check the self test immediately. Review any concepts that were missed.

ACTIVITY:

Do Worksheet 7.

Have a child read the title.

Have another child read the directions. Instruct them to cut out the four words at the bottom and to paste the words in the box under the right picture.

Check the worksheet together.

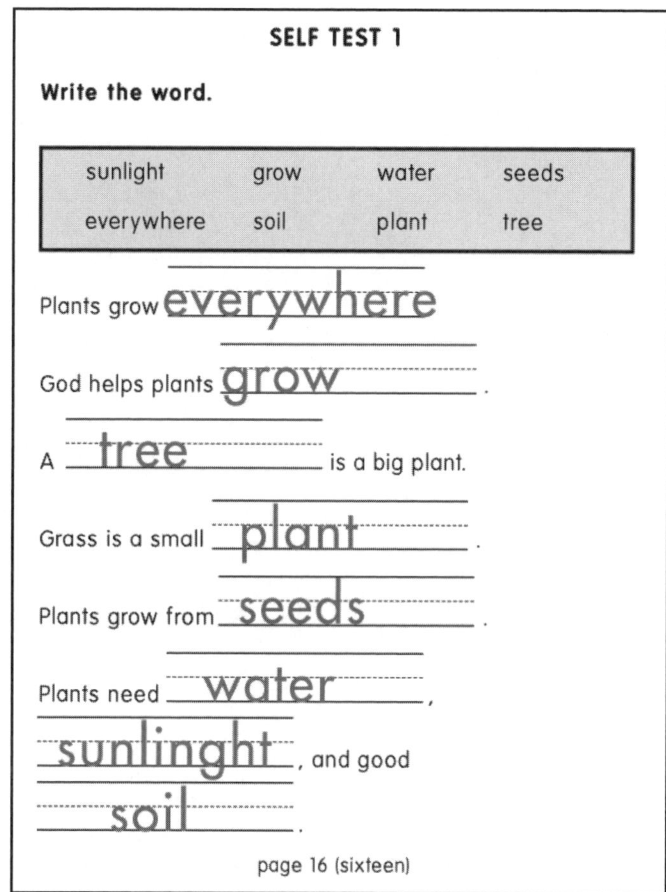

SELF TEST 1

Write the word.

sunlight	grow	water	seeds
everywhere	soil	plant	tree

Plants grow everywhere

God helps plants grow.

A tree is a big plant.

Grass is a small plant.

Plants grow from seeds.

Plants need water, sunlinght, and good soil.

page 16 (sixteen)

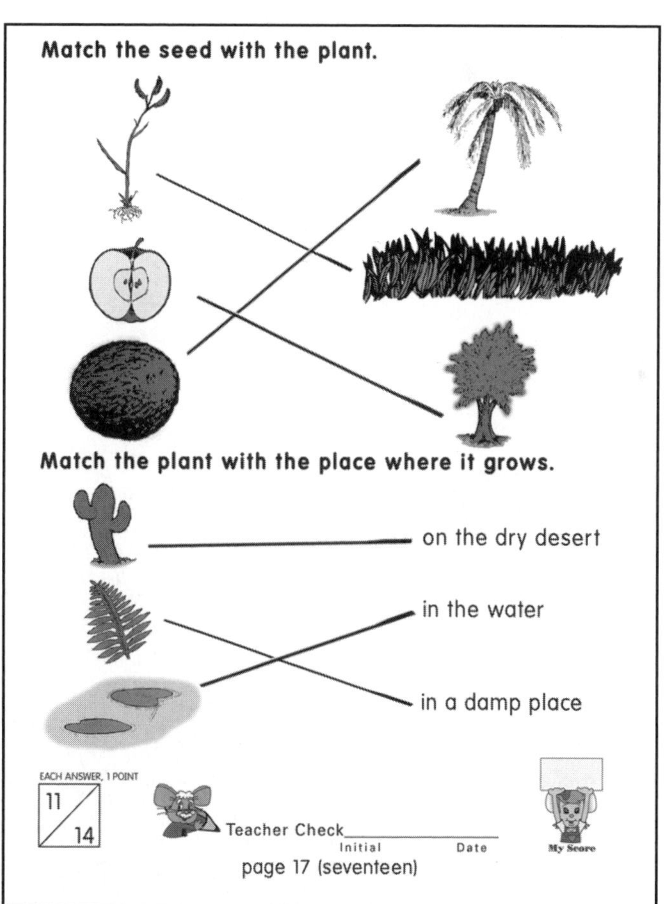

Match the seed with the plant.

Match the plant with the place where it grows.

on the dry desert

in the water

in a damp place

EACH ANSWER, 1 POINT

11/14

Teacher Check ________ Initial Date

My Score

page 17 (seventeen)

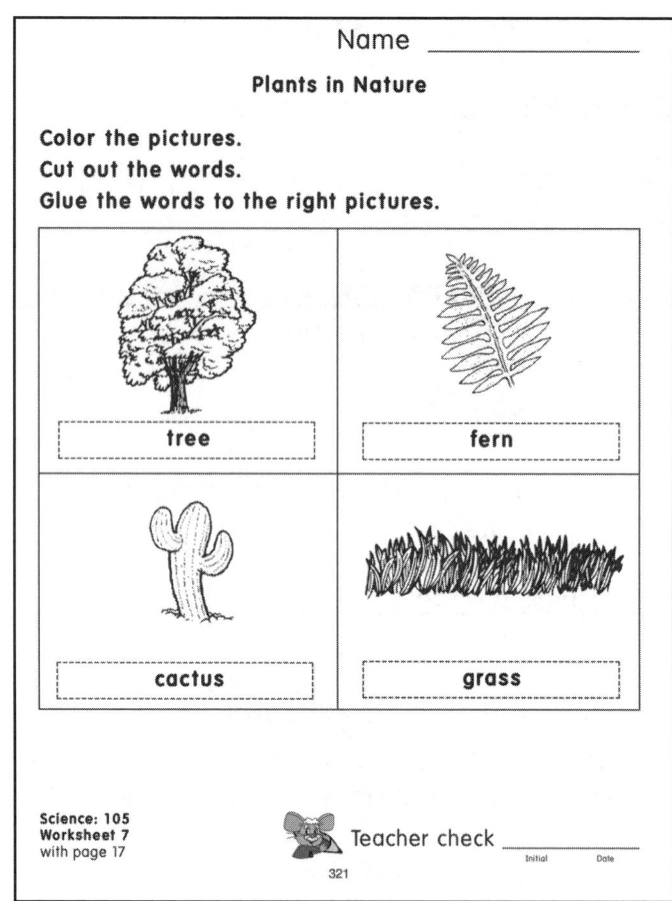
Name ____________

Plants in Nature

Color the pictures.
Cut out the words.
Glue the words to the right pictures.

tree	fern
cactus	grass

Science: 105
Worksheet 7
with page 17

Teacher check ____________
Initial Date

321

II. PART TWO

Page 18 : Plants on a Farm

CONCEPTS: Farmers grow many things. They must care for the plants they grow on the farm.

OBJECTIVE: I can tell about some plants that grow on a farm.

PROCESS: observing

READING INTEGRATION: rhyming, main idea, listening, speaking in a group

VOCABULARY: corn, hay, vegetables, wheat

MATERIALS NEEDED: pictures of plants growing on a farm, pictures representing the vocabulary words

TEACHING PAGE 18:

Provide some time for the children to share what they already know about what grows on a farm.

Present the vocabulary words by matching the words with corresponding pictures.

Read the poem aloud to the children. Read it again. Have the children follow along.

Spend some time discussing ways God helps the farmer take care of his plants.

Reread the poem together. Have the vocabulary and rhyming words identified.

ACTIVITIES:

1. Provide a book table including books about farm plants and how they are used.
2. To challenge the most capable child, do this activity:

Provide paper to make a book about a farm plant. The child should include pictures of the seed, the growing plant, the part or parts that are used, and the way the plant is used.

II. PLANTS ON A FARM

Wheat and corn,
Some vegetables,
Apples on a tree–
The farmer grows
So many things–
Food for you and me.

Corn for pigs and chickens,
Hay for cow and horse–
The farmer cares
For all his plants,
With God's help, of course.

page 18 (eighteen)

Page 19: Activity Page

MATERIALS NEEDED: crayons

TEACHING PAGE 19:

Have the children look at the picture.

Ask: "How do you think the farmer is feeling?" (happy, thankful)

"Why do you think he feels that way?" (He is glad his plant is growing so well and he is thankful for God's blessings on his crop.)

Ask for a volunteer to read the direction.

Have the children complete the page independently.

Color the farmer.
page 19 (nineteen)

Page 20: Grain Plants

CONCEPT: Farmers grow grain to feed animals and people.

OBJECTIVE: I can tell about some plants that grow on a farm.

PROCESSES: observing, classifying

READING INTEGRATION: recalling detail, vocabulary development

VOCABULARY: grain, pig, bread, cereal (corn, wheat, chicken, people)

MATERIALS: pictures representing vocabulary words

TEACHING PAGE 20:

Present the vocabulary by matching the words with the corresponding pictures.

Remind children that they have learned about grasses that grow in nature.

Grains are grasses that have been "tamed" and are grown by farmers.

Read the sentences to the children.

Have the vocabulary words identified.

Ask these questions:

"What kind of plant is grain?" (grass)

"Name two kinds of grain." (corn and wheat)

"Who eats corn?" (children, pigs, people)

"What are bread and cereal made of?" (wheat) (Some cereals are made of other grains.)

Read the discussion question. Have the children name some of the other grains (oats, rye, rice). Help them if necessary.

GRAIN PLANTS

Farmers grow grain.
Grain is a kind of grass.
Corn and wheat are grains.

Farmers grow corn.
Chickens, pigs, and people eat corn.

Farmers grow wheat.
Breads and cereals are made of wheat.

Can you name some other grains?

page 20 (twenty)

Page 21: Grains

CONCEPTS: Farmers grow grain to feed animals and people. Grains need water, sunlight, and good soil.

OBJECTIVES:
I can tell about some plants that grow on a farm.
I can tell what plants need to live and grow.

PROCESSES: observing, comparing

READING INTEGRATION: vocabulary development, following directions, speaking in a group

VOCABULARY: (hay)

MATERIALS NEEDED: pencils, pictures of hay in stacks or bales and of hay growing in a field

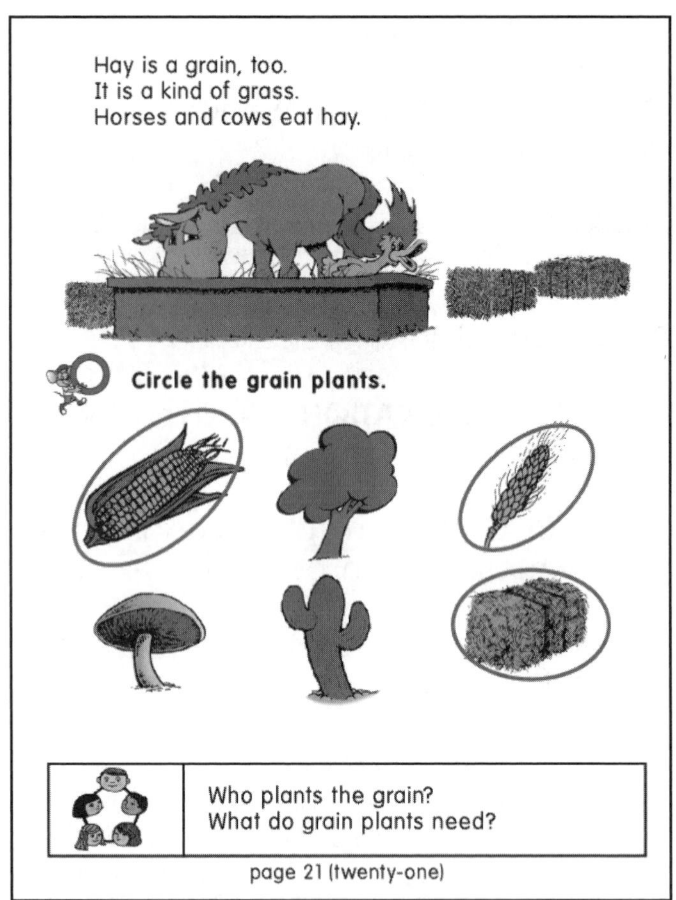

Hay is a grain, too.
It is a kind of grass.
Horses and cows eat hay.
Circle the grain plants.
Who plants the grain?
What do grain plants need?
page 21 (twenty-one)

TEACHING PAGE 21:

Present the vocabulary word. Show the pictures for identification and compare to the grains presented on page 20.

Read the sentences or have them read by a volunteer.

Note: The non-edible parts of the grain plants are called straw and are used as bedding materials and to help keep the barn clean.

Ask a volunteer to read the direction.

Have the children complete the activity independently.

Discussion questions: Read them or have them read. Have the children answer.

"Who plants the grains?" (the farmer)

"What do grain plants need?" (water, sunlight, and good soil)

ACTIVITY:

The sprouts of many grain plants are edible and an excellent addition to a salad, as a substitute for lettuce on a sandwich, or as a nutritious snack.

Sprouts can be grown easily in the classroom. Follow these steps:

a. Provide a large glass jar (mayonnaise jars are good) and wheat or alfalfa seeds.

b. Place about two tablespoons of seeds in the jar. Rinse with water. Pour off excess. Close jar and place on its side in a dark place.

c. Repeat the rinsing daily, returning the seeds to a dark place until the seeds begin to sprout.

d. When most of the seeds have sprouted, place them in the light so that the sprouts show green.

e. Sprouts keep well in a refrigerator for a week. If you continue frequent rinsing, they will continue to grow slowly.

Page 22: Vegetables

CONCEPT: Most of the vegetables we eat are grown by farmers.

OBJECTIVE: I can tell about some plants that grow on a farm.

PROCESSES: observing, classifying

READING INTEGRATION: vocabulary development, speaking in a group, main idea

VOCABULARY: peas, squash, spinach, tomatoes, (vegetables)

MATERIALS NEEDED: pictures representing vocabulary words, pictures of other vegetables (try to provide root vegetables as well as leafy vegetables), Worksheet 8, crayons

TEACHING PAGE 22:

Present the vocabulary. Match with corresponding pictures.

Discuss the part of the vegetable plant that we eat (leaves, stems, roots, and so on).

Read or have a volunteer read the sentences and picture captions.

Discuss the vegetables pictured. *Ask:* "What part of the plant do we eat?"

Discussion questions: Have a volunteer read the questions:

Can you name some vegetables a farmer might grow? Have the children name as many vegetables as they can. For each ask what part they eat.

Who eats the vegetables a farmer grows? (We all do. The farmer sends his vegetables to the stores where we can buy them.)

ACTIVITY:

Provide Worksheet 8.

Read the directions.

Discuss root and leafy vegetables.

Let the children do the page independently.

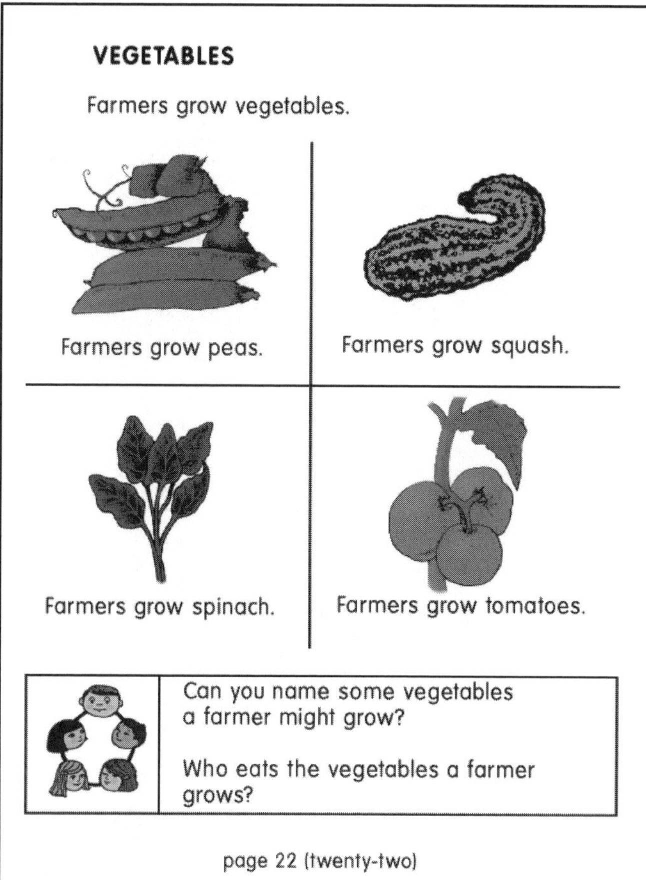

VEGETABLES
Farmers grow vegetables.
Farmers grow peas.
Farmers grow squash.
Farmers grow spinach.
Farmers grow tomatoes.
Can you name some vegetables a farmer might grow?
Who eats the vegetables a farmer grows?
page 22 (twenty-two)

Check the worksheets together. If children have the wrong color or vegetable type, have them correct it.

Name ______________

Draw a root vegetable. Color it.

Draw a leafy vegetable. Color it.

Science: 105
Worksheet 8
with page 22

Teacher check ______________
Initial Date

Page 23: Activity Page

MATERIALS NEEDED: pencils

TEACHING PAGE 23:

Read the sentences at the top of the page, or have them read by a volunteer. Compare the needs of vegetables with those of other plants. (All need sun, water, and good soil.)

Ask a volunteer to find and read the directions. When the children understand how to do the activities, have them complete the page independently. Check it together.

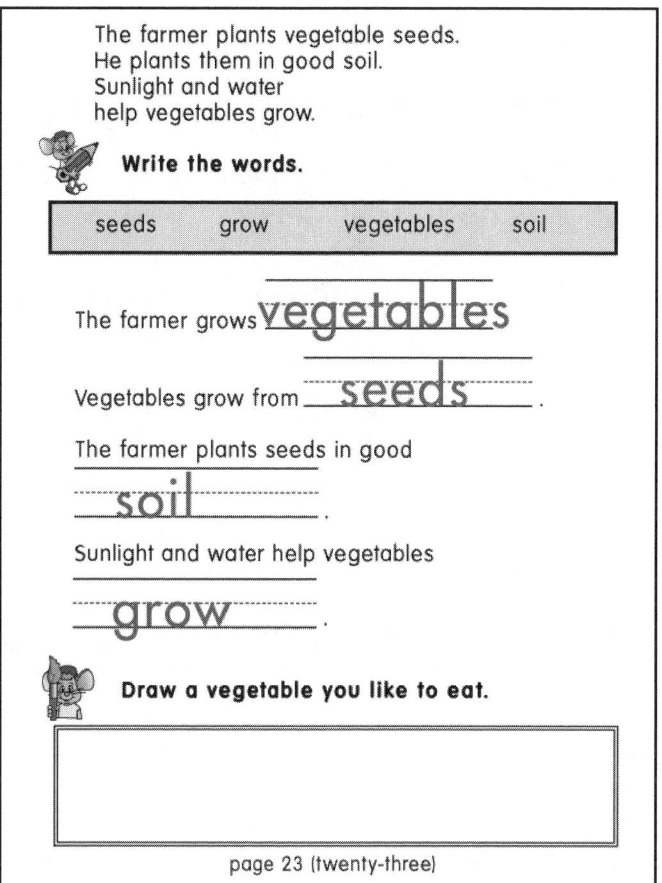

The farmer plants vegetable seeds.
He plants them in good soil.
Sunlight and water
help vegetables grow.

Write the words.

seeds grow vegetables soil

The farmer grows vegetables

Vegetables grow from seeds .

The farmer plants seeds in good soil .

Sunlight and water help vegetables grow .

Draw a vegetable you like to eat.

page 23 (twenty-three)

Page 24: Fruits

CONCEPT: Farmers grow fruit.

OBJECTIVE: I can tell about some plants that grow on a farm.

PROCESSES: observing, comparing, classifying

READING INTEGRATION: vocabulary development, speaking in a group, recalling detail

VOCABULARY: fruit, bushes, vines

MATERIALS NEEDED: pictures representing vocabulary words; assorted fruits or pictures of fruits selected from those that grow on trees, bushes, and vines; LIFEPAC Tablets, pencils

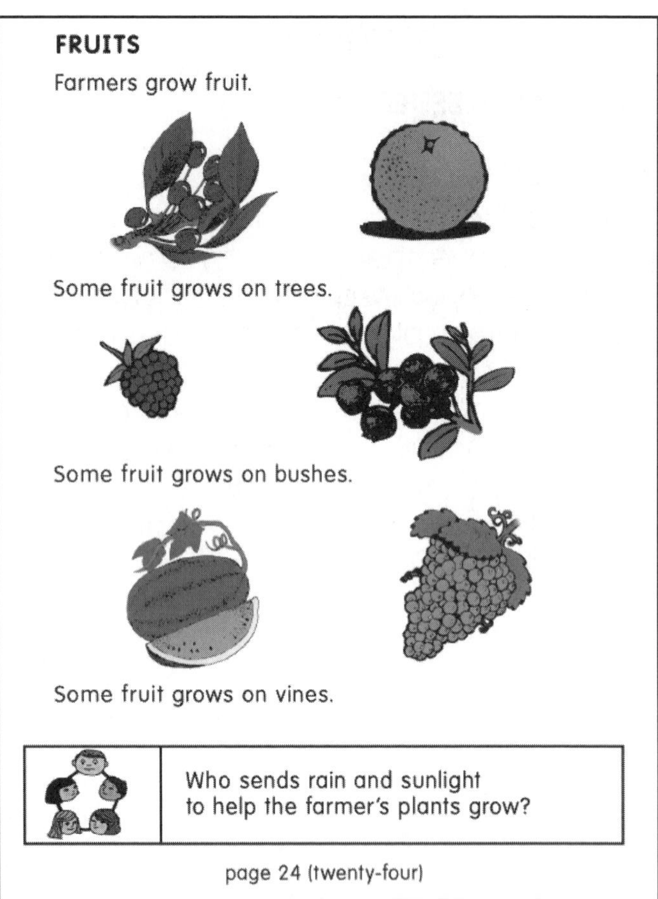
FRUITS
Farmers grow fruit.
Some fruit grows on trees.
Some fruit grows on bushes.
Some fruit grows on vines.
Who sends rain and sunlight
to help the farmer's plants grow?
page 24 (twenty-four)

TEACHING PAGE 24:

Present the vocabulary. Match the vocabulary with the corresponding pictures.

Display fruits (or pictures of fruits). Have the children sort (classify) the fruits into groups according to how they grow.

Read the sentences one by one. Discuss each in turn.

Discussion question: Have the questions read by a volunteer. "Who sends rain and sunlight to help the farmer's plants grow?" Let the children answer. (God)

Have the children write this sentence in their Tablets. *Thank you, God, for sunlight and rain.*

ACTIVITY:

Make a fruit salad. Have each child bring in one fresh fruit. Encourage them to bring a variety.

a. In the morning, peel and slice the fruit into a large bowl. Refrigerate if possible.

b. Have the children take turns stirring the fruit about once every half hour to mingle the juices.

c. Add miniature marshmallows and/or sour cream if desired.

d. Serve in the afternoon.

e. This may be an opportunity to introduce unfamiliar fruits if available (mango, pomegranate, papaya).

Page 25: Activity Page

MATERIALS NEEDED: crayons, pencils

TEACHING PAGE 25:

Ask for a volunteer to read the direction.

Have the children complete the activity independently. Check it together.

Discussion questions: "Can you name the vegetables?" (ask volunteers)

"Tell what fruits need." (sunlight, water, and good soil)

"Who takes care of the fruits?" (the farmer, with God's help)

Give each child an opportunity to participate.

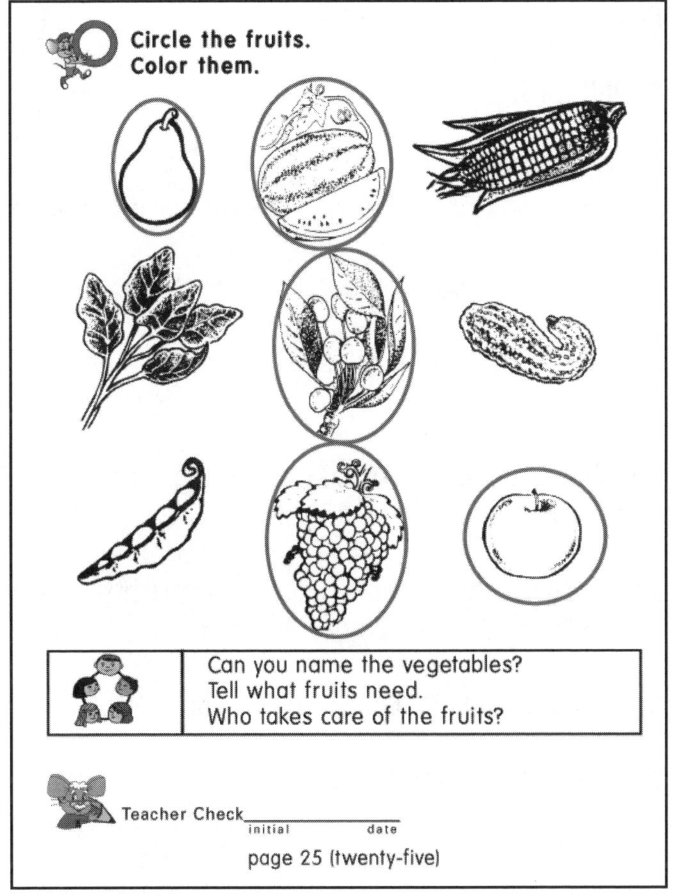

Pages 26 and 27: Self Test 2

CONCEPT: evaluation

OBJECTIVES:

I can tell about some plants that grow in nature.

I can tell about some plants that grow on a farm.

I can tell what plants need to live and grow.

READING INTEGRATION: following directions, main idea, recalling details

VOCABULARY: review all vocabulary from Sections 1 and 2

MATERIALS NEEDED: pencils, Worksheet

TEACHING PAGES 26 and 27:

Review the vocabulary and concepts for Sections 1 and 2.

Practice matching the vocabulary words to the pictures.

Review classifications skills (group grains, vegetables, fruits, and so on).

Read all the directions with the children. Be sure they are understood.

The general proficiency of your group will dictate whether you choose to direct the self test or allow the children to proceed independently, once directions are given. In either case you should be available to answer questions and to help with vocabulary, as needed.

Check the self test immediately. Go over the tests individually so that children learn their strengths and weaknesses.

ACTIVITIES:

1. Do Worksheet 9.

Read the direction or have a child read it.

Use this Worksheet for enrichment or for a retest for children who did not successfully complete the self test.

SELF TEST 2

Circle plants that grow on a farm.

Circle plants that grow in nature.

© Ivan Korolev/Dreamstime.com

page 26 (twenty-six)

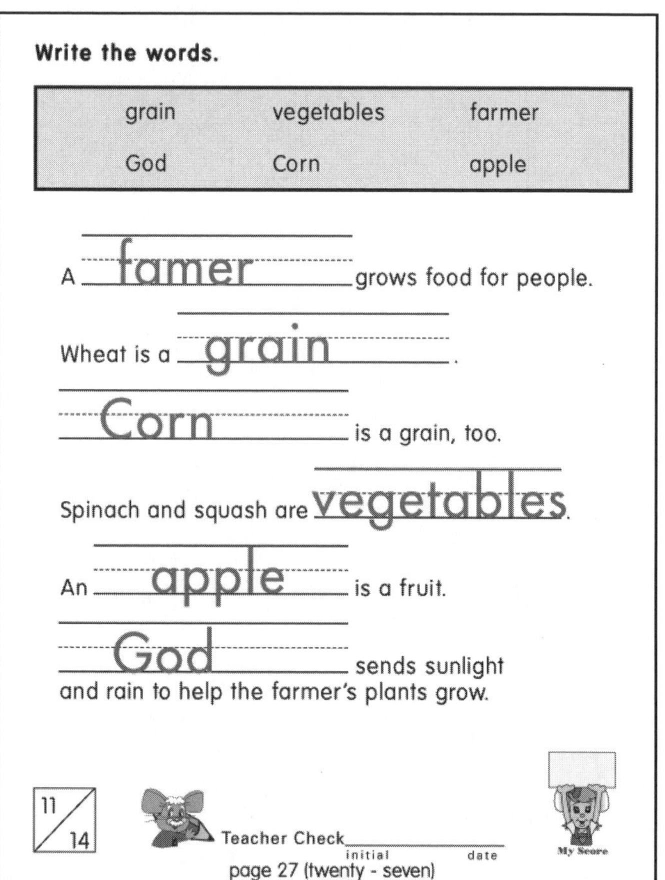

Write the words.

grain	vegetables	farmer
God	Corn	apple

A famer grows food for people.

Wheat is a grain.

Corn is a grain, too.

Spinach and squash are vegetables.

An apple is a fruit.

God sends sunlight and rain to help the farmer's plants grow.

11/14

Teacher Check ________ initial date

My Score

page 27 (twenty - seven)

2. Have the children who need the review go over the first two sections with their parents or a classroom helper. Then give the worksheet as a second check.

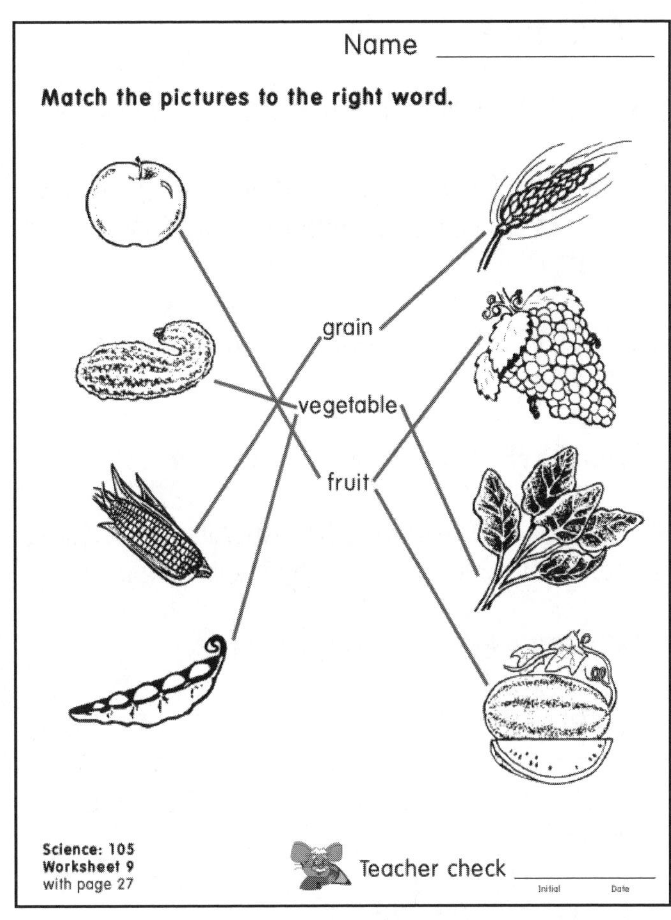

Name
Match the pictures to the right word.
grain
vegetable
fruit
Science: 105
Worksheet 9
with page 27
Teacher check
Initial
Date

III. PART THREE

Page 28: Plants at Home

CONCEPT: Many plants can be grown at home, in a yard, a window box, or in the house.

OBJECTIVE: I can tell about some plants that grow at home.

PROCESSES: observing, classifying

READING INTEGRATION: listening, rhyming, vocabulary development, main idea

VOCABULARY: (garden, yard)

MATERIALS NEEDED: pictures of plants growing in and around the home, Worksheet 10, crayons, LIFEPAC Tablets, pencils

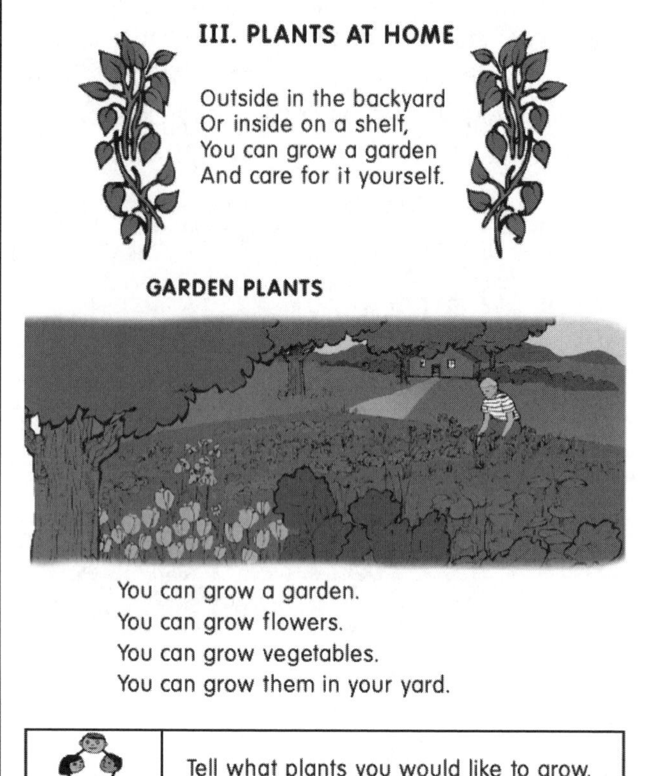

III. PLANTS AT HOME
Outside in the backyard
Or inside on a shelf,
You can grow a garden
And care for it yourself.
GARDEN PLANTS
You can grow a garden.
You can grow flowers.
You can grow vegetables.
You can grow them in your yard.
Tell what plants you would like to grow.
page 28 (twenty-eight)

TEACHING PAGE 28:

Display the pictures of plants that are grown around the home. Have the children tell what kind of plants are most often grown at home (probably flowers, green plants, and a few vegetables and fruits). Discuss reasons people might have plants around their home. (To make the house look nice. To provide fruits and vegetables for the family.)

Read the poem aloud to the class. Ask a child to tell the main idea of the poem in his own words. Reread the poem with the children reading along in chorus.

Read the sentences to the children or have them read by volunteers.

Discussion sentence: "Tell what plants you would like to grow." Let each of the children contribute ideas.

ACTIVITIES:

1. Have the children write the poem in their Tablets.
2. For those with less ability have them write this sentence. "I can grow a garden."
3. Provide Worksheet 10.

Read the directions. Talk about flowers that grow around the yard.

Have the children point out flowers they recognize.

Let them complete the Worksheet.

Check to see that they have colored only the flowers.

Name
Color the flowers in the garden.
Science: 105
Worksheet 10
with page 28
Teacher check
Initial
Date

Page 29: Activity Page

MATERIALS NEEDED: seeds (radishes, marigolds, or some other seed suited to small gardens), space or box for planting, Worksheet 11 and 12, pencils, scissors, paste or glue, crayons

TEACHING PAGE 29:

Show the children the materials they will use. Explain that this page will tell them what to do.

As you show the seeds ask the children what they will become.

Ask: "How do you think the seeds know what kind of plant to be."

Encourage acknowledgment of God's plan for all things that live and grow .

Read through the directions for planting a small garden. Ask the children to tell the directions in the right order. "What do you do first, second, and so on?"

If you have planting space at school, go through each step as you plant your garden.

Give the children a chance to share in the experience.

If you are using cups in which to plant, modify the steps as follows:

1) Put soil into your cup.

2) Make small holes in the soil with your pencil. (Adjust depth of hole according to directions on seed packet).

3) Place seeds into the holes.

4) Cover the seeds with soil.

5) Water your seeds regularly.

6) Watch the plants grow.

Sequencing activity: Read the directions to the class. Have them look at the pictures carefully, then number them as they should go.

Discuss some plants people might grow in a garden. Discuss what garden plants need to live and grow.

ACTIVITIES:

1. Do Worksheets 11 and 12.

Worksheet 11 has pictures of a seed, seedling, plant with flower, and plant with fruit. The children are to color, cut out, and paste the pictures in order onto Worksheet 12.

Check the work together and discuss the life cycle of several other familiar plants.

2. In their Tablets have the children write this sentence. *Garden plants need sunlight, water, and good soil.*

Plant a garden.
Get a package of seeds.
Choose a small spot in your yard.
Dig up the soil.
Make rows in the soil.
Put seeds in the rows.
Cover the seeds with soil.
Water your garden.
Watch the plants grow.
Number the pictures 1, 2, 3 to show how they should go.
1
3
2
page 29 (twenty-nine)

Name ______________

Color the pictures.
Cut them apart.
Put them in the order they should go. Glue the pictures on Worksheet 12.

Science: 105
Worksheet 11
with page 29

Teacher check ______________
Initial Date

Name ______________

See how the pumpkin grows.
Put the pictures in the proper order.

Science: 105
Worksheet 12
with page 29

Teacher check ______________
Initial Date

Page 30: House Plants

CONCEPT: You can grow plants inside the house.

OBJECTIVES:

I can tell about some plants that grow at home.

I can tell what plants need to live and grow.

PROCESSES: observing, classifying, predicting

READING INTEGRATION: vocabulary development, speaking in a group

VOCABULARY: flowers, ivy, leafy, house plant

MATERIALS NEEDED: pictures representing vocabulary, include several examples of house plants, have examples of the living plants if available

HOUSE PLANTS
You can grow a plant in the house.
You can grow flowers.
You can grow ivy.
You can grow leafy plants.
Can you grow food plants in the house?
What do house plants need?
Who gives house plants what they need?
page 30 (thirty)

TEACHING PAGE 30:

Present the vocabulary. Match the vocabulary with the corresponding pictures.

Read the sentences to the children or have them read by a volunteer.

Identify the vocabulary words. Using the picture, have the children identify flowering houseplants, ivy, and leafy plants.

Discussion questions: Read each question separately and discuss.

"Can you grow food plants in the house?" (Some people grow herbs indoors. Chives, parsley, rosemary, and so on are used for seasoning foods.)

"What do houseplants need?" (Sunlight (special plant lights are also used), water, and good soil.)

"Who gives houseplants what they need?" (The people who have them, perhaps the children do. God gives the sunlight, soil, and water so that they can provide them to their plants.)

ACTIVITY:

This would be a good opportunity to have a visitor who specializes in indoor plants come and visit the class (a florist, a nurseryman, or perhaps a qualified parent). Check your local sources.

Page 31: Activity Page

VOCABULARY: sweet potato, (glass)

MATERIALS NEEDED: sweet potato, glass, toothpicks, carrot tops, flat dish, pebbles

TEACHING PAGE 31:

Read the sentences to the class, or have them read by a volunteer. Prepare the sweet potato as directed. If the potato is too small for the glass, prop it up by inserting toothpicks that will hold it up.

Read the directions for the activity at the bottom of the page. Review the words to be used. Have the children fill in the blanks and read the completed sentence aloud.

ACTIVITIES:

1. Grow a carrot top garden. This can be a class project or can be done individually in the discovery center.
   a) Put the carrot top into a flat dish .
   b) Put pebbles around it.
   c) Put water in the dish. Keep it wet.
   d) Watch the carrot top grow. As the carrot top is kept moist it will grow roots and send up shoots of green leaves.
2. As a measuring activity have the children keep daily track of the height of the carrot leaves. Use centimeters or inches as the unit of measurement.
3. Birdseed also makes an interesting house plant.

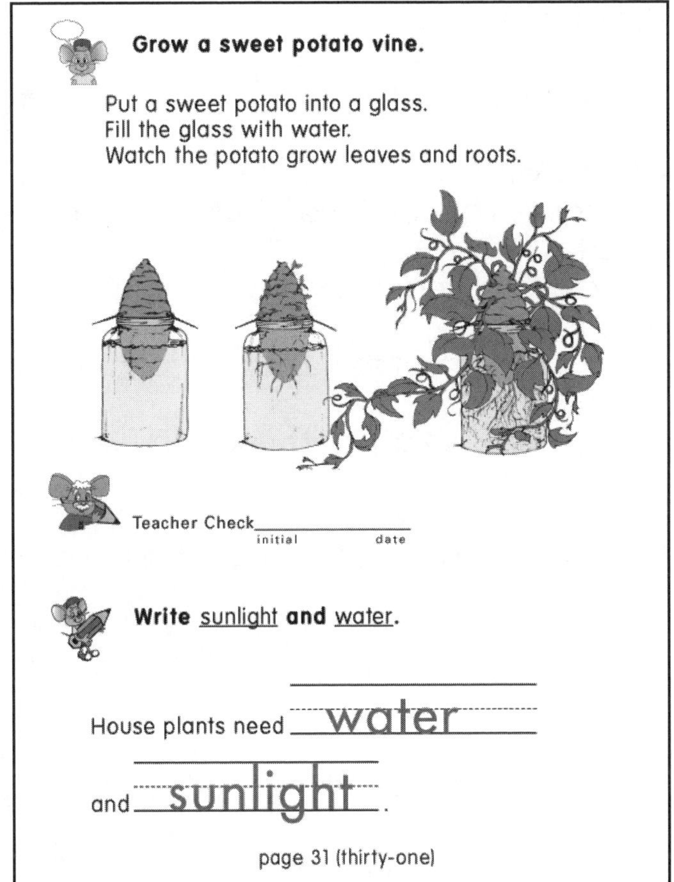
Grow a sweet potato vine.

Put a sweet potato into a glass.
Fill the glass with water.
Watch the potato grow leaves and roots.

Teacher Check ____________
initial date

Write sunlight and water.

House plants need water

and sunlight.

page 31 (thirty-one)

Pages 32 and 33: Self Test 3

CONCEPT: evaluation

OBJECTIVES:
I can tell about some plants that grow in nature.
I can tell about some plants that grow on a farm.
I can tell about some plants that grow at home.
I can tell what plants need to live and grow.

READING INTEGRATION: following directions, recalling details

VOCABULARY: Review all LIFEPAC vocabulary words.

MATERIALS NEEDED: pencils

TEACHING PAGES 32 and 33:

Review the vocabulary words and concepts for the entire LIFEPAC, with special emphasis on Section 3.

Read through the directions for the self test with the group. Answer any questions they might have.

The general proficiency of your group will dictate whether you choose to direct the self test or allow the children to proceed independently, once directions are given. In either case, you should be available to answer questions and help with vocabulary, as needed.

Check the self test immediately. Go over the tests individually so that the child sees his strengths and weaknesses. Review all concepts missed.

For those children who need extra help, have them work with a classroom helper or a parent to prepare for the LIFEPAC Test.

SELF TEST 3

Circle plants in nature.

Circle plants on a farm.

Circle plants in the house.

Circle words that tell what plants need.

grass water
sunlight soil

page 32 (thirty-two)

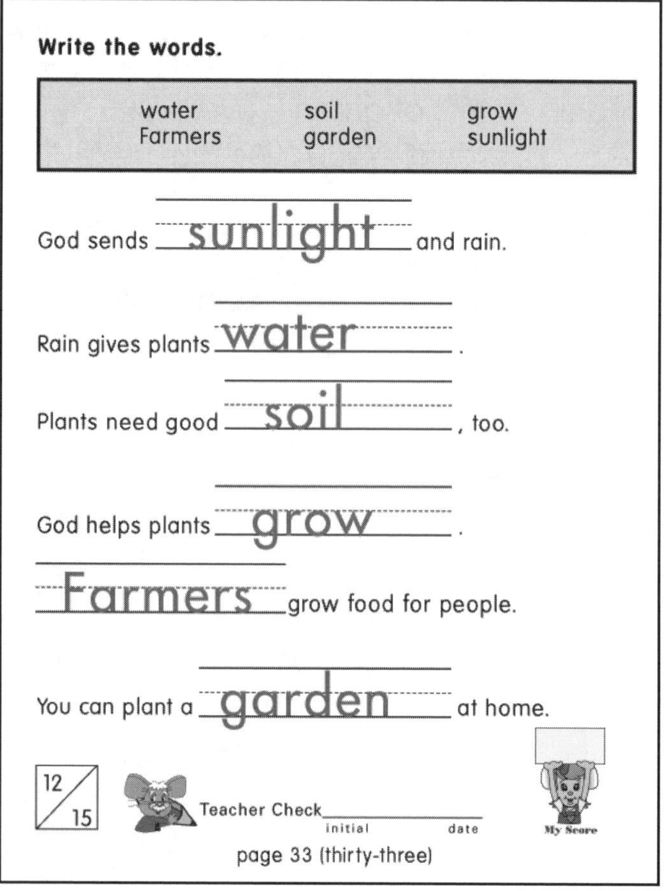
Write the words.

water	soil	grow
Farmers	garden	sunlight

God sends sunlight and rain.

Rain gives plants water.

Plants need good soil, too.

God helps plants grow.

Farmers grow food for people.

You can plant a garden at home.

12/15 Teacher Check ______ initial date

My Score

page 33 (thirty-three)

LIFEPAC TEST AND ALTERNATE LIFEPAC TEST:

Administer the test to the class as a group. Ask to have directions read or read them to the class. In either case, be sure that the children clearly understand. Put examples on the board if it seems necessary. Give ample time for each activity to be completed before going on to the next.

Correct immediately and discuss with the child.

Review any concepts that have been missed.

Give those children who do not achieve the 80% score additional copies of the worksheets and a list of vocabulary words to study. A parent or a classroom helper should help in the review.

When the child is ready, give the Alternate LIFEPAC Test. Use the same procedure as for the LIFEPAC TEST.

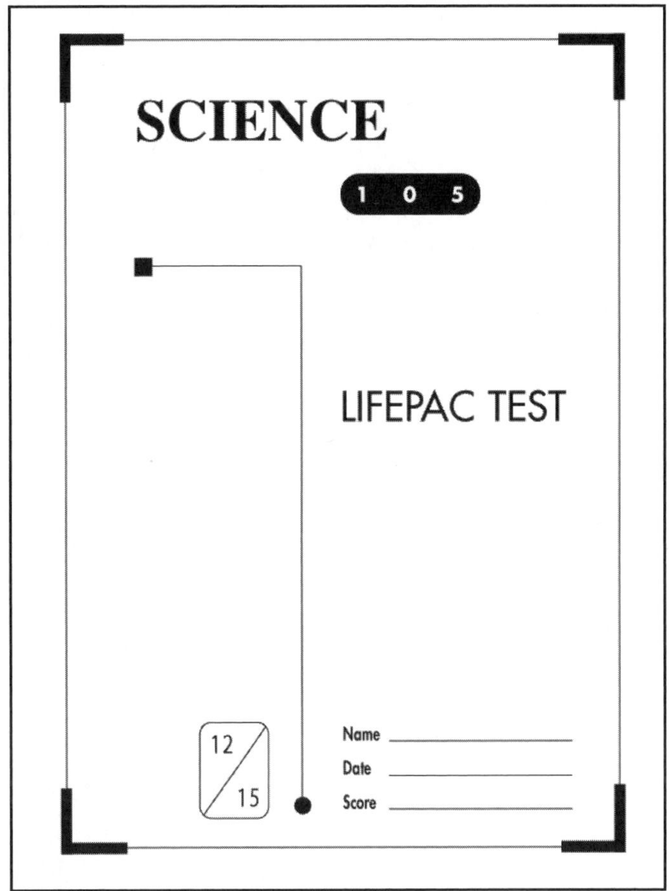

SCIENCE

105

LIFEPAC TEST

12/15

Name ______

Date ______

Score ______

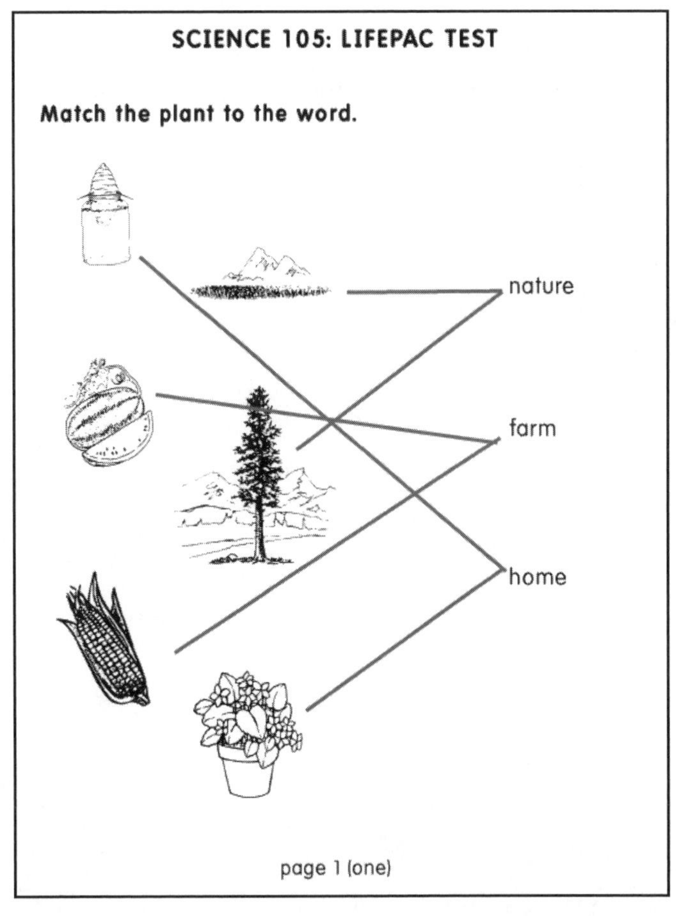

SCIENCE 105: LIFEPAC TEST

Match the plant to the word.

page 1 (one)

Number the picture 1, 2, 3 to show how they should go.

1 3 2

Write the words.

desert	grains	trees
food	soil	water

Plants need sunlight, water, and good soil.

Farmers grow food for people.

Apples grow on trees.

A cactus grows in the desert.

page 2 (two)

Seaweed grows in the water.

Corn and wheat are grains.

NOTES

page 3 (three)

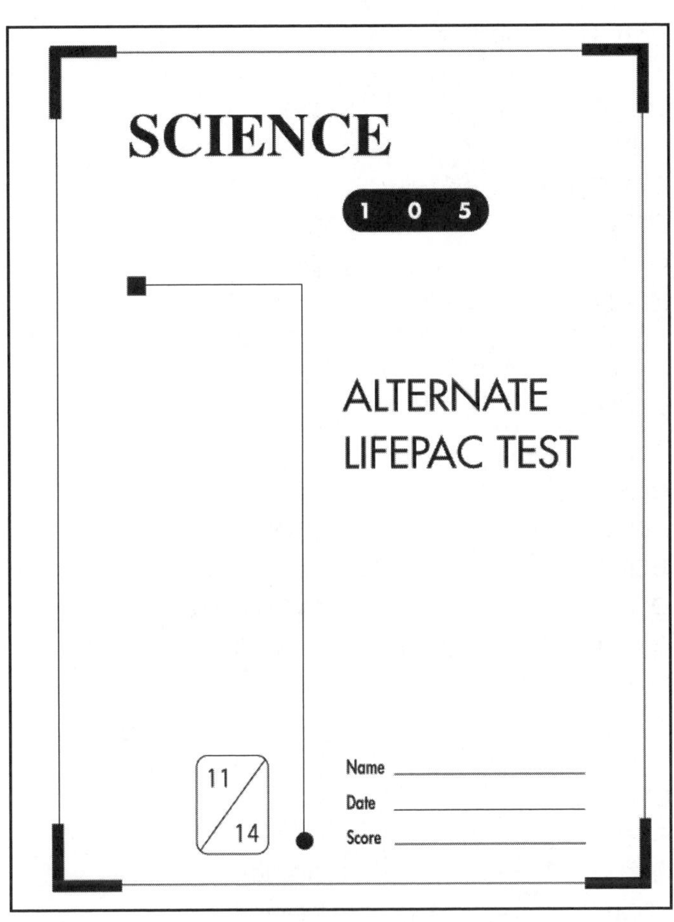
SCIENCE
1 0 5
ALTERNATE
LIFEPAC TEST
11
14
Name
Date
Score

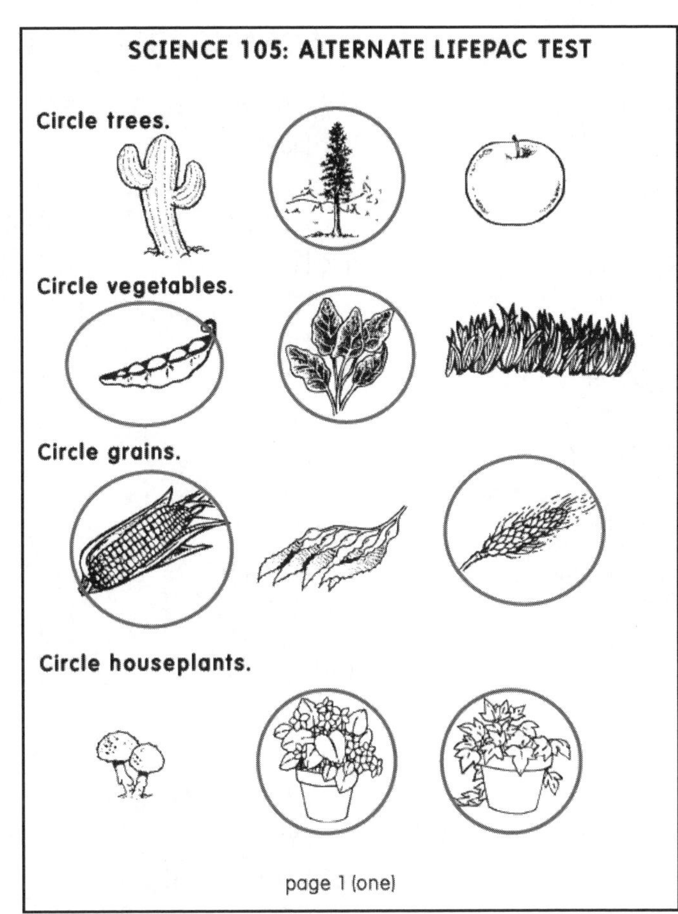
SCIENCE 105: ALTERNATE LIFEPAC TEST
Circle trees.
Circle vegetables.
Circle grains.
Circle houseplants.
page 1 (one)

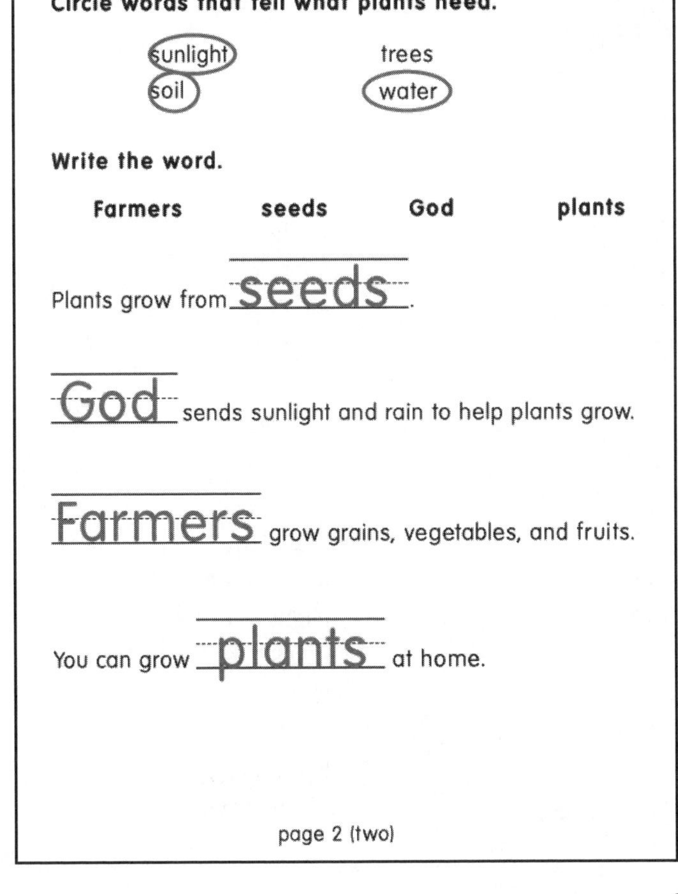
Circle words that tell what plants need.
sunlight
trees
soil
water
Write the word.
Farmers
seeds
God
plants
Plants grow from seeds.
God sends sunlight and rain to help plants grow.
Farmers grow grains, vegetables, and fruits.
You can grow plants at home.
page 2 (two)

NOTES
page 3 (three)

SCIENCE 101–110: CUMULATIVE WORD LIST

act
air
almost
angry
animal
answer
anything
apple
atom
autumn
ax
back
banana
bear
beat
belong
berries
better
big
bigger
bird
bitter
black
blue
board
body
bowl
brain
bread
breakfast
breathe
brown
buds
buffalo
build
burn
bushes
cactus
cacti
cage
calf
cannot
car
cat
catch
cereal
change
changes
check
cheese
chick
chicken
chop
church
circle
cities
clean
climate
clippers
clock
cloud
coal
coconut
cold
color
community
cone
cooler
cook
corn
cover
cow
creature
cub
damp
dark
date
deer
den
desert
dew
different
dinner
dog
dolphin
donkey
doorstop
dot
dove
down
drink
drive
driving
drop
dry
eagle
eaglet
ears
earth
easier
easily
easy
eat
eggs
electricity
elephants
energy
engines
exercise
eye
eyes
fact
fantasy
farm
farmer
feather
feeling
feet
fern
first
fish
fisherman
fit
flag
flower
fluffy
force
food
forest
forth
fruit
fuel
fulcrum
garden
gasoline
gear(s)
gills
giraffe
glass
goat
goldfish
good
grain
grass
grassland
green
grew
group
grown-up
guard
hamster
hands
happy
harm
hay
healthy
hear
heaven
heavy
hedge
help
herd
high
hippopotamus
hole
home
honey
horse
hot
hours
house
house plant
hunter
important
inclined plane
invisible
ivy
jump
jumping
kitchen

kitten
knife
lake
land
leaf
leaves
lemons
lemonade
lever
lift
lilypad
lion
light
living
lizard
load
long
loud
louder
low
machine
magnifying glass
make-believe
mane
maple
march
Mary
match
meadow
meat
massage
metal
microscope
middle
milk
morning
mouse
mountain
move
moving
munch
mushroom
muscles
mysterious
mail
narrow
nature

nerves
nest
nestling
Noah
noise
nose
nuclear
nutcracker
oak
oar
oarlock
ocean
o'clock
oil
open
orange
outer
outside
owner
pain
pair
parakeet
peanut butter
peas
pencil
pick
picnic
picture
pig
pine
pink
pitch
place
plains
plant
playing
pliers
plow
prairie
praise
pulley(s)
purple
push
push-up
raccoon
rain
rainbow

raindrop
ramp
read
rectangle
red
replace
rest
rhythm
ring
river
roadrunner
rock
root
rope(s)
rough
run
sad
safe
sailing ships
salty
same
sand
sandwich
school
scientist
scissors
seaweed
seashore
season
screw
screwdriver
see
seed
shape(s)
sharp
sheep
side
simple machine
sing
singing
sit-up
size(s)
skin
skip
sleep
slippery
small

smaller
smell
smooth
snack
snake
snow
soft
soil
solar
solid
sour
sound
sparrow
spinach
spring
square
squash
stalk
starfish
stayed
steam
sticky
still
stone(s)
strong
stronger
struck
sugar
summer
sunlight
sunshine
supper
sweet
sweet potato
tail
taller
taste
teach
themselves
thick
thin
through
thunder
tight
toe-touch
tomato
tone

tool
toolbox
touch
teach
trains
travel
tree
triangle
trucks
true
trunk
turn
turtle
useful
valley
vegetables
vibrate
vibration
vines
voice
wagon
walk
warmer
waste
watch
water
waves
weather
wedge
wet
wheat
wheel(s)
wheelchair
white
wide
wildflower
wind
windmill
winter
wood(s)
woodland
work
write
yard
yellow

LIFEPAC

WORKSHEETS

Reproducible Worksheets
for use with the Science 100
Teacher's Guide

Name ____________________

Science 101
Worksheet 1
with page 4

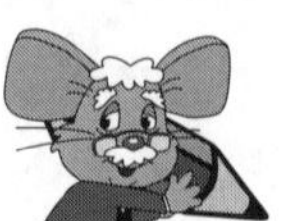

Teacher check ____________________
Initial Date

Name ____________________

Color the circles.

Write the color word.

yellow + blue = ____________________

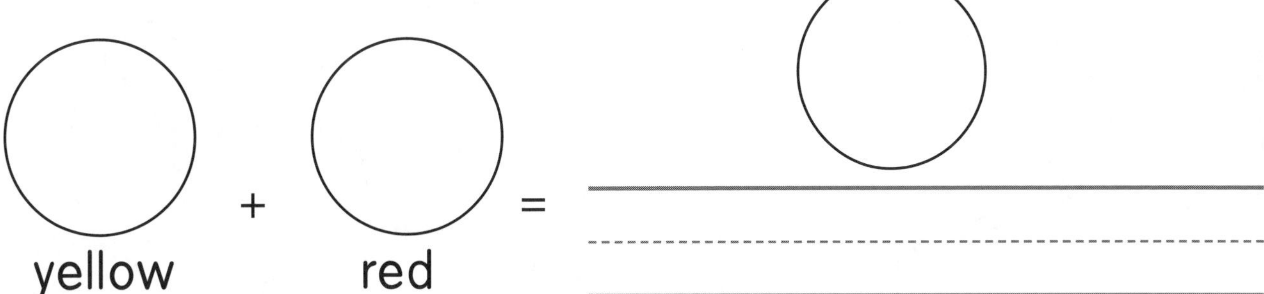

blue + red = ____________________

Teacher check ____________________
Initial Date

Name ____________________

Read the color words.

Color the pictures.

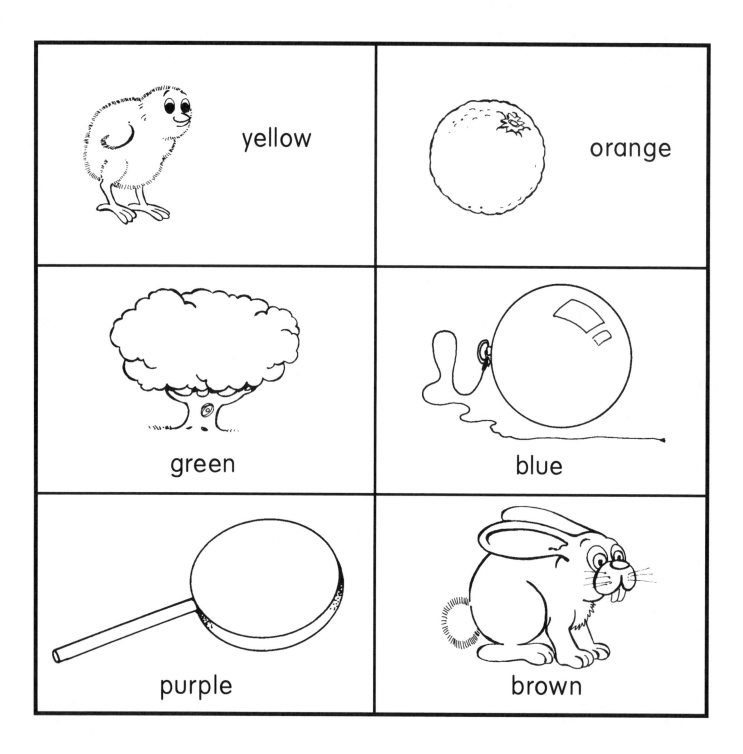

yellow	orange
green	blue
purple	brown

Science 101
Worksheet 2
with page 3

Teacher check ____________________
Initial Date

Name ______________________

Color the flag.

Teacher check ______________________
Initial Date

Name ______________________

Pick a color.

Draw 4 things that are that color.

Teacher check ______________________
Initial Date

Name ______________

Science 101
Worksheet 5
with page 11

Teacher check ______________
Initial Date

Name ____________________

5 2 4 1 6 3

Color 1: blue
Color 2: green
Color 3: red

Color 4: yellow
Color 5: brown
Color 6: orange

Science 101
Worksheet 6
with page 11

Teacher check ____________________
Initial Date

Name ____________________

Draw a square. Color it red.

Draw a circle. Color it yellow.

Draw a rectangle. Color it blue.

Teacher check ____________________
Initial Date

Name ______________________

Color the triangles red.
Color the squares yellow.
Color the circles blue.
Color the rectangles green.

Science 101
Worksheet 8
with page 15

Teacher check ______________________
Initial Date

Name ____________________

Find the shape that helps.

Color 1: pink **Color 2: brown** **Color 3: blue**

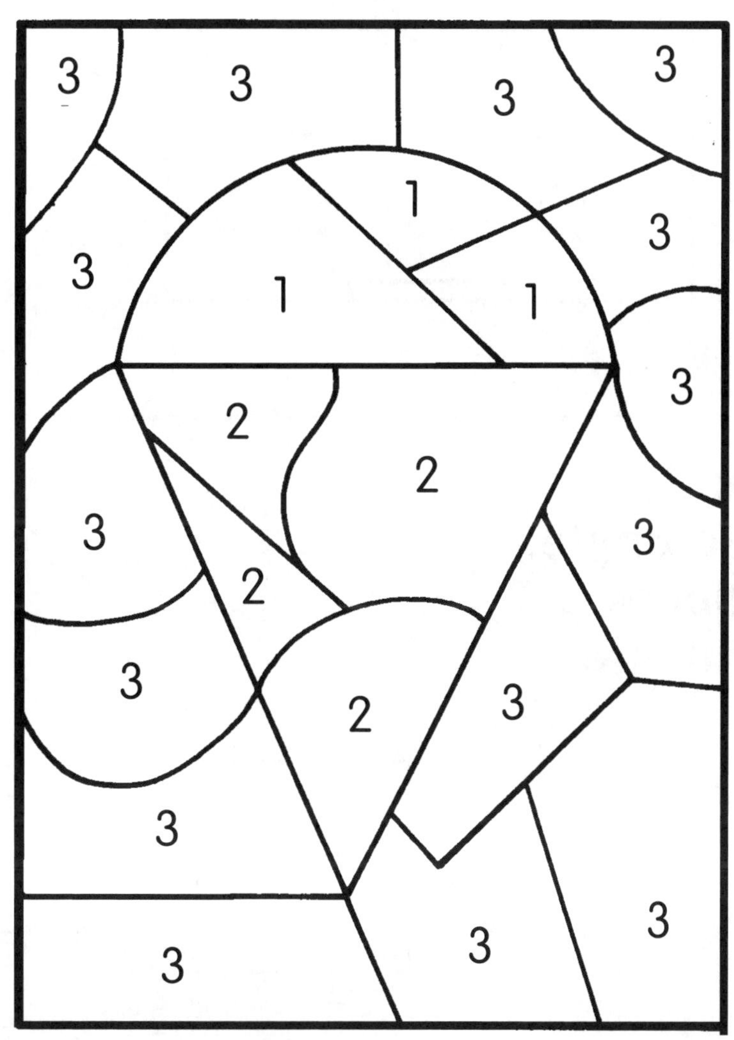

Name the shape you found.

____

circle
rectangle
square
triangle

Teacher check ____________________
Initial Date

Name ____________________

Draw the missing shape.

Color the picture.

Write C for circle.
Write R for rectangle.
Write S for square.
Write T for triangle.

red

blue

black

pink

Read the color words.

Color the shapes.

Science 101
Worksheet 10
with page 22

Teacher check ____________________
Initial Date

Name ___________________

Draw a big **flower. Draw a** small **flower.**

Draw a big **balloon. Draw a** small **balloon.**

Color your pictures.

Science 101
Worksheet 11
with page 24

Teacher check ___________________
Initial Date

Name ______________________

Color the long **crayon yellow.**

Color the short **crayon orange.**

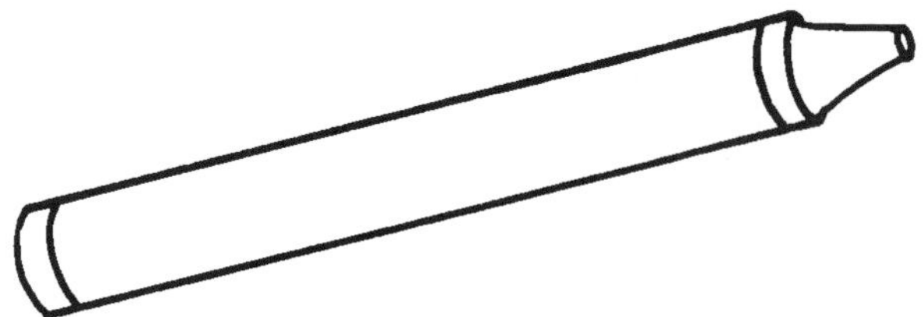

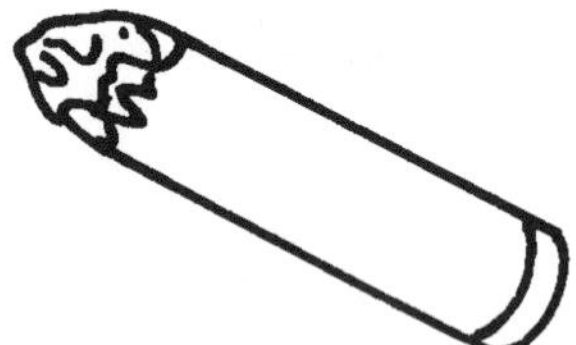

Color the long **truck brown.**

Color the short **truck green.**

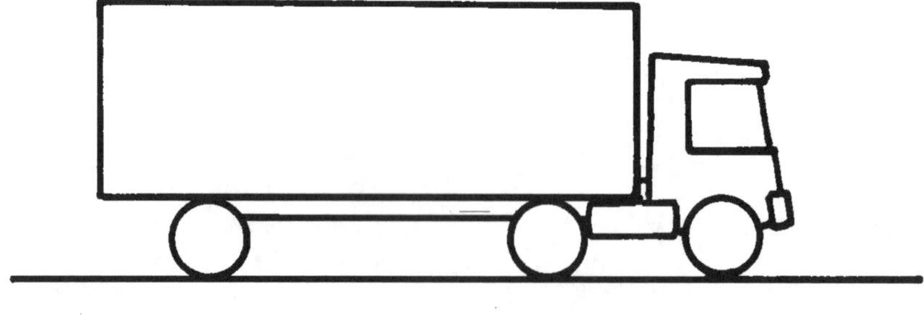

Teacher check ______________________
Initial Date

Name ______________

Who am I?

I am a **big** animal.

I have a **small** head.

I have a **long, narrow** neck.

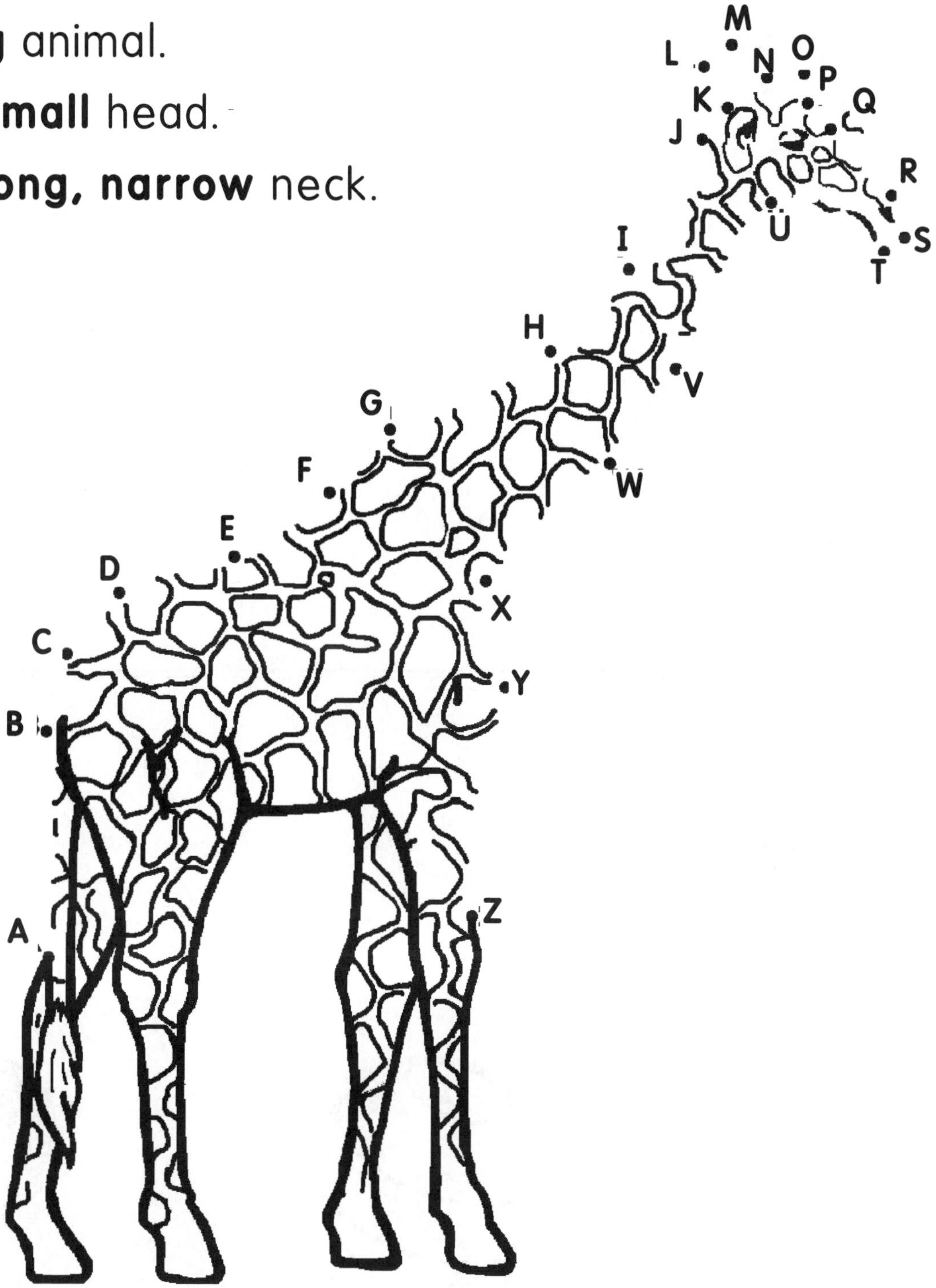

M L N O K P Q J R I U S T H V G W F E D X C Y B A Z

Color me.

I am a ______________.

Teacher check ______________
Initial Date

Name ____________________

Color the balls.
Cut them out.
Paste **them in** order.
Put the small ball first.

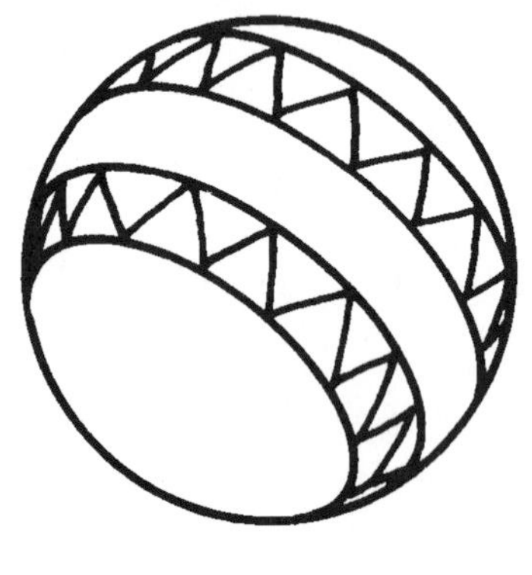

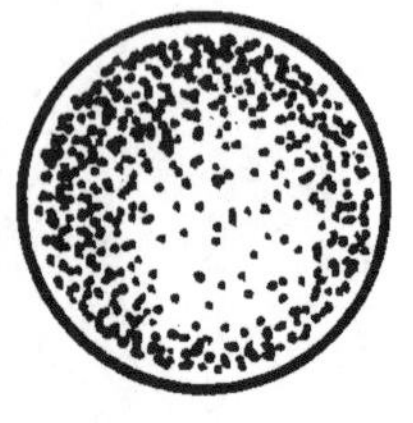

Teacher check ____________________
Initial Date

Name ____________________

Hi, My name is Patches. I need a house.

Draw my house just the right size.

Use a square **and a** triangle. **The door can be a** circle **or a** rectangle.

Color my house red.

Color the roof black.

Science 101
Worksheet 15
with page 30

Teacher check ____________________
Initial Date

Name ____________________

Circle the ones that ring.
Color the pictures.

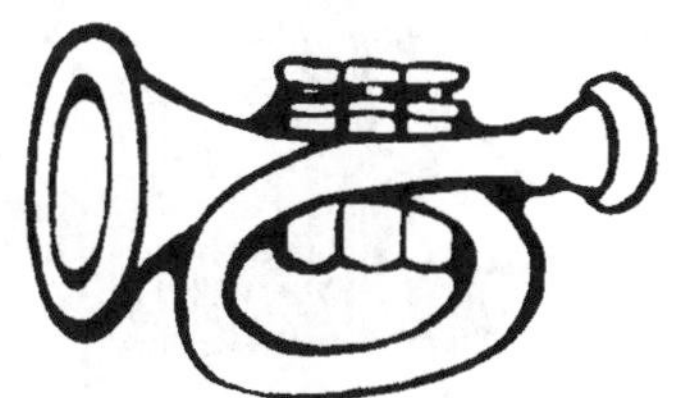

Science: 102
Worksheet 1
with page 2

Teacher check ____________________
Initial Date

Name ____________________

Circle the ones that whistle.
Color the pictures.

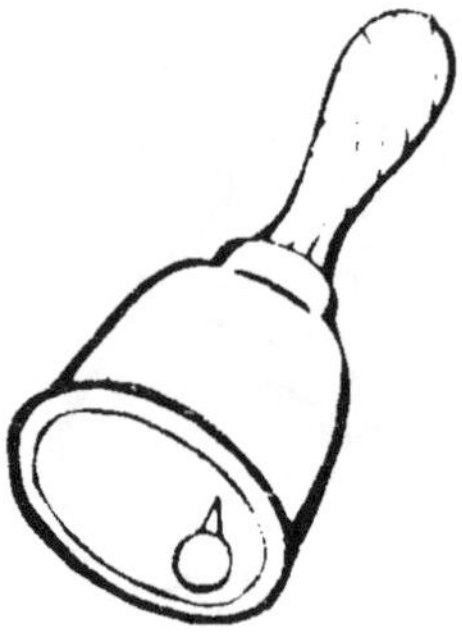

Science 102
Worksheet 2
with page 2

Teacher check ____________________
Initial Date

Name ____________________

I wake up early.
I say, "Cock-a-doodle-doo!"
Who am I?

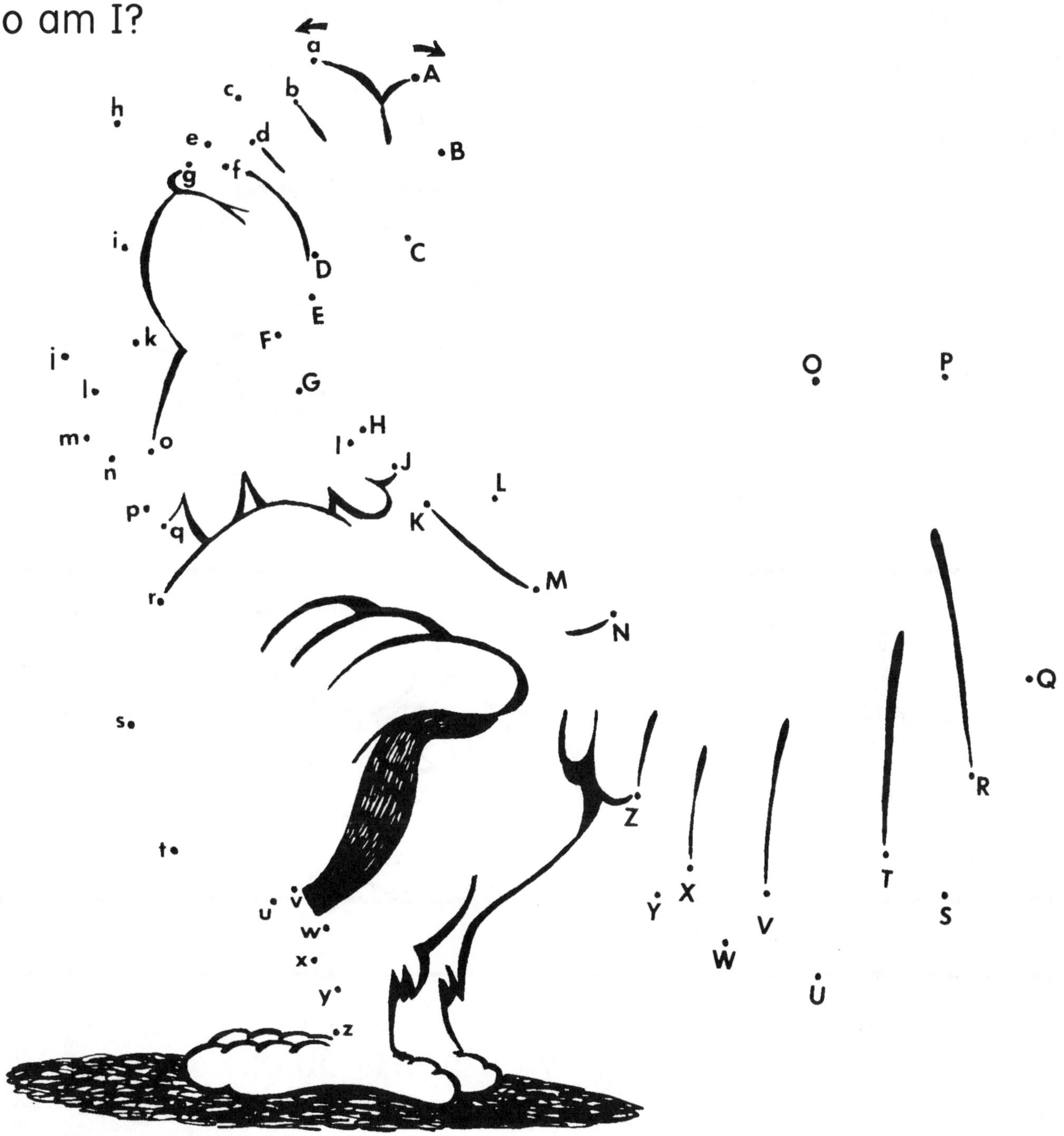

Write my name.

____

Teacher check ____________________
Initial Date

Name ______________________

Cut out the sentences.

Glue each sentence under its picture.

Color the pictures.

Write the sentences in your Tablet.

____

____

____

____

- -

cut Some weather is quiet.

- -

cut I can hear wind and rain.

- -

Science: 102
Worksheet 4
with page 7

Teacher check ______________________
Initial Date

Name ____________________

Circle the one you should listen to at home.

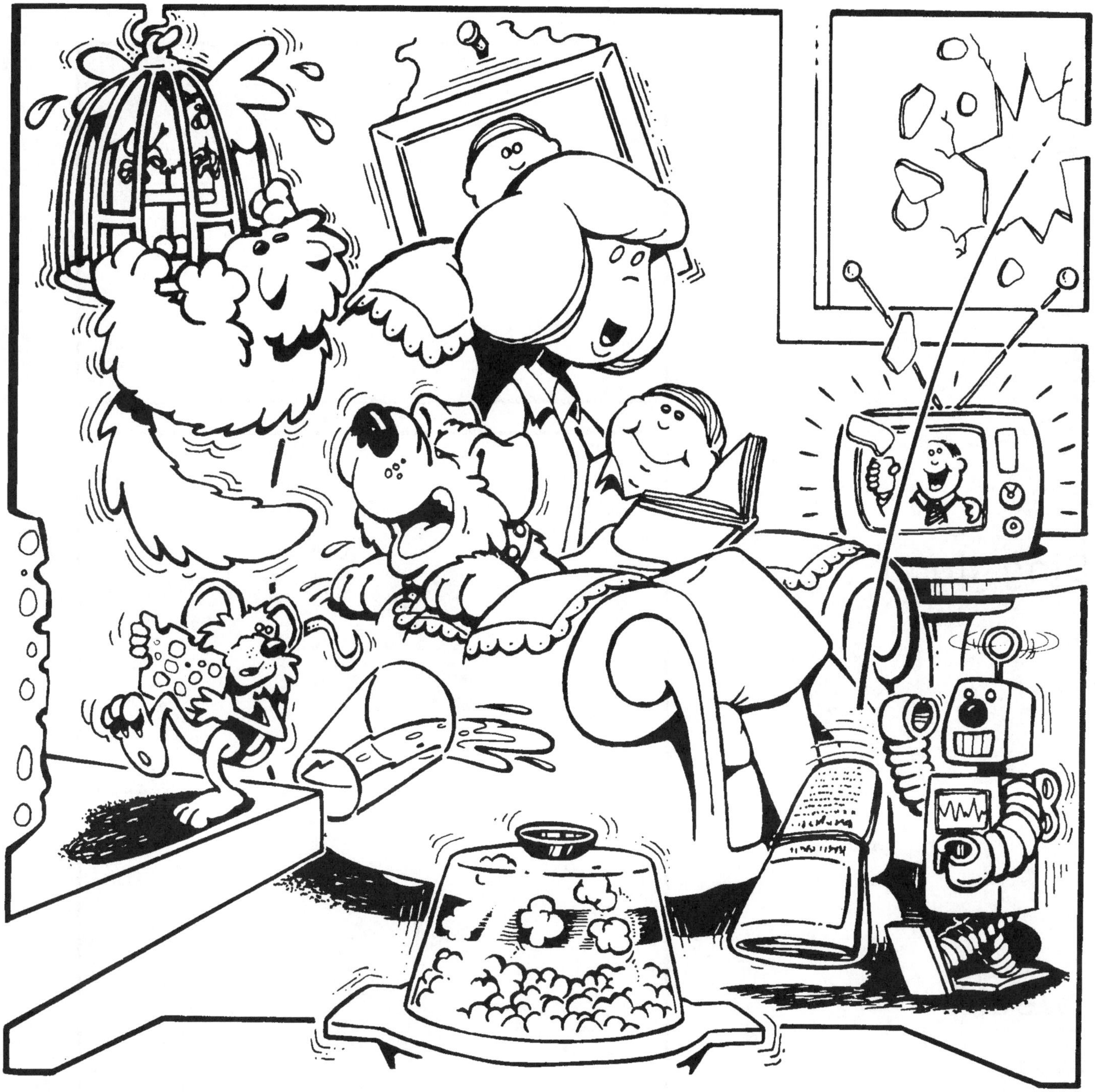

Color the picture.

Teacher check ____________________
Initial Date

Name ____________

Draw a picture for each sound.

Buzz

Ding-dong

Tweet

Teacher check ____________
Initial Date

Name ________________

Use a word from the box to name a sound you might hear.

Baa-baa	pitter-patter	bow-wow

____

____

____

Science: 102
Worksheet 7
with page 13

Teacher check ________________
Initial Date

Name ______________________

Color the pictures.

Cut them apart.

Glue them onto Worksheet 9 in the right order.

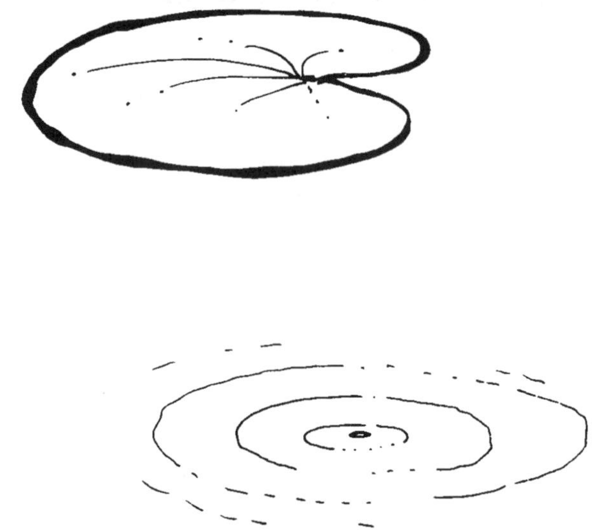

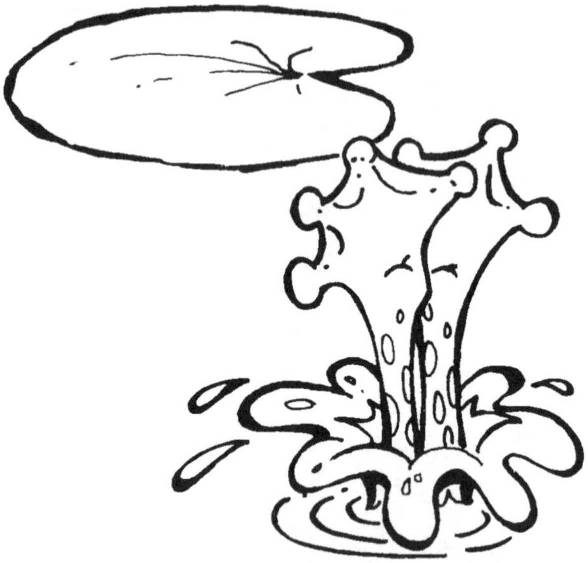

Teacher check ______________________

Initial Date

Name ______________________

The Hungry Frog

Write a sentence about the hungry frog.

Science: 102
Worksheet 9
with page 16

Teacher check ______________________
Initial Date

Name ____________________

How can these animals hear?
Color them.
Name them.

____

____

____

____

Science: 102
Worksheet 10
with page 20

Teacher check ____________________
Initial Date

Name ______________________

Write the word that fits.

Animals	**hear**	**vibrate**

You ______________________ with your ears.

______________________ have special ears.

Sound makes your eardrums

______________________ .

Draw the ears on this animal.
Color it.

Teacher check ______________________
Initial Date

Name ____________________

Write voice, hands, or feet to name what you might use to make these sounds.

Science: 102
Worksheet 12
with page 24

Teacher check ____________________
Initial Date

Name ______________________

Write tone **or** pitch.

Your voice changes ______________________ when you talk or read.

The ______________________ of your voice tells your feelings.

Write high **or** low.

Patches voice has a ______________________ pitch.

Color Patches.

He has brown spots.

Science: 102
Worksheet 13
with page 27

Teacher check ______________________
Initial Date

Name ______________________

Here is a nose smelling something nice.

Draw the rest of the face.

Science: 103
Worksheet 1
with page 5

Teacher check ______________________
Initial Date

Name ____________________

This nose is smelling something it does not like.

Draw the rest of the face.

Science: 103
Worksheet 2
with page 7

Teacher check ____________________
Initial Date

Name ____________________

Write the taste words.

sweet	sour	salt	bitter

____

____

____

____

____

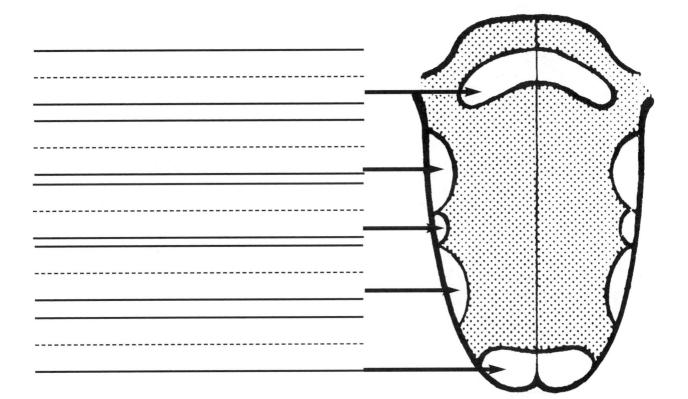

Science: 103
Worksheet 3
with page 8

Teacher check ____________________
Initial Date

Name ____________________

Match the picture with the word.

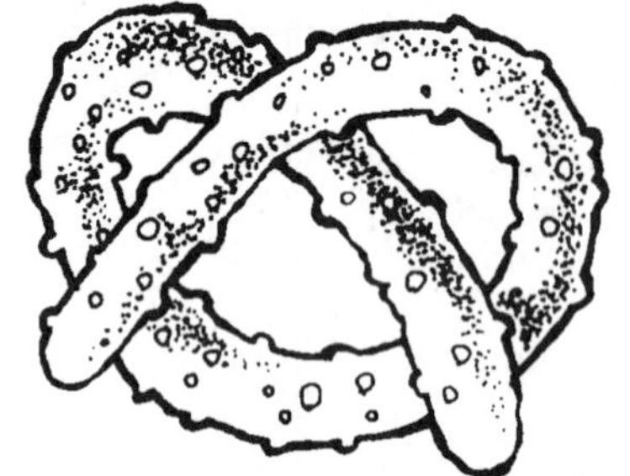

nose

tongue

sour

salty

Color the pictures.

Teacher check ____________________
Initial Date

Name ____________________

Follow the dots to find something that tickles.

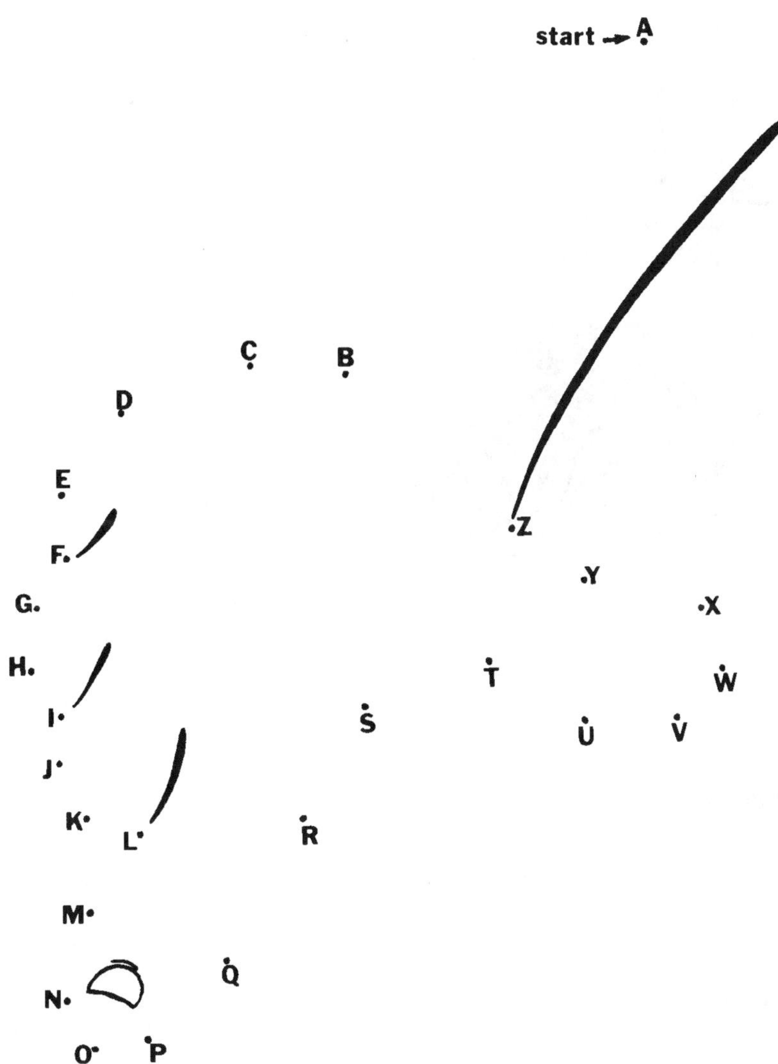

Color the picture.

Science: 103
Worksheet 5
with page 13

Teacher check ____________________
Initial Date

Name ____________________

Match the words to the picture.
Color the pictures.

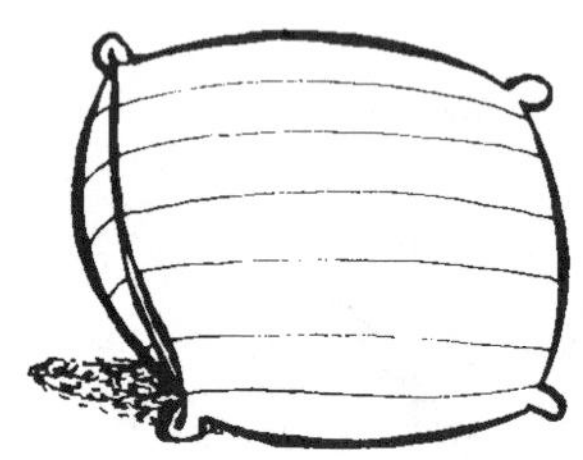

smooth

cold

soft

hard

Teacher check ____________________
Initial Date

Name ______________________

Write the words to tell how things feel.

soft	rough	cold	wet	hot

A feels ______________________.

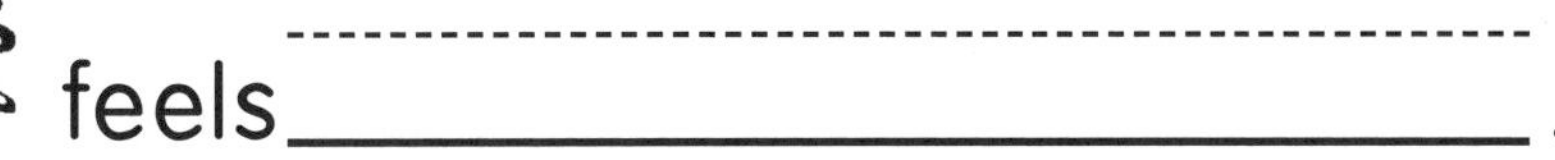

A feels ______________________.

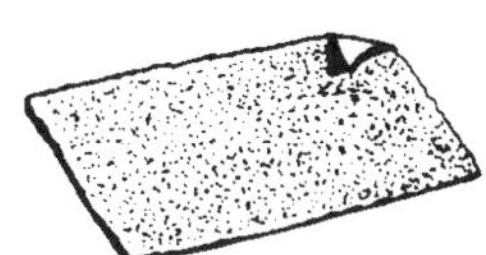

feels ______________________.

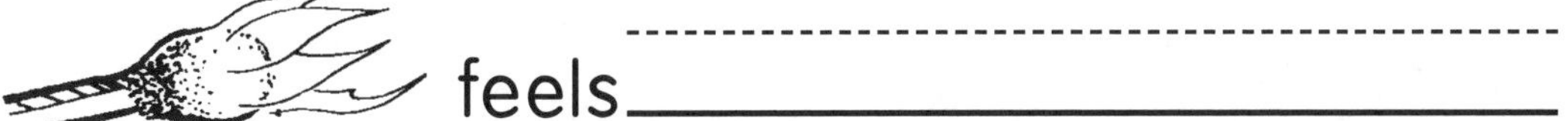

A feels ______________________.

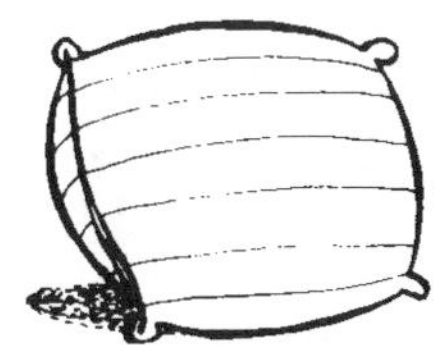

A feels ______________________.

Science: 103
Worksheet 7
with page 18

Teacher check ______________________
Initial Date

Name ____________________

Draw and color a picture of someone cleaning the sticky, messy kitchen.

Science: 103
Worksheet 8
with page 19

Teacher check ____________________
Initial Date

Name ______________________

Write the words that tell how things smell, taste, **or** feel.

sticky	hot	sour	slippery	sweet

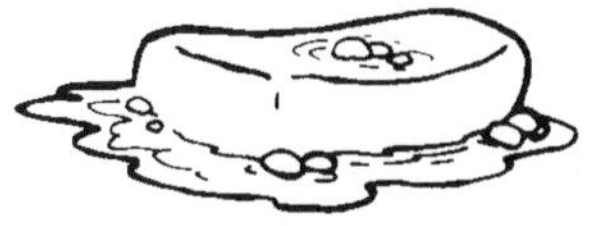 is ______________________ .

 is ______________________ .

A  tastes ______________________ .

A  smells ______________________ .

An 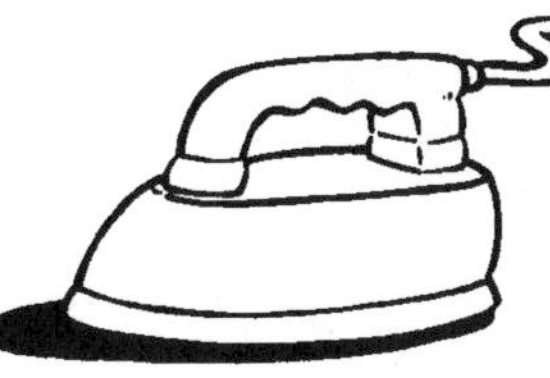 can be ______________________ .

Science: 103
Worksheet 9
with page 21

 Teacher check ______________________
Initial Date

Name ____________________

Follow the dots to see who hurt his foot on a tack.

Color the picture.

Science: 103
Worksheet 10
with page 23

Teacher check ____________________
Initial Date

Name ____________________

Match the part of the body to the sense that goes with it.

sight

hearing

smell

taste

touch

Teacher check ____________________
Initial Date

Name ______________________

Draw a picture of something you can see, hear, touch, taste, **and** smell.

Science: 103
Worksheet 12
with page 29

Teacher check ______________________
Initial Date

Name ____________________

Choose the right word.

brain	message	senses	nerves

My ____________________ send messages to my brain.

Messages move along ____________________ .

Each sense sends a special kind of

____________________ .

The ____________________ knows what the messages mean.

Teacher check ____________________
Initial Date

Name ______________________

Draw an animal.

Write three words to tell what the animal needs.

______________________ ______________________

____

Science 104
Worksheet 1
with page 3

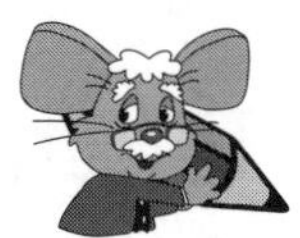

Teacher check ______________________
Initial Date

Name ______________________

Follow the dots.
Color the picture.

Write meat **or** wolf.

I am a ______________________ .

I eat ______________________ .

Teacher check ______________________
Initial Date

Name ____________________

Color the mother bear and her cub.

Color the mother cat and her kittens.

Teacher check ____________________
Initial Date

Name ____________________

This is a bullfrog.

Bullfrogs eat insects.

Insects are meat.

Color the bullfrog.

Science 104
Worksheet 4
with page 6

Teacher check ____________________
Initial Date

Name ____________________

The **hippopotamus** eats grass and water plants.
Follow the dots to see the hippopotamus.

Color the hippopotamus brown.

Color the grass green.

Science 104
Worksheet 5
with page 8

Teacher check ____________________
Initial Date

Name ______________________

Help the bird find the bird seed.

FINISH

START

Science 104
Worksheet 6
with page 9

Teacher check ______________________
Initial Date

Name ____________________

Color the picture.

Write the word.

The polar bear is ____________________.

black / white

Polar bears live where it is very ____________________.

cold / hot

Teacher check ____________________
Initial Date

Name ____________________

This crow wants to eat the farmer's corn.
Draw a scarecrow to keep him away.
Color the picture.

Science 104
Worksheet 8
with page 12

Teacher check ____________________
Initial Date

Name ____________________

Circle the one that does not **belong.**

Circle the one that does not **belong.**

Circle the one that does not **belong.**

Science 104
Worksheet 9
with page 13

Teacher check ____________________
Initial Date

Name ______________________

Animals That Eat Plants	Animals That Eat Meat	Animals That Eat Both

Cut out the animals.

Glue them into the right column.

Science 104
Worksheet 10
with page 15

Teacher check ______________________
Initial Date

Name ______________________

I live on a farm.

I honk.

I make a good Christmas dinner.

My feathers make a very soft pillow.

Follow the dots to see who I am.

Science 104
Worksheet 11
with page 17

Teacher check ______________________
Initial Date

Name ______________________

Match the baby to its mother.

Color the animals.

Science 104
Worksheet 12
with page 20

Teacher check ______________________
Initial Date

Name ______________________

Write the words.

grass	corn	slops	boy	Farmer Jim

______________________ had gone away.

The cows wanted ______________________ .

The pigs wanted ______________________ .

The chickens wanted ______________________ .

A ______________________ helped the animals.

Science 104
Worksheet 13
with page 21

Teacher check ______________________
Initial Date

Name ____________________

Cut out the animal names.
Glue the names in the right place.

Wild Animals	Farm Animals

cow	lion	cat	bear	horse
lamb	raccoon	pig	chicken	
deer	wolf	bullfrog		

Circle three **things the animals need.**

shoes	sleep	food
water	paper	cars

Teacher check ____________________
Initial Date

Name ____________________

Follow the dots.

Color the picture.

Science 104
Worksheet 15
with page 26

Teacher check ____________________
Initial Date

Name ___________________

Can you help the turtle find his bowl?.

FINISH

START

Science 104
Worksheet 16
with page 29

Teacher check ___________________
Initial Date

Name ____________________

Draw a pet that lives in a bowl.

Draw a pet that lives in a cage.

Science 104
Worksheet 17
with page 29

Teacher check ____________________
Initial Date

Name ____________________

Draw the animal who lives here.
Color the picture.

Science 104
Worksheet 18
with page 30

Teacher check ____________________
Initial Date

Name ______________________

Write wild, farm, **or** pet.

____

____

____

____

____

____

Teacher check ______________________
Initial Date

The following pages are reproducible worksheet patterns for Science 104.

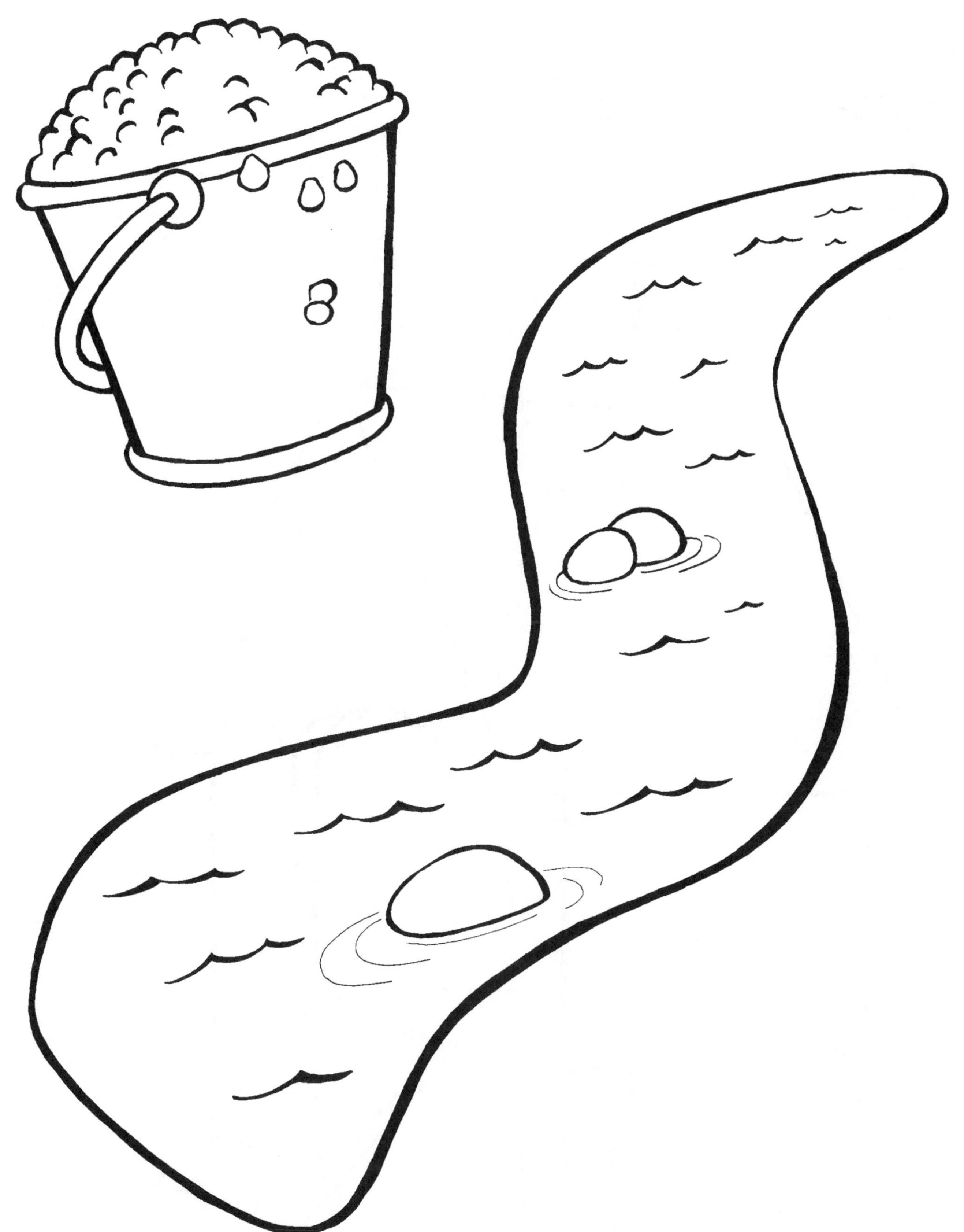

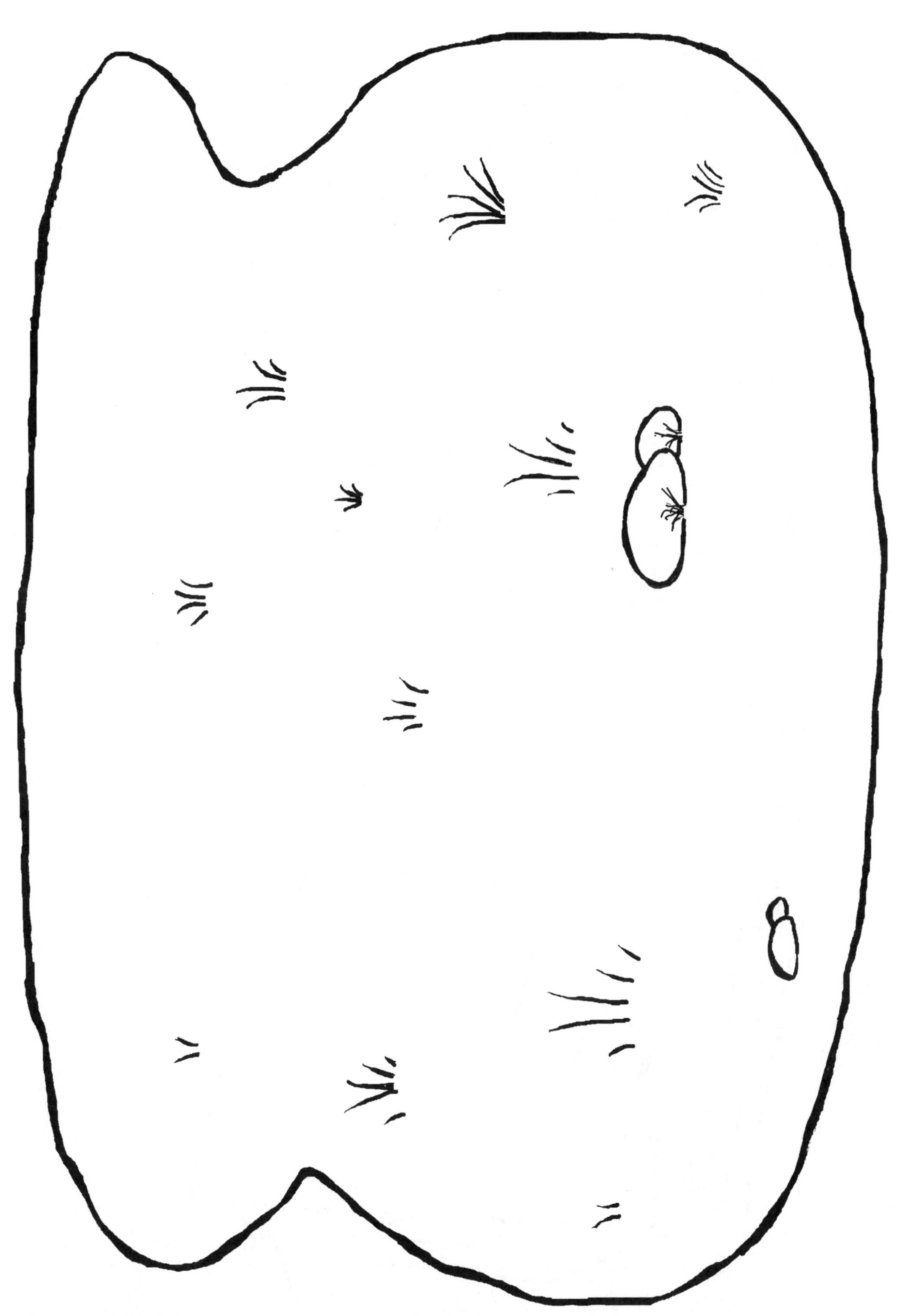

PIGS

Name ____________________

Color the plants.

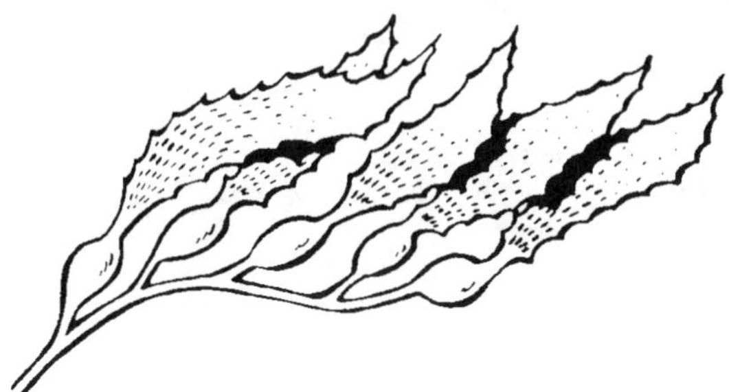

seaweed

cactus

grass

tree

Teacher check ____________________
Initial Date

Name ____________________

Name the parts of a tree.
Use these words.

root trunk leaves seed

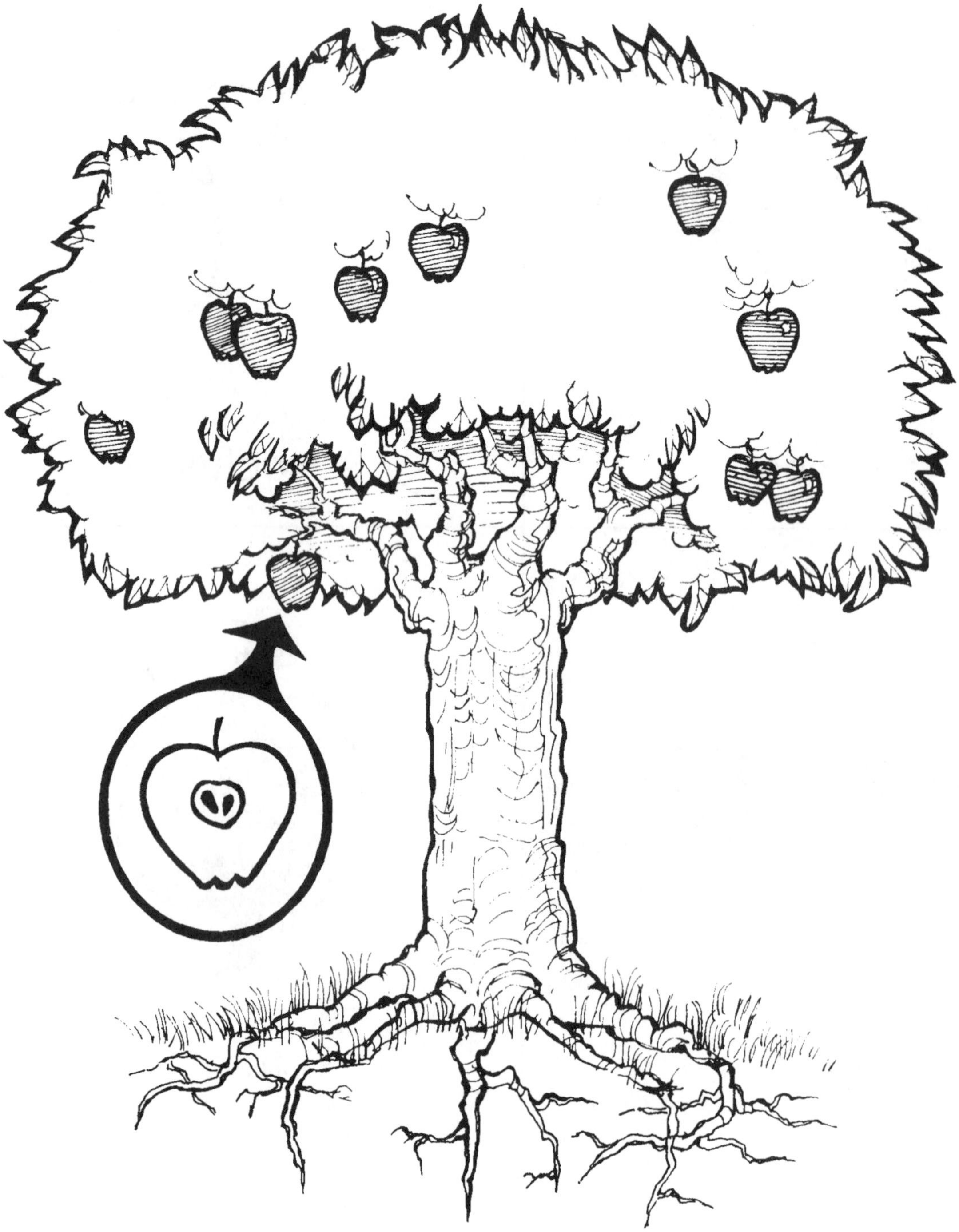

Teacher check ____________________
Initial Date

Name ____________________

Color the pictures.

Cut on the dotted lines.

Glue onto Worksheet 4 in the right order.

A big tree.

A seedling.

A young tree.

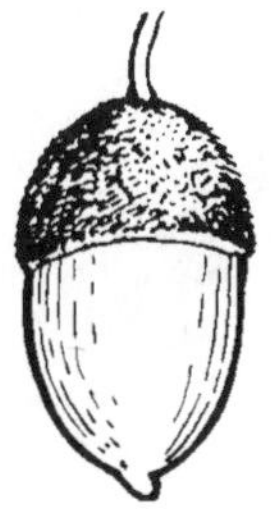

A seed.

Teacher check ____________________
Initial Date

Name ______________________

A tree grows from a seed.

1.	2.
3.	4.

Science: 105
Worksheet 4
with page 7

Teacher check ______________________
Initial Date

Name ______________________

Name the parts of a grass plant.
Use these words.

leaf roots seeds stalk

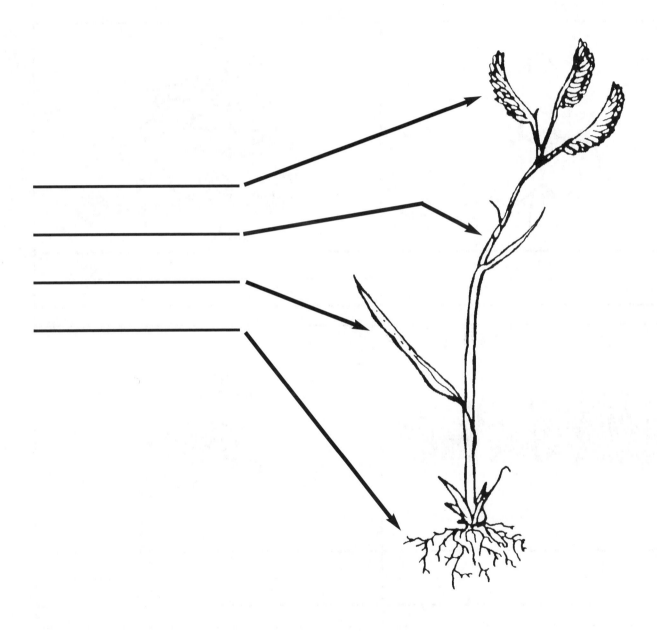

____

____

____

____

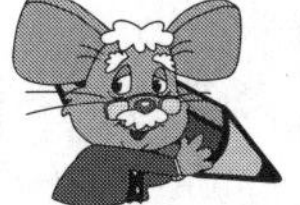

Teacher check ______________________
Initial Date

Name ____________________

Name the plant.
Write these words.

tree vine grass wild flower

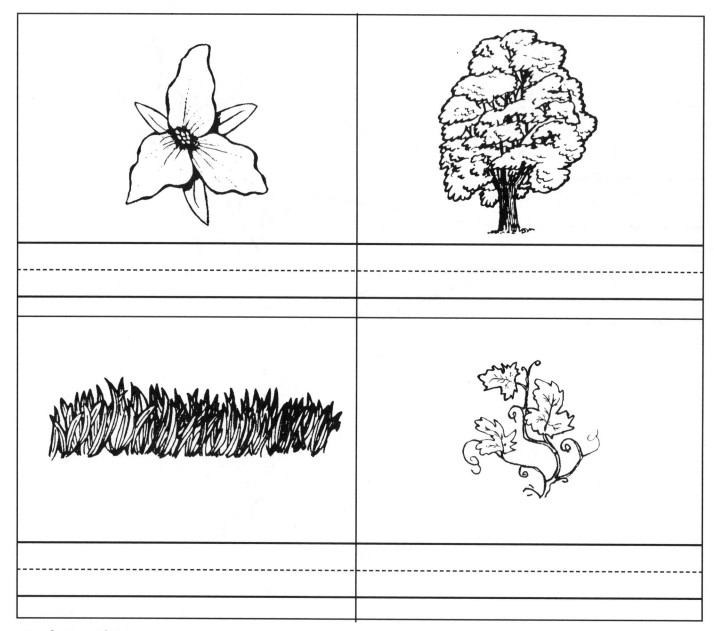

Color the pictures.

Science: 105
Worksheet 6
with page 11

Teacher check ____________________
Initial Date

Name ____________________

Plants in Nature

Color the pictures.
Cut out the words.
Glue the words to the right pictures.

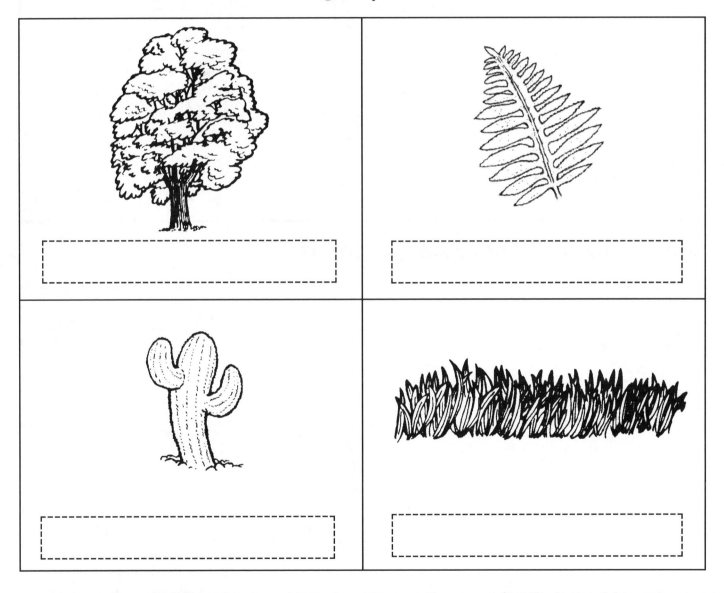

fern	tree
grass	cactus

Science: 105
Worksheet 7
with page 17

Teacher check ____________________
Initial Date

Name ____________________

Draw a root vegetable. Color it.

Draw a leafy vegetable. Color it.

Science: 105
Worksheet 8
with page 22

Teacher check ____________________
Initial Date

Name ___________________

Match the pictures to the right word.

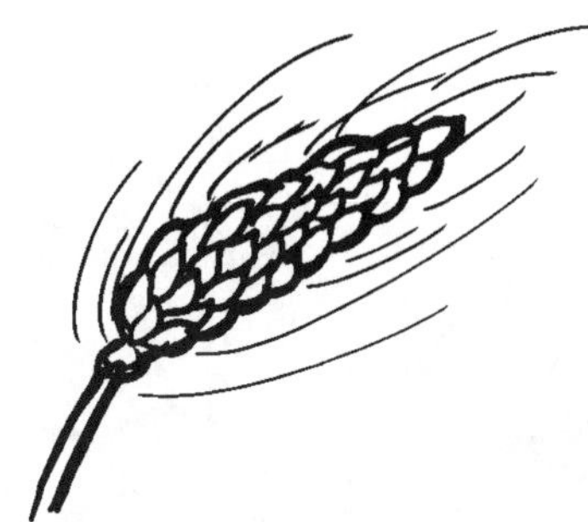

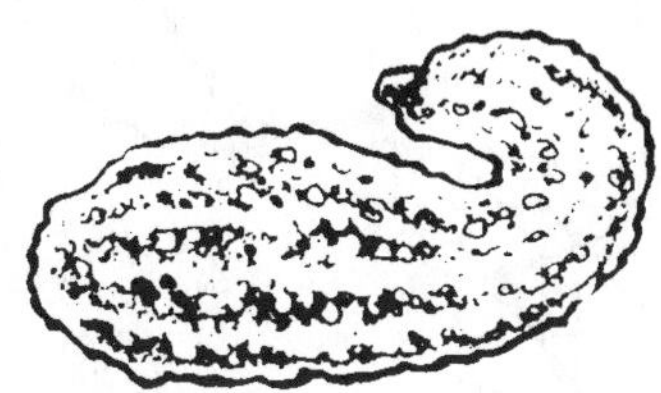

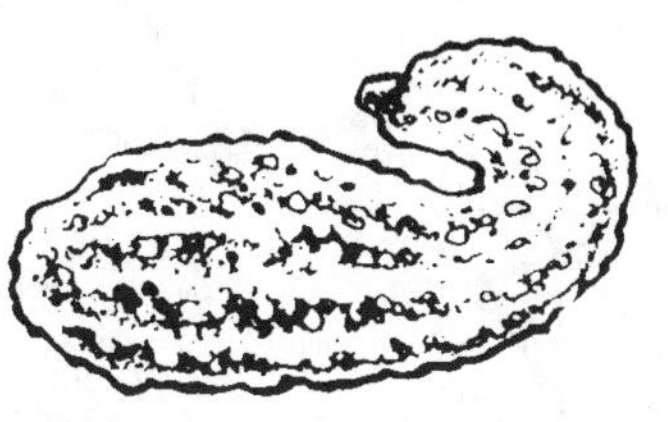

grain

vegetable

fruit

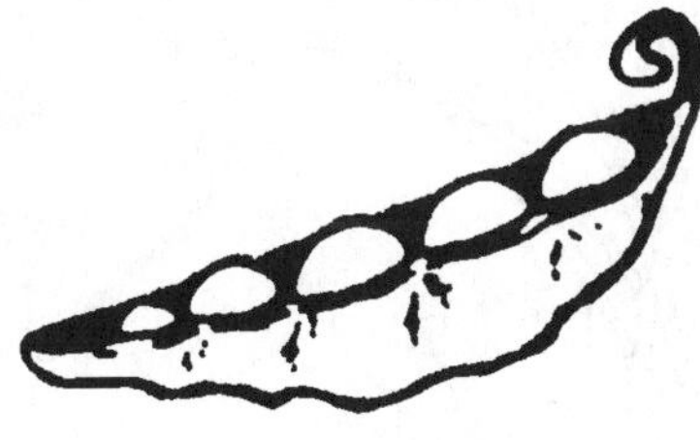

Science: 105
Worksheet 9
with page 27

Teacher check ___________________
Initial Date

Name ____________________

Color the flowers in the garden.

Teacher check ____________________
Initial Date

Science: 105
Worksheet 10
with page 28

Name ____________________

Color the pictures.
Cut them apart.
Put them in the order they should go. Glue the pictures on Worksheet 12.

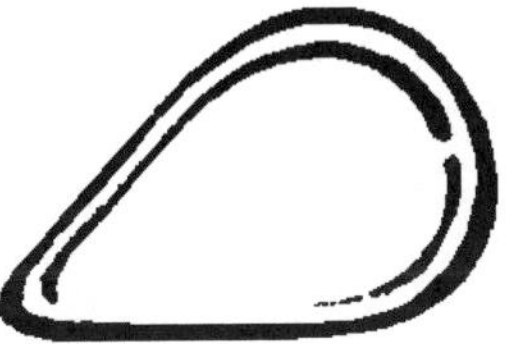

Teacher check ____________________
Initial Date

Name ______________________

See how the pumpkin grows.
Put the pictures in the proper order.

1.	**2.**
3.	**4.**

Teacher check ______________________
Initial Date

ALTERNATE

TESTS

Reproducible Tests
for use with the Science 100
Teacher's Guide

SCIENCE

1 0 1

ALTERNATE LIFEPAC TEST

11/13

Name ____________________

Date ____________________

Score ____________________

SCIENCE 101: ALTERNATE LIFEPAC TEST

Color the smaller circle red.

Color the bigger triangle green.

Color the widest rectangle blue.

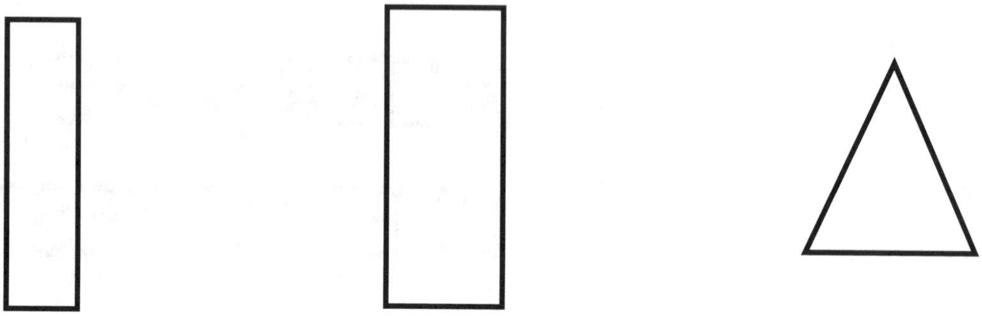

Color the smaller square yellow.

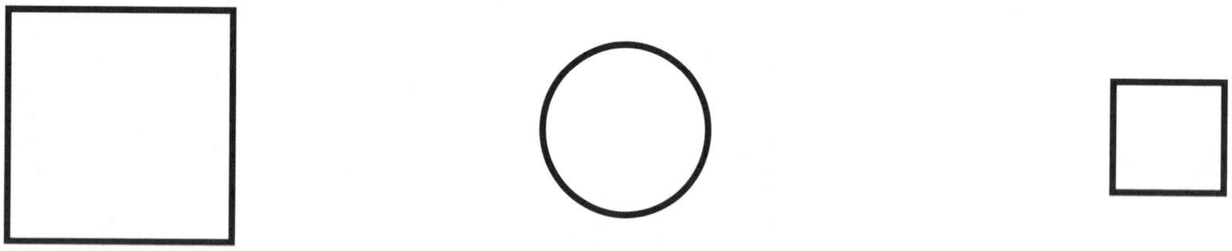

Color the shortest pencil orange.

Color the longer balloon pink.

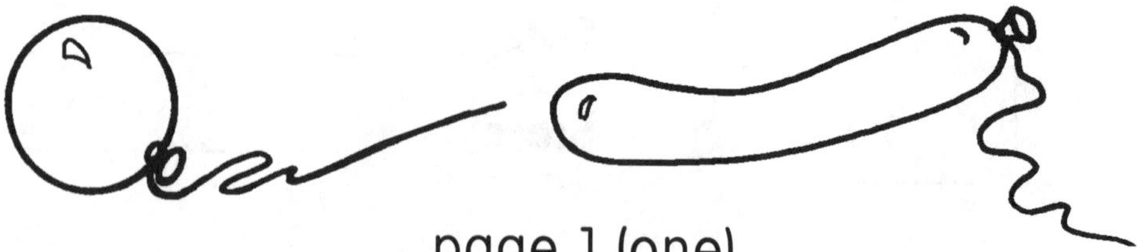

Color the circles.

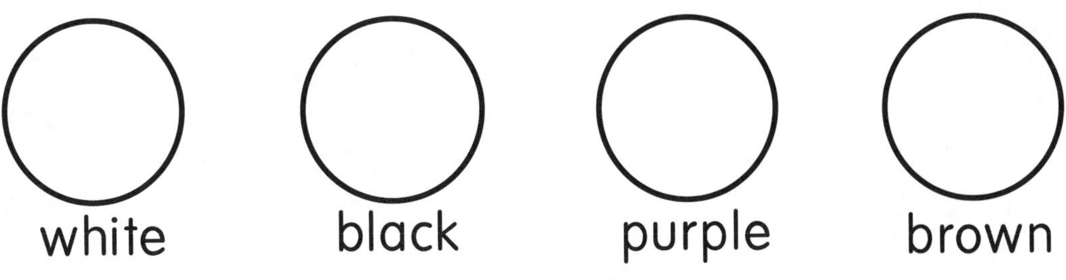

Draw the shape that will help.

Match the foot to the shoe that fits.

Circle the one that is different.

NOTES

page 3 (three)

SCIENCE

1 0 2

ALTERNATE LIFEPAC TEST

14/17

Name ______________________

Date ______________________

Score ______________________

SCIENCE 102: ALTERNATE LIFEPAC TEST

Put an X on some sounds people make.

Draw a line under each word that tells how you learn with your ears.

vibration	see	color	hear
shape	listen	look	sound

Write the word that fits.

A ______________ says, "Gar-rump."
dog / frog

God gave animals special ______________.
sounds / music

Your ______________ catch sound.
ears / eyes

I should ______________ to my teacher.
look / listen

I can ______________ praises to the LORD.
sing / walk

Sound waves ______________ through air,
move / sing

water, and solids.

page 2 (two)

Write the word that fits.

Your voice has ____________________. It can be
tone/clouds
loud or soft.

A song has ____________________. It can go
shout/pitch
high or low.

Music has ____________________. You can
air/rhythm
hear a beat.

Say your Bible verses (Psalm 100:1 and 2).

SCIENCE

1 0 3

ALTERNATE LIFEPAC TEST

12/16

Name ____________________

Date ____________________

Score ____________________

SCIENCE 103: ALTERNATE LIFEPAC TEST

Match the berry to the senses you might use to learn about it

sight

hearing

taste

smell

touch

Match the horn to the senses you might use to learn about it

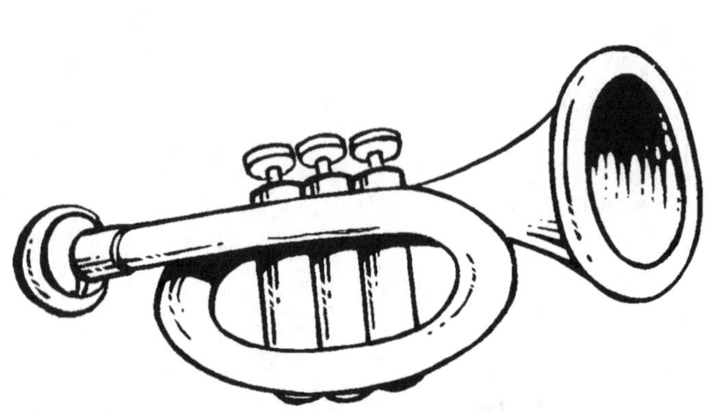

sight

hearing

taste

smell

touch

Draw a line under the words that fit.

Your________________________help you taste.

nose and tongue / eyes and ears

You can feel things with your______________________.

nose / skin

You can observe with all of your____________________.

toes / senses

You cannot _________________________ when you

smell / see

have a bad cold.

Circle the words that name your senses.

tone	smell	circle
touch	blue	taste
small	sight	hearing

SCIENCE

1 0 4

ALTERNATE LIFEPAC TEST

11/14

Name ______________________

Date ______________________

Score ______________________

SCIENCE 104: ALTERNATE LIFEPAC TEST

Write food, water, **and** sleep.

all animals need ______________________,

______________________, and ______________________.

Match the animal to the word.

wild

farm

pet

Circle the animals that gives us food.

Circle the wild animals that eat meat.

Circle pets that live in cages.

Write the word.

farmer	wild	You

__________ animals take care of themselves.

The __________ takes care of his animals.

__________ take care of your pets.

SCIENCE

105

ALTERNATE LIFEPAC TEST

11/14

Name ____________________

Date ____________________

Score ____________________

SCIENCE 105: ALTERNATE LIFEPAC TEST

Circle trees.

Circle vegetables.

Circle grains.

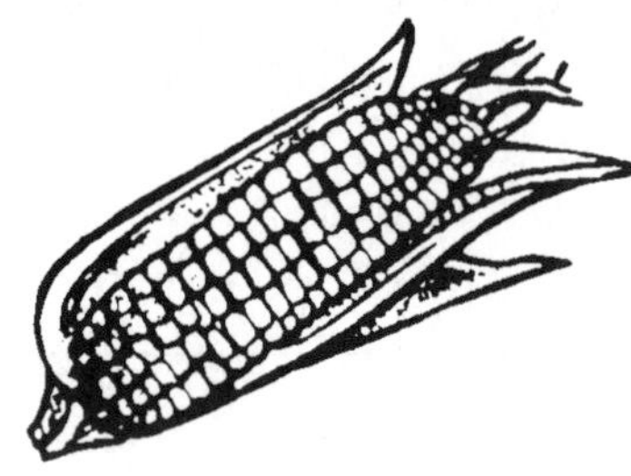
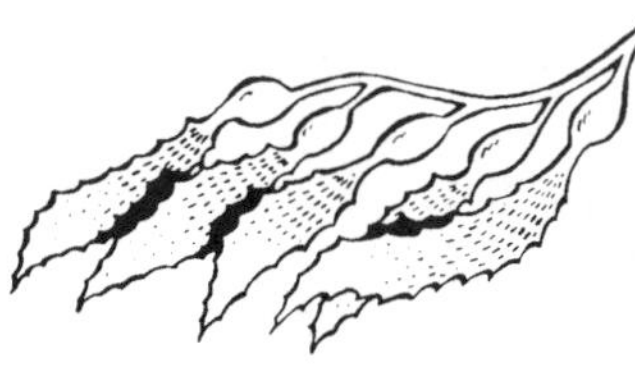

Circle houseplants.

Circle words that tell what plants need.

sunlight trees

soil water

Write the word.

Farmers	**seeds**	**God**	**plants**

Plants grow from ____________________.

__________ sends sunlight and rain to help plants grow.

______________ grow grains, vegetables, and fruits.

You can grow ______________ at home.

NOTES

page 3 (three)